Table of Contents

25 ESSENTIAL GRAPHIC NOVELS

ALAN MOORE'S UNFORGETTABLE MEDITATION ON THE RAZOR-THIN LINE BETWEEN SANITY AND INSANITY, HEROISM AND VILLAINY, COMEDY AND TRAGEDY

BATMAN: THE KILLING JOKE

In this groundbreaking work, Moore weaves together a twisted tale of insanity and human perseverance featuring Batman's greatest foe, the Joker.

Looking to prove that any man can be pushed past his breaking point into madness, the Joker attempts to drive Commissioner Gordon insane. Refusing to give up even after suffering a tremendous personal tragedy, Gordon struggles to maintain his sanity with the help of Batman in a desperate effort to best the madman.

With art by Brian Bolland, one of comics' best illustrators, *Batman: The Killing Joke* remains DC's best-selling graphic novel more than 25 years after its inception.

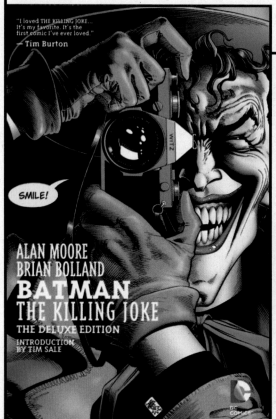

"I loved THE KILLING JOKE... It's my favorite. It's the first comic I've ever loved."
— Tim Burton

SMILE!

ALAN MOORE
BRIAN BOLLAND
BATMAN
THE KILLING JOKE
THE DELUXE EDITION
INTRODUCTION BY TIM SALE

"EASILY THE GREATEST JOKER STORY EVER TOLD, BATMAN: THE KILLING JOKE IS ALSO ONE OF ALAN MOORE'S FINEST WORKS. IF YOU'VE READ IT BEFORE, GO BACK AND READ IT AGAIN. YOU OWE IT TO YOURSELF." —IGN

"I LOVED BATMAN: THE KILLING JOKE IT'S MY FAVORITE. IT'S THE FIRST COMIC I EVER LOVED." —TIM BURTON

"A GENUINELY CHILLING PORTRAYAL OF BATMAN'S GREATEST FOE." —BOOKLIST

BATMAN: THE KILLING JOKE

Writer: Alan Moore | Artist: Brian Bolland | ISBN: 9781401216672 | Diamond Code: NOV150279 | Price: $17.99/$20.99 CAN | Format: HC

FOR MATURE READERS

BATMAN:
THE DARK KNIGHT RETURNS

FRANK MILLER'S INFLUENTIAL GRAPHIC NOVEL JUGGERNAUT THAT ALTERED THE PERCEPTION OF THE GENRE

"GROUNDBREAKING."
–USA TODAY

"CHANGED THE COURSE OF COMICS." –ROLLING STONE

"REVISIONIST POP EPIC." –SPIN

"IT'S FILM NOIR IN CARTOON PANELS." –VANITY FAIR

Ten years after an aging Batman retired, Gotham City has sunk deeper into decadence and lawlessness. Now, when his city needs him most, the Dark Knight returns in a blaze of glory. Joined by Carrie Kelley, a teenage, female Robin, Batman must take back the streets.

But for a man his age, a return to a life of crime-fighting is not easy. After facing off against two of his greatest enemies, the Joker and Two-Face, a haggard Batman finds himself in mortal combat with his former ally Superman, in a battle that only one of them will survive.

Hailed as a comics masterpiece, *Batman: The Dark Knight Returns* is Frank Miller's (*300* and *Sin City*) reinvention of Gotham's legendary protector. It remains one of the most influential stories ever told in comics, with its echoes felt in all media forms of DC storytelling.

BATMAN: THE DARK KNIGHT RETURNS
FRANK MILLER with KLAUS JANSON and LYNN VARLEY INTRODUCTION BY FRANK MILLER
30TH ANNIVERSARY EDITION

BATMAN: THE DARK KNIGHT RETURNS

Writer: Frank Miller | Artist: Frank Miller | ISBN: 9781401263119 | Diamond Code: NOV150279 | Price: $19.99/$25.99 CAN | Format: TP

THE DEFINITIVE DC VERTIGO SERIES BY THE LEGENDARY NEIL GAIMAN

THE SANDMAN VOL. 1: PRELUDES & NOCTURNES 30TH ANNIVERSARY EDITION

The *New York Times* best-selling author Neil Gaiman's transcendent series *The Sandman* is often labeled as not only the definitive DC Vertigo title, but also one of the finest achievements in graphic storytelling.

In *The Sandman Vol. 1: Preludes & Nocturnes,* an occultist attempting to capture Death to bargain for eternal life traps her younger brother Dream instead. After his seventy-year imprisonment and eventual escape, Dream, also known as Morpheus, goes on a quest for his lost objects of power to reclaim his reign.

Gaiman, a celebrated storyteller and award-winning creator the world over, has forged an incredible legacy with this groundbreaking saga, the ripples of which are still felt today.

"THE SANDMAN JUST MIGHT BE THE SMARTEST COMIC BOOK EVER WRITTEN."
—USA TODAY

"NEIL GAIMAN'S LONG-RUNNING SERIES MADE COOL COMICS FANTASTICAL AND FANTASTICAL COMICS COOL. *THE SANDMAN* IS A MODERN MYTH, AS WELL AS A PRÉCIS ON WHY THE STORIES WE TELL MATTER SO MUCH."
—PLAYBOY

"THE GREATEST EPIC IN THE HISTORY OF COMIC BOOKS."
—LOS ANGELES TIMES MAGAZINE

THE SANDMAN VOL. 1: PRELUDES & NOCTURNES 30th ANNIVERSARY EDITION

Writer: Neil Gaiman | Artists: Sam Kieth, Malcolm Jones III & Mike Dringenberg | ISBN: 9781401284770

Diamond Code: JUL180774 | Price: $19.99/$25.99 CAN | Format: TP | On sale: 10/30/2018 | FOR MATURE READERS

BATMAN

THE COURT OF OWLS SAGA (DC ESSENTIAL EDITION)

ESSENTIAL EDITIONS

A NEW ERA FOR THE DARK KNIGHT AND GOTHAM CITY BEGINS HERE IN THIS #1 *NEW YORK TIMES* BESTSELLER!

"[WRITER SCOTT SNYDER] PULLS FROM THE OLDEST ASPECTS OF THE BATMAN MYTH, COMBINES IT WITH SINISTER COMIC ELEMENTS FROM THE SERIES' BEST PERIOD AND GIVES THE WHOLE THING A TERRIFIC FORWARD-SPIN BY SETTING UP AN HONEST-TO-GOSH MYSTERY FOR BATMAN TO SOLVE." –ENTERTAINMENT WEEKLY

"A STUNNING DEBUT.... THIS IS DEFINITELY IN THE TOP RANK OF THE REVAMP." –A.V. CLUB/THE ONION

Batman has heard tales of Gotham City's Court of Owls: that the members of this powerful cabal are the true rulers of Gotham. The Dark Knight dismissed the stories as rumors and old wives' tales. Gotham was his city. Until now.

A brutal assassin is sinking his razor-sharp talons into the city's best and brightest, as well as its most dangerous and deadly. If the dark legends are true, his masters are more powerful predators than the Batman could ever imagine.

With every year that passes, Scott Snyder and Greg Capullo's masterpiece becomes more entrenched in this medium's pantheon of the greatest stories ever told.

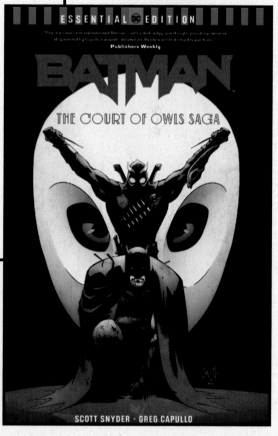

"THIS IS A CLEVER AND SOPHISTICATED BATMAN—WITH A DARK, EDGY, AND THOUGHT-PROVOKING NARRATIVE ABLY ABETTED BY CAPULLO'S PULPISH, DETAILED ART. READERS WILL FIND IT HARD TO PUT DOWN." –PUBLISHERS WEEKLY, STARRED

BATMAN: THE COURT OF OWLS SAGA (DC ESSENTIAL EDITION)

Writer: Scott Snyder | Artist: Greg Capullo | ISBN: 9781401284336 | Diamond Code: JUN180569 | Price: $24.99/$33.99 CAN | Format: TP

A DARK
PORTRAIT OF
OPPRESSION
AND
RESISTANCE
SET AGAINST
THE BACKDROP
OF DYSTOPIAN
FUTURE
ENGLAND

"DARK, GRIPPING
STORYTELLING."
–ENTERTAINMENT
WEEKLY

V FOR VENDETTA

A visionary graphic novel that defines sophisticated storytelling, Alan Moore's best-selling *V For Vendetta* is a terrifying portrait of totalitarianism and resistance, superbly illustrated by artist David Lloyd.

Set in a futuristic, totalitarian England, a country without freedom or faith, a mysterious man in a white porcelain mask strikes back against the oppressive overlords on behalf of the voiceless. This powerful story detailing the loss of and fight for individuality has become a cultural touchstone and an enduring allegory for current events.

ALAN **MOORE**   DAVID **LLOYD**
WITH **STEVE WHITAKER** AND **SIOBHAN DODDS**

V FOR VENDETTA

VERTIGO

"A DARKLY PHILOSOPHICAL VOICE IN THE MEDIUM
OF COMIC BOOKS—A RARE TALENT."
–THE NEW YORK TIMES

V FOR VENDETTA

Writer: Alan Moore | Artist: David Lloyd | ISBN: 9781401208417 | Diamond Code: SEP088030 | Price: $19.99/$23.99 CAN | Format: TP

SUPERGIRL: BEING SUPER

A COMING-OF-AGE TALE FULL OF HEART AND TEENAGE IRONY

"A PERFECT BALANCE BETWEEN WHAT ONE MIGHT EXPECT IN A MORE REALISTIC, 'LITERATURE'-STYLE COMIC BOOK AND A SUPERHERO COMIC."
—SCHOOL LIBRARY JOURNAL

"A GATEWAY FOR NEW READERS."
—HOLLYWOOD REPORTER

"THIS IS THE MOST GROUNDED, AUTHENTIC SUPERGIRL I THINK I'VE EVER READ."
—THE MARY SUE

From Mariko Tamaki, author of the Caldecott Honor, Printz, Eisner and Ignatz award-winning book *This One Summer*.

Kara Danvers isn't any different from the other teenagers in her hometown. Problems with school. Problems with boys. Problems with friends. But while growing pains shake up Kara's world, a series of earthshaking events hits her hometown, leaving her with the choice of blending in with the crowd, or being different. Being an outcast. Being super.

Supergirl: Being Super is more than just a tale about heroics, flying and crushing diamonds with your bare hands. It's the heartfelt story of Kara and her attempts to balance the arduous roles of teenager and hero.

"This is the most grounded, authentic Supergirl I think I've ever read." —The Mary Sue

"AN INTERESTING CHOICE FOR THOSE LOOKING FOR MORE THAN THE USUAL HERO FARE."
—KIRKUS REVIEWS

SUPERGIRL: BEING SUPER

Writer: Mariko Tamaki | Artist: Joëlle Jones | ISBN: 9781401268947 | Diamond Code: FEB180311 | Price: $16.99/$22.99 CAN | Format: TP

BATMAN: HUSH

IN ONE OF THE MOST ACCESSIBLE GRAPHIC NOVELS EVER WRITTEN, SUPERSTAR CREATORS JEPH LOEB AND JIM LEE DIG DEEP INTO THE DARK KNIGHT'S ROGUES GALLERY FOR THIS EPIC ADVENTURE

"THE REAL STAR ... IS JIM LEE'S ART, WHICH JUST MIGHT BE HIS BEST WORK IN HIS TIME AT DC COMICS." –IGN

Gotham City's worst criminals have emerged to throw Batman's life into utter chaos. However, these villains—the Joker, Riddler, Ra's al Ghul, Clayface and others—are part of a much more elaborate, sinister scheme to destroy the Dark Knight once and for all. Pushed past his breaking point, Batman will need to use more than the world's greatest detective skills to uncover the true mastermind behind this murderous plot before those closest to Bruce Wayne suffer the consequences.

In this truly unforgettable story by two of comics' top talents, writer Jeph Loeb and DC publisher Jim Lee present the Caped Crusader's most personal case yet.

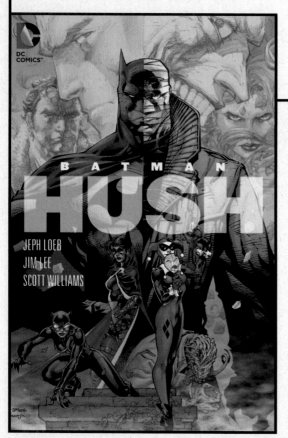

"IT'S BEAUTIFUL STUFF. CATWOMAN HAS RARELY LOOKED SO SEDUCTIVE, NOR HAS BATMAN'S HEROIC BUT FEARSOME IMAGE OFTEN BEEN USED SO WELL. [HUSH] MAKE[S] READERS LOOK AT BATMAN AND HIS COLLEAGUES WITH A FRESH, ENTHUSIASTIC EYE." –PUBLISHERS WEEKLY

BATMAN: HUSH

Writer: Jeph Loeb | Artist: Jim Lee | ISBN: 9781401223175 | Diamond Code: MAY090178 | Price: $24.99/$33.99 CAN | Format: TP

BATMAN:
WHITE KNIGHT

"UNLIKE ANYTHING WE'VE SEEN BEFORE." —NERDIST

The impossible has happened: the Joker has become ... sane. Calling himself Gotham's newest protector, the Joker now spearheads a task force to take down the dangerous masked vigilante known as Batman. After years of epic battles, the Clown Prince of Crime's fight for good in Gotham City may just cause Batman to go over the edge of his own sanity.

Writer/artist Sean Murphy (*Punk Rock Jesus*) takes the helm of this Batman/Joker story like no one else could, delivering an alternative examination of the relationship between the greatest rivals in the DC Universe and exploring the darkest corners of justice and madness.

Batman: White Knight is the first graphic novel in the new DC Black Label imprint. DC Black Label, a new publishing imprint from DC Entertainment, gives premier talent the opportunity to expand upon the canon of DC's iconic superhero comic book characters with unique, provocative standalone stories that are outside of the current DC Universe continuity.

"CINEMATIC AND GRAPHIC." —A.V. CLUB

"MURPHY WAS TRULY BORN TO DRAW BATMAN." —IGN

BATMAN: WHITE KNIGHT

Writer: Sean Murphy | Artist: Sean Murphy | ISBN: 9781401279592 | Diamond Code: JUL180733 | Price: $19.99/$25.99 CAN | Format: TP

CRITICALLY ACCLAIMED WRITER BRIAN AZZARELLO TEAMS WITH CLIFF CHIANG AND TONY AKINS TO CREATE A NEW WONDER WOMAN MYTHOLOGY

WONDER WOMAN VOL. 1: BLOOD

Experience a bold new beginning for the iconic character in *Wonder Woman Vol. 1: Blood*—a critically acclaimed and best-selling series!

Wonder Woman's world is shattered when a secret her mother, Hippolyta, queen of the Amazons, kept all her life is revealed: Diana is not clay brought to life, but is in fact the child of Zeus! In this reimagining of Diana's history, superheroics and mythology seamlessly blend as Brian Azzarello (*Joker, 100 Bullets*) creates a new direction for one of the world's best-known heroes. With stunning art by Cliff Chiang and Tony Akins, Wonder Woman has never looked better.

"BEAUTIFULLY ILLUSTRATED AND BRINGS A FRESH, FASCINATING AND FUN TAKE TO THE AMAZON PRINCESS AND HER WORLD." —IGN

"AZZARELLO IS ... REBUILDING THE MYTHOLOGY OF WONDER WOMAN." —MAXIM

"IT'S A DIFFERENT DIRECTION FOR WONDER WOMAN, BUT ONE STILL STEEPED IN MYTHOLOGY ... GREAT THINGS FROM AZZARELLO AND CHIANG." —A.V. CLUB/THE ONION

WONDER WOMAN VOLUME 1: BLOOD

Writer: Brian Azzarello | Artists: Cliff Chiang & Tony Akins | ISBN: 9781401235628 | Diamond Code: OCT120256

Price: $14.99/$17.99 CAN | Format: TP

BATMAN:
YEAR ONE

THE TIMELESS ORIGIN STORY OF THE DARK KNIGHT

> "IT'S NOT ONLY ONE OF THE MOST IMPORTANT COMICS EVER WRITTEN, IT'S ALSO AMONG THE BEST." —IGN

In 1986 Frank Miller and David Mazzucchelli produced this groundbreaking reinterpretation of the origin of Batman—who he is, and how he came to be. Sometimes careless and naive, this Dark Knight is far from the flawless vigilante he is today. In his first year on the job, Batman feels his way around a Gotham City far darker than the one he left. His solemn vow to extinguish the town's criminal element is only half the battle; along with Lieutenant James Gordon, the Dark Knight must also fight a police force more corrupt than the scum in the streets.

Batman: Year One stands next to *Batman: The Dark Knight Returns* as one of the greatest Batman graphic novels of all time. Timeless in its appeal, Frank Miller and David Mazzucchelli's masterpiece would stand out in the crowded comics field even today.

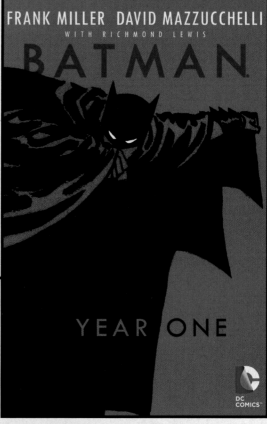

> "THERE'S NEVER BEEN STORYTELLING QUITE LIKE THIS. IT TOOK SOMEONE WHO VIEWS COMICS AS AN ART TO CREATE IT." —WASHINGTON POST

> "THIS IS A STORY NO TRUE BATMAN FAN SHOULD BE ABLE TO RESIST." —SCHOOL LIBRARY JOURNAL

BATMAN: YEAR ONE

Writer: Frank Miller | Artist: David Mazzucchelli | ISBN: 9781401207526 | Diamond Code: OCT060163
Price: $14.99/$17.99 CAN | Format: TP

ALL-STAR SUPERMAN

"MANIACALLY BRILLIANT."
–THE NEW YORK TIMES

THE CRITICALLY ACCLAIMED, GENRE-BENDING SERIES THAT HEARKENS BACK TO THE GOLDEN AGE OF SUPERMAN

The Underverse ruled by Bizarros. The time-eating Chronovore. Jimmy Olsen, superhero? Nothing is impossible in *All-Star Superman*.

The unstoppable creative team of writer Grant Morrison and artist Frank Quitely join forces once more to take Superman back to basics. In an emotionally and visually stunning graphic novel harkening back to the Golden Age of Comics, *All-Star Superman* creates a new, and at the same time familiar, take on the world's first superhero.

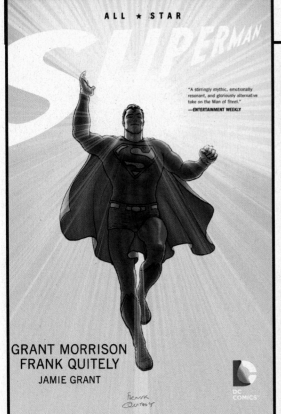

ALL ★ STAR
SUPERMAN

"A stirringly mythic, emotionally resonant, and gloriously alternative take on the Man of Steel."
—ENTERTAINMENT WEEKLY

GRANT MORRISON
FRANK QUITELY
JAMIE GRANT

DC COMICS

"A STIRRINGLY MYTHIC, EMOTIONALLY RESONANT, AND GLORIOUSLY ALTERNATIVE TAKE ON THE MAN OF STEEL." –ENTERTAINMENT WEEKLY

"TAKING THE MAN OF STEEL BACK TO HIS ROOTS AND INTO THE FUTURE AT THE SAME TIME, ALL-STAR SUPERMAN IS EXCITING, BOLD AND SUPERCOOL … ALL THE MAKINGS OF A CLASSIC." –VARIETY

ALL-STAR SUPERMAN

Writer: Grant Morrison | Artist: Frank Quitely | ISBN: 9781401232054 | Diamond Code: JUL110247

Price: $29.99/$35.00 CAN | Format: TP

THE FLASH:

STARTING LINE (DC ESSENTIAL EDITION)

ESSENTIAL EDITIONS

"A VISUAL TREAT ... ANY READER CAN EASILY JUMP ON BOARD."
—THE NEW YORK TIMES

A BOLD NEW VISION OF THE SCARLET SPEEDSTER, BREATHTAKINGLY RENDERED BY ONE OF COMICS' BEST ARTISTS

Struck by a bolt of lightning and doused in chemicals, Central City police scientist Barry Allen was transformed into the Fastest Man Alive. But there are some things even the Flash can't outrun. Trying since his youth to solve his mother's murder, Barry has often ignored what was in front of his very eyes. And that personal grudge might end up affecting the Flash just as much as his alter ego.

Written and gorgeously illustrated by the creative tag team of Francis Manapul and Brian Buccellato, *The Flash: Starting Line (DC Essential Edition)* is the perfect vision of the Scarlet Speedster brought to life. This stunning graphic novel is one of the fastest and easiest entry points in all of DC Comics' vast library.

"THE FLASH IS SIMPLY COMICS AT ITS FINEST."
—POPMATTERS

"THIS IS WHY COMIC BOOKS ARE AWESOME."
—CRAVEONLINE

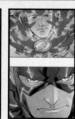

THE FLASH: STARTING LINE (DC ESSENTIAL EDITION)

Writers: Francis Manapul & Brian Buccellato | Artist: Francis Manapul | ISBN: 9781401284763

Diamond Code: JUL180755 | Price: $24.99/$33.99 CAN | Format: TP | On sale: 10/30/2018 | COVER NOT FINAL

MISTER MIRACLE

ALREADY A CLASSIC IN THE MAKING, THIS MISTER MIRACLE IS MAGICAL, DARK, INTIMATE AND UNLIKE ANYTHING YOU'VE READ BEFORE

From Hugo and Eisner Award-winning writer Tom King and artist Mitch Gerads, the team behind *The Sheriff Of Babylon*, comes an ambitious new take on one of Jack Kirby's most beloved New Gods in *Mister Miracle*!

Scott Free is the greatest escape artist who ever lived. So great, he escaped Granny Goodness' gruesome orphanage and the dangers of Apokolips to travel across galaxies and set up a new life on Earth with his wife, Big Barda. Using the stage alter ego of Mister Miracle, he has made quite a career for himself showing off his acrobatic escape techniques. He even caught the attention of the Justice League, which has counted him among its ranks.

You might say Scott Free has everything—so why isn't it enough? Mister Miracle has mastered every illusion, achieved every stunt, pulled off every trick—except one. He has never escaped death. Is it even possible? Our hero is going to have to kill himself if he wants to find out.

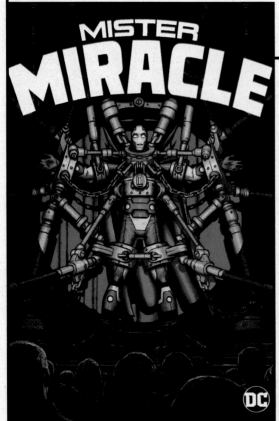

"HEARTBREAKING, FUNNY, AND HUMAN, IT'S AN ALL-TIME CLASSIC IN THE MAKING." —WIRED

"ONE OF THE MOST MIND-BENDING SUPERHERO COMICS CURRENTLY ON STANDS." —ENTERTAINMENT WEEKLY

MISTER MIRACLE

Writer: Tom King | Artist: Mitch Gerads | ISBN: 9781401283544 | Diamond Code: STL096816 | Price: $24.99/$33.99 CAN | Format: TP

On sale: 1/22/2019 | FOR MATURE READERS | COVER NOT FINAL

DC SUPER HERO GIRLS: FINALS CRISIS

WELCOME TO SUPER HERO HIGH! CLASS IS NOW IN SESSION!

"A YOUTHFUL TWIST ON POPULAR CHARACTERS."
—LOS ANGELES TIMES

A NEW YORK TIMES BESTSELLER

Prepping for high school finals is hard enough, but at Super Hero High, even the tests are super-tough! Supergirl, Bumblebee, Wonder Woman, Batgirl, Harley Quinn, Katana and Poison Ivy are studying hard when they are trapped by a mysterious villain! Will the students outsmart their captor, save Metropolis, and still pass their finals?

DC Super Hero Girls is an exciting new universe of super heroic storytelling that helps build character and confidence, and empowers girls to discover their true potential. Developed for girls ages 6-12, this graphic novel series features DC Comics' most powerful and diverse lineup of female characters as relatable teens. *DC Super Hero Girls: Finals Crisis* has bridged the gap between over seventy years of DC storytelling and a brand-new audience of young readers who want to read more about them. Beginning with *Finals Crisis*, this line of graphic novels is not just a powerful piece of graphic storytelling, but a piece of literature that parents can use to share their love of DC characters with their children.

"DC COMICS FANS GET A NICE INTRODUCTION TO THE FUN, FUNNY WORLD OF SUPER HERO HIGH."
—SCHOOL LIBRARY JOURNAL

DC SUPER HERO GIRLS: FINALS CRISIS

Writer: Shea Fontana | Artist: Yancey Labat | ISBN: 9781401262471 | Diamond Code: APR160322 | Price: $9.99/$13.50 CAN | Format: TP

DARK NIGHTS: METAL

A JAM-PACKED ROCK 'N' ROLL MYSTERY THAT SPANS THE ENTIRE HISTORY OF THE DC UNIVERSE! FROM *NEW YORK TIMES* BEST-SELLING *BATMAN* TEAM AND MASTER STORYTELLERS SCOTT SNYDER AND GREG CAPULLO

The Dark Multiverse is coming, and nothing will ever be the same! Beyond our universe is the Multiverse ... and beneath the Multiverse is a nightmare realm where every fear that has ever been felt on our Earth becomes reality. When the door between worlds opens, it's not just any nightmares that come spilling out. They call themselves the Dark Knights, and each one is a twisted version of Batman from a world where one of his worst fears has come true.

Best-selling writer Scott Snyder and artist Greg Capullo use the broad expanse of the DC Universe for their next great epic, as they obliterate expectations and weave a Multiverse-spanning saga in this incredible graphic novel.

"METAL IS A CELEBRATION OF THE WACKIEST, CRAZIEST, MOST OUTRIGHT FUN ELEMENTS OF THE DC UNIVERSE." –ENTERTAINMENT WEEKLY

"WHERE NIGHTMARES AND REALITY COLLIDE." –WASHINGTON POST

"THIS IS THE WORK OF TWO MEN AT THE TOP OF THEIR GAMES." –NEW YORK POST

"THIS IS A BOOK YOU NEED TO READ. WHETHER YOU'RE A FAN OF COMICS OR NOT." –HUFFINGTON POST

"PACKED AS IT IS WITH BOTH REAL STEEL AND ROCK 'N ROLL." –SYFY WIRE

DARK NIGHTS: METAL: DELUXE EDITION

Writer: Scott Snyder | Artist: Greg Capullo | ISBN: 9781401277321 | Diamond Code: JAN180379 | Price: $29.99/$39.99 CAN | Format: HC

A CLASSIC BATMAN MURDER MYSTERY BY THE ICONIC CREATIVE TEAM OF JEPH LOEB AND TIM SALE

BATMAN: THE LONG HALLOWEEN

Just after Batman's first year in Gotham City, the Dark Knight finds himself working alongside District Attorney Harvey Dent and Lieutenant James Gordon, trying to vanquish the criminal element. However, a serial killer known only as Holiday has been killing friends and foes each month. Batman races against the calendar trying to discover the assassin's identity, fighting the entirety of Gotham's rogues gallery along the way.

The magnificent creative team of Jeph Loeb and Tim Sale reach their apex in *Batman: The Long Halloween*, propelling the graphic novel to its place among comics' finest murder mystery stories.

> "*THE LONG HALLOWEEN* STRETCHES BEYOND THE NORMAL BOUNDARIES OF COMICS TO CREATE A LEGENDARY STORY OF ONE MAN'S CRUSADE AGAINST AN INSANE WORLD." —IGN

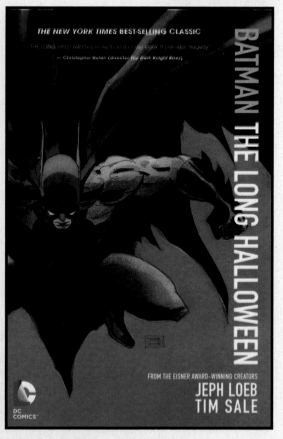

> "*THE LONG HALLOWEEN* IS MORE THAN A COMIC BOOK. IT'S AN EPIC TRAGEDY." —CHRISTOPHER NOLAN (DIRECTOR OF *BATMAN BEGINS*, *THE DARK KNIGHT* AND *THE DARK KNIGHT RISES*)

BATMAN: THE LONG HALLOWEEN

Writer: Jeph Loeb | Artist: Tim Sale | ISBN: 9781401232597 | Diamond Code: JUL110251 | Price: $24.99/$33.99 CAN | Format: TP

AQUAMAN:
WAR FOR THE THRONE

AN EPIC TALE OF CONFLICT AND CONQUEST FROM AWARD-WINNING AUTHOR GEOFF JOHNS

"IT'S DRAMATIC, ENGAGING AND EXPERTLY RENDERED." -IGN

Six years ago he was a surface dweller, raised as the son of a lighthouse keeper. Then tragedy struck. Destiny was revealed. And young Arthur Curry claimed his birthright:

The Throne of Atlantis.

But his reign was brief. When darkness threatened the surface world, he rose to meet it. As Aquaman, he joined the team of heroes called the Justice League, leaving the rule of his kingdom behind. But even underwater, the past will not stay buried. A sinister force is pushing Aquaman's two worlds to the brink of war, with the fate of the planet in the balance. If Arthur does not reclaim his throne, the throne may well claim his life....

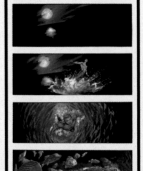

AQUAMAN: WAR FOR THE THRONE
Writers: Geoff Johns | Artist: Ivan Reis | ISBN: 9781401283582 | Diamond Code: AUG180587 | Price: $12.99/$17.50 CAN

Format: TP | On sale: 11/27/2018 | COVER NOT FINAL

IDENTITY CRISIS

BEST-SELLING AUTHOR BRAD MELTZER WEAVES A MURDER MYSTERY IN THE DC UNIVERSE!

> "THE *IDENTITY CRISIS* MYSTERY INVOLVES THE BIGGEST DC HEROES ... AND USE[S] ALL OF MR. MELTZER'S SKILLS AS A THRILLER NOVELIST."
> —THE NEW YORK TIMES

New York Times best-selling author Brad Meltzer (*The President's Shadow*, *House of Secrets*) delivers a look into the all-too-human lives of superheroes. When the spouse of a member of the Justice League of America is brutally murdered, the entire superhero community searches for the killer, fearing their own loved ones may be the next targets. But before the mystery is fully solved, long-buried secrets rise to the surface, threatening to tear apart and divide the heroes before they can bring the mysterious killer to justice.

Rife with intrigue and tragedy, Meltzer brings the nuance and suspense of a mystery novel to the printed page, turning our conception of the mythological Justice League on its head and showing the deep humanity in our favorite heroes. With pencils by the divine Rags Morales, *Identity Crisis* is one of the great tales in Justice League lore.

> "MORALES'S MUSCULAR NATURALISM RENDERS THE PLAYERS BOTH TIMELESSLY ICONIC AND BELIEVABLY HUMAN...." —WASHINGTON POST

> "REFRESHING ... UNDERSCORE[S] THAT THESE ARE VERY HUMAN CHARACTERS IN A VERY RISKY BUSINESS." —ENTERTAINMENT WEEKLY

DC COMICS™

FROM #1 *NEW YORK TIMES* BEST-SELLING NOVELIST

BRAD MELTZER
RAGS MORALES

IDENTITY CRISIS™

"The IDENTITY CRISIS mystery involves the biggest DC heroes. . . And use[s] all of Mr. Meltzer's skills as a thriller novelist."
THE NEW YORK TIMES

IDENTITY CRISIS

Writer: Brad Meltzer | Artist: Rags Morales | ISBN: 9781401263133 | Diamond Code: NOV150278 | Price: $19.99/$25.99 CAN | Format: TP

GREEN LANTERN: EARTH ONE VOL 1.

AN *ALIEN*-MEETS-*INTERSTELLAR* ORIGIN STORY FOR HAL JORDAN THAT HEARKENS BACK TO HAL JORDAN'S SILVER AGE ROOTS

Hal Jordan yearns for the thrill of discovery, but the days when astronaut and adventure were synonymous are long gone. His gig prospecting asteroids for Ferris Galactic is less than fulfilling—but at least he's not on Earth, where technology and culture have stagnated.

When Jordan finds a powerful ring, he also finds a destiny to live up to. There are worlds beyond his own, unlike anything he ever imagined. But revelation comes with a price: the Green Lantern Corps has fallen, wiped out by ruthless killing machines known as Manhunters. The odds against reinstating the Corps are nearly impossible ... but doing the impossible is exactly what Hal Jordan was trained to do!

From creators Gabriel Hardman and Corinna Bechko comes a soaring intergalactic adventure, reimagining Hal Jordan and the Green Lantern Corps for a new generation.

> "THE EARTH ONE LINE IS INTRODUCING DC'S HEROES TO A NEW GENERATION." —*THE NEW YORK TIMES*

> "A GRITTY SCI-FI APPROACH AKIN TO *ALIEN*." —*IGN*

> "A MODERN, GROUNDED SCI-FI STORY." —*HOLLYWOOD REPORTER*

> "PUTS A FEMINIST SPIN ON A FAMILIAR SUPERHERO STORY." —*BUST*

GREEN LANTERN: EARTH ONE VOL. 1

Writer: Gabriel Hardman and Corrina Bechko | Artist: Gabriel Hardman | ISBN: 9781401241865 | Diamond Code: DEC170239

Price: $24.99/$33.99 CAN | Format: HC

JUSTICE LEAGUE VOL. 1:
ORIGIN

GEOFF JOHNS AND JIM LEE UNITE FOR THE FIRST TIME TO LAUNCH THE BOLD NEW BEGINNING OF THE DC UNIVERSE'S PREMIER SUPERHERO TEAM!

Two of the greatest titans of the comics industry come together to tell the definitive story featuring the World's Greatest Super Heroes in *Justice League Vol. 1: Origin*.

It's the dawn of a new age of superheroes, frightening to the world at large. Superman. Batman. The Flash. Wonder Woman. Green Lantern. Aquaman. Cyborg. Though young and inexperienced, brash and overconfident, each one alone is a powerful force in the battle of good against evil. Together, they may be the only thing on Earth that can stop the alien warlord Darkseid from claiming our planet as his own. Together they will become the Justice League!

This indelible recasting of the World's Greatest Heroes has only grown in stature as the years have worn on, with fans everywhere gaining a greater and greater appreciation for this masterwork in the genre. *Justice League Vol. 1: Origin* has come to be emblematic of the word "Essential."

"WRITER GEOFF JOHNS AND ARTIST JIM LEE TOSS YOU—AND THEIR HEROES—INTO THE ACTION FROM THE VERY START AND DON'T PUT ON THE BRAKES. DC'S ÜBER-CREATIVE TEAM CRAFT AN INVITING WORLD FOR THOSE WHO ARE TRYING OUT A COMIC FOR THE FIRST TIME." –USA TODAY

"A MUST-READ." –COMPLEX MAGAZINE

GEOFF **JOHNS** JIM **LEE** SCOTT **WILLIAMS**

"WELCOMING TO NEW FANS LOOKING TO GET INTO SUPERHERO COMICS FOR THE FIRST TIME AND OLD FANS WHO GAVE UP ON THE FUNNY-BOOKS LONG AGO." –MTV GEEK

JUSTICE LEAGUE VOL. 1: ORIGIN

Writer: Geoff Johns | Artist: Jim Lee | ISBN: 9781401237882 | Diamond Code: OCT120252 | Price: $16.99/$19.99 CAN | Format: TP

BATMAN VOL. 1:
I AM GOTHAM

ACCLAIMED WRITER TOM KING (*THE SHERIFF OF BABYLON, THE VISION*) INTRODUCES STARTLING NEW HEROES INTO THE WORLD OF BATMAN!

The Caped Crusader has never been stopped. Not by the Joker. Not by Two-Face. Not even by the Justice League. But now, in the wake of *DC Universe: Rebirth*, Batman faces his most challenging foe ever—the idealistic superhero known as Gotham, who wants to save the city from Batman himself!

When sinister forces are unleashed that can warp the minds of men and make heroes into monsters, the time will come for Batman and his allies to decide once and for all whether Gotham is a force for good or evil.

Writer Tom King installs himself amongst the greatest *Batman* writers of all time with this incredible jumping-on-point graphic novel, as he takes the Dark Knight on a psychological journey as few other authors could.

DC UNIVERSE REBIRTH

BATMAN

VOL.1 I AM GOTHAM
TOM KING • DAVID FINCH

"[TOM KING] CRAFTS AN INCREDIBLE STORY." —NERDIST

"A CLEAN, SIMPLE GATEWAY INTO THE BATMAN FRANCHISE...." —IGN

"KING SETS A NEW STAGE AND TONE FOR BATMAN AND GOTHAM." —POPMATTERS

BATMAN VOL. 1: I AM GOTHAM

Writer: Tom King | Artist: David Finch | ISBN: 9781401267773 | Diamond Code: OCT160291 | Price: $16.99/$22.99 CAN | Format: TP

SUICIDE SQUAD:
KICKED IN THE TEETH

The story begins with the Suicide Squad defeated, imprisoned and being interrogated about their newest mission. Harley Quinn, King Shark, Deadshot and company must make it out alive without revealing who's pulling the strings behind their illegal operations. Who will be the first to crack under the pressure? More importantly, will they all make it out alive?

Adam Glass, writer and co-creator of the CW show *Supernatural*, rolls out an all-new team of death-row super-villains recruited by the government to take on missions so dangerous, they're sheer suicide!

> "A CLEVERLY WRITTEN, OUTSTANDING READ FROM BEGINNING TO END." —USA TODAY

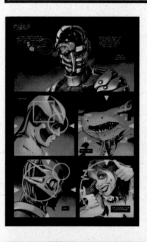

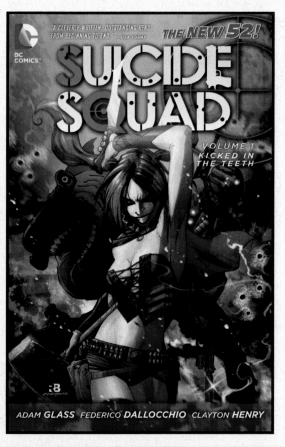

> "ITS HIGH-OCTANE NUTTINESS IS, AT TIMES, A ROCK-AND-ROLL DELIGHT." —VULTURE

SUICIDE SQUAD: KICKED IN THE TEETH

Writer: Adam Glass | Artist: Federico Dallocchio | ISBN: 9781401235444 | Diamond Code: APR120250

Price: $14.99/$17.99 CAN | Format: TP

WATCHMEN

THE GREATEST
GRAPHIC NOVEL OF ALL TIME

One of the most influential graphic novels of all time and a perennial bestseller, *Watchmen* is considered a gateway title to the entire graphic storytelling medium. Alan Moore and Dave Gibbons' seminal story is the benchmark against which all other graphic novels and comic books are judged.

A murder mystery turned nationwide conspiracy, *Watchmen* examines the lives of a former superhero team as they seem to decay alongside the ever-darkening America around them. Rorschach, Nite Owl, Silk Spectre, Dr. Manhattan and Ozymandias reunite to investigate who's behind a teammate's murder, but find that the truth may be even more grim than the world they seek to protect.

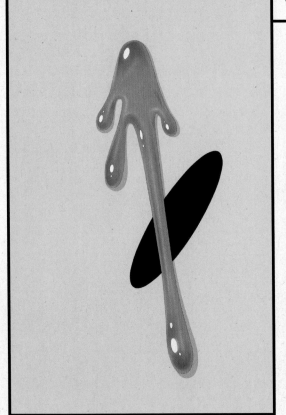

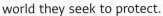

"A WORK OF RUTHLESS PSYCHOLOGICAL REALISM, IT'S A LANDMARK IN THE GRAPHIC NOVEL MEDIUM. IT WOULD BE A MASTERPIECE IN ANY."
–TIME, TIME'S 100 BEST ENGLISH-LANGUAGE NOVELS FROM 1923 TO THE PRESENT

"REMARKABLE. THE WOULD-BE HEROES OF **WATCHMEN** HAVE STAGGERINGLY COMPLEX PSYCHOLOGICAL PROFILES."
–THE NEW YORK TIMES BOOK REVIEW

"DARK, VIOLENT AND BLACKLY FUNNY, **WATCHMEN** IS A COMIC BOOK LIKE NO OTHER. [IT IS] THE CRIME AND PUNISHMENT OF GRAPHIC NOVELS."
–THE LONDON TIMES

WATCHMEN

Writer: Alan Moore | Artist: Dave Gibbons | ISBN: 9781401245252 | Diamond Code: FEB140265 | Price: $19.99/$25.99 CAN | Format: TP

DC UNIVERSE: REBIRTH
THE DELUXE EDITION

From Crisis, to Zero Hour, to a Flashpoint in time, to a New 52 universe, nothing has affected the World's Greatest Heroes as much as the threat that's careening toward them. Meanwhile, a mysterious force ripples across the cosmos, trying to warn them of this impending doom. That force? A returning Wally West.

This graphic novel brings together the incredible legacy of DC, with decades of mythology colliding with new characters and adventures, all launching us into a new era of vivid storytelling called DC Rebirth.

Written by Geoff Johns and illustrated by four of the industry's best artists—Gary Frank, Ivan Reis, Ethan Van Sciver and Phil Jimenez—*DC Universe: Rebirth* shatters all the unwritten rules in comics and from those pieces creates an all-new status quo for the DC Universe.

> THE COURSE OF THE DC UNIVERSE IS CHANGED FOREVER IN THIS HEARTFELT TALE OF LOVE, LOSS AND HOPE, ALL LEADING UP TO ONE OF THE MOST SHOCKING ENDINGS IN COMICS HISTORY

> "GEOFF JOHNS IS INJECTING HEART AND HUMANITY BACK INTO THE LIVES AND ADVENTURES OF DC COMICS' ICONIC SUPERHEROES."
> —USA TODAY

> "DELIVERS A JAW-DROPPING TWIST THAT WILL HAVE IMPLICATIONS FOR YEARS TO COME." —YAHOO! MOVIES

> "A COMPASS FOR THE NEW ERA."
> —WALL STREET JOURNAL

GEOFF JOHNS
GARY FRANK
ETHAN VAN SCIVER
IVAN REIS
PHIL JIMENEZ

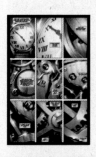

DC UNIVERSE: REBIRTH THE DELUXE EDITION

Writer: Geoff Johns | Artists: Gary Frank, Ivan Reis, Ethan Van Sciver and Phil Jimenez | ISBN: 9781401270728

Diamond Code: AUG160316 | Price: $17.99/23.99 CAN | Format: HC

THE WATCHMEN INVADE THE DC UNIVERSE

BATMAN/ THE FLASH: THE BUTTON DELUXE EDITION

> "KING, FABOK AND HOWARD PORTER PROVIDE ENOUGH ACTION FOR AN ENTIRE SUMMER'S WORTH OF BLOCKBUSTER MOVIES." –LIBRARY JOURNAL

During the unforgettable events of *DC Universe: Rebirth*, Batman encountered a mystery he can't even begin to solve—a strange bloodstained smiley-face button embedded in the Batcave wall. All analysis suggests the button is not of this universe ... so where did it come from? And who left it here? These are questions only the Flash can help answer.

When the button is stolen by the Reverse-Flash, Batman and Flash follow his trail to a parallel world, a twisted alternate timeline that shouldn't exist. Someone is sending the heroes on a bizarre trip through reality, showing them glimpses of fallen loved ones and forgotten friends—but who? Wally West warned the Flash of an unseen force influencing our world—distorting histories, pulling the strings, watching all—and the strange yellow button could be the key to finding it.

> "THERE'S NO MORE EXCITING STORYLINE IN SUPERHERO COMICS RIGHT NOW." –IGN

BATMAN/THE FLASH: THE BUTTON DELUXE EDITION

Writers: Tom King & Joshua Williamson | Artists: Jason Fabok & Howard Porter | ISBN: 9781401276447 | Diamond Code: JUN170380

Price: $19.99/$25.99 CAN | Format: HC

The *Watchmen* characters and the DC Universe come together for the first time! The story that began in *DC Universe: Rebirth* comes to a thrilling and unexpected crescendo in the pages of this titanic series by the creative team of writer Geoff Johns and artist Gary Frank.

Secrets will be revealed as the Doomsday Clock ticks on....

DOOMSDAY CLOCK
No. 1 of 12

DC

THE END IS HERE

JANUARY 2018

"Doomsday Clock has echoes aplenty.... Should look very familiar to *Watchmen* readers."
—*Entertainment Weekly*

'There seems to be two kinds of comics—gritty, dark, and serious on the one hand, lighthearted and funny on the other. Somehow, the first installment of *Doomsday Clock* does the impossible:

New York Gazette
THE GREAT LIE

DC Black Label, a new publishing imprint from DC Entertainment, gives premier talent the opportunity to expand upon the canon of DC's iconic superhero comic book characters with unique, standalone stories that are outside of the current DC Universe continuity. An all-star lineup of creative teams will craft their own personal definitive DC stories in the tradition of compelling literary works like *Batman: The Killing Joke*, *DC: The New Frontier* and *Kingdom Come*.

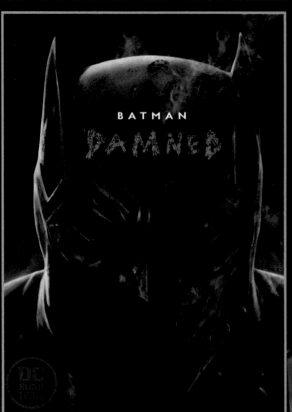

Batman: Damned is a supernatural horror story told by two of comics' greatest modern creators, *New York Times* best-selling author Brian Azzarello (*100 Bullets*, *Joker*) and visionary artist Lee Bermejo (*Luthor*, *Joker*). This is a visceral thrill-ride that proudly puts the "black" in Black Label.

The Joker is dead. There is no doubt about that, but whether Batman finally snapped his scrawny neck is still a mystery. But even Batman can't remember—and the more he digs into this labyrinthian case, the more his mind starts to doubt everything he's uncovering. So who better to set him straight than … John Constantine? With John's "help," the pair will delve into the sordid underbelly of Gotham as they race toward the mind-blowing truth of who murdered The Joker.

BATMAN: DAMNED

Writer: Brian Azzarello | Artist: Lee Bermejo | ISBN: 9781401291402 | Diamond Code: JUN188708 | Price: $24.99/$33.99 CAN

Format: HC | On sale: 6/18/2019

BATMAN: WHITE KNIGHT

Visionary creator Sean Murphy unveils his radical take on the greatest rivalry in comics.

The impossible has happened: the Joker has become ... sane. Calling himself Gotham's newest protector, the Joker now spearheads a task force to take down the dangerous masked vigilante known as Batman. After years of epic battles, the Clown Prince of Crime's fight for good in Gotham City may just cause Batman to go over the edge of his own sanity.

Writer: Sean Murphy | Artist: Sean Murphy | ISBN: 9781401279592 | Diamond Code: JUL180733
Price: $19.99/$25.99 CAN | Format: TP | On sale: 10/9/2018

"UNLIKE ANYTHING WE'VE SEEN BEFORE." —NERDIST

SUPERMAN: YEAR ONE

A groundbreaking, definitive treatment of Superman's classic origin story in honor of his 80th anniversary.

Superman: Year One details new revelations that reframe the Man of Steel's most famous milestones—from Kal-El's frantic escape from Krypton, to Clark Kent's childhood in Kansas, to his inevitable rise to become the most powerful and inspiring superhero of all time. From best-selling author Frank Miller (*Batman: The Dark Night Returns, Batman: Year One*) and artist John Romita Jr. (*All-Star Batman*).

Writer: Frank Miller | Artist: John Romita Jr. | ISBN: 9781401291372 | Price: $24.99/$33.99 CAN
Diamond Code: JUN188709 | Format: HC | On sale: 9/10/2019

KINGDOM COME

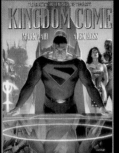

Mark Waid and artist Alex Ross's multiple Eisner and Harvey Award-winning, seminal masterpiece *Kingdom Come* is now part of DC Black Label.

In the near-future world of *Kingdom Come*, superheroes are ubiquitous, but heroism is rare. After decades as Earth's champions, the members of the Justice League have all retreated out of the public eye, replaced with a new generation of crime-fighters whose brand of harsh justice leaves humanity terrified, rather than inspired. But with the planet's future in jeopardy, Superman, Wonder Woman and Batman must come out of retirement to make one last stand for truth and justice.

"ONE OF THE BEST COMIC STORIES EVER TOLD."
—*WASHINGTON EXAMINER*

Writer: Mark Waid | Artist: Alex Ross | ISBN: 9781401290962 | Diamond Code: JUN188688 | Price: $19.99/$25.99 CAN | Format: TP | On sale: 4/23/2019

EXPLORE THESE GRAPHIC NOVELS BY JEPH LOEB

BATMAN: THE LONG HALLOWEEN

Working with District Attorney Harvey Dent and Lieutenant James Gordon, Batman races against the calendar as he tries to discover who Holiday is before he claims his next victim each month. A mystery that has the reader continually guessing the identity of the killer, this story also ties into the events that transform Harvey Dent into Batman's deadly enemy, Two-Face.

Writer: Jeph Loeb | Artist: Tim Sale | ISBN:9781401292881 | $24.99/$33.99 CAN | Format: TP | On sale: 11/5/2019

BATMAN: DARK VICTORY

Once a place controlled by organized crime, Gotham City suddenly finds itself being run by lawless characters such as Poison Ivy, Mr. Freeze and the Joker.

Writer: Jeph Loeb | Artist: Tim Sale | ISBN:9781401292898
$24.99/$33.99 CAN | Format: TP | On sale: 11/26/2019

BATMAN: HAUNTED KNIGHT

The creative team behind *Batman: The Long Halloween* and *Batman: Dark Victory* brings you their prelude to their all-time classic graphic novels in *Batman: Haunted Knight!*

Writer: Jeph Loeb | Artist: Tim Sale | ISBN:9781401292904
$19.99/$25.99 CAN | Format: TP | On sale: 12/17/2019

ALL-STAR SUPERMAN

In an emotionally and visually stunning graphic novel harkening back to a Golden Age of comics, ALL-STAR SUPERMAN creates a new, and simultaneously familiar, take on the world's first superhero.

Writer: Grant Morrison | Artist: Frank Quitely | ISBN: 9781401290832
Diamond Code: AUG180593 | Price: $29.99/$39.99 CAN | Format: TP | On sale: 12/4/2018

DC: THE NEW FRONTIER

DC: The New Frontier takes readers on an epic journey from the end of the Golden Age of heroes to the beginnings of the legendary Justice League of America.

Writer: Darwyn Cooke | Artist: Darwyn Cooke| ISBN: 9781401290924
Diamond Code: JUN188674 | Price: $34.99/$45.99 CAN | Format: TP | On sale: 2/19/2019

ALL-STAR BATMAN & ROBIN, THE BOY WONDER VOL. 1

The high-octane origin story of Dick Grayson's transformation into Robin, the Boy Wonder. This ultimate tale of the Dynamic Duo features guest appearances by Superman, Wonder Woman, Green Lantern, Black Canary and Batgirl as you've never seen them before.

FRANK MILLER + JIM LEE

"MILLER ... RETURNS TO WRITE THE ICONIC CHARACTER ONCE AGAIN IN A SERIES THAT TAKES THE TROPES OF SUPERHERO EXCESS AND EXPLODES THEM INTO SATIRE."
—PUBLISHERS WEEKLY

Writer: Frank Miller | Artist: Jim Lee | ISBN: 9781401291242 | $19.99/$25.99 CAN | TP | On sale: 6/11/2019

EXPLORE FRANK MILLER'S DARK KNIGHT UNIVERSE

BATMAN: THE DARK KNIGHT RETURNS

It is ten years after an aging Batman retired and Gotham City has sunk deeper into decadence and lawlessness. Now as his city needs him most, the Dark Knight returns in a blaze of glory. Joined by Carrie Kelley, a teenage female Robin, Batman takes to the streets to end the threat of the mutant gangs that have overrun the city.

Writer: Frank Miller | Artist: Lynn Varley
ISBN: 9781401291525 | $19.99/$25.99 CAN | Format: TP | On sale: 6/18/2019

BATMAN: THE DARK KNIGHT RETURNS: THE LAST CRUSADE

As the Joker is manically returned to Arkham Asylum, Bruce Wayne is struggling to train his sidekick and heir apparent, the new Robin, Jason Todd. What does night after night of danger and brutality do to a child? And what is the Joker planning?

Writer: Frank Miller | Artist: John Ramita Jr.
ISBN: 9781401291624 | $14.99/$19.99 CAN | Format: TP | On sale: 6/25/2019

BATMAN: THE DARK KNIGHT STRIKES AGAIN

The Dark Knight returns once again with a vitality unseen since the first years of his war on crime. Together with his army of Bat-soldiers, the Dark Knight wages a new war on a diseased world that's become completely lost.

Writer: Frank Miller | Artist: Lynn Varley
ISBN: 9781401291464 | $19.99/$25.99 CAN | Format: TP | On sale: 6/18/2019

BATMAN: THE DARK KNIGHT: MASTER RACE

A new war is beginning. An army of unimaginable power led by Superman's own daughter is preparing to claim Earth as their new world.

Writer: Frank Miller | Artists: Andy Kubert, Klaus Janson, John Romita Jr.
ISBN: 9781401291600 | $24.99/$33.99 CAN | Format: TP | On sale: 6/25/2019

BATMAN: YEAR ONE

A young Bruce Wayne has spent his adolescence and early adulthood traveling the world to hone his body and mind into the perfect fighting and investigative machine. But now as he returns to Gotham City, he must find a way to focus his passion and bring justice to his city.

Writer: Frank Miller | Artist: David Mazzucchelli | ISBN: 9781401291228 | $16.99/$22.99 CAN
Format: TP | On sale: 6/11/2019

FRANK MILLER'S RONIN

In this tale of a legendary warrior, the Ronin, a dishonored, masterless 13th-century samurai, is mystically given a second chance to avenge his master's death, suddenly finding himself reborn in a futuristic and corrupt 21st-century New York City.

Writer: Frank Miller | Artist: Frank Miller| ISBN: 9781401290979
Diamond Code: JUN188679 | $19.99/$25.99 CAN | Format: TP | On sale: 5/7/2019

DC BOOKS FOR YOUNG READERS

DC Books for Young Readers brings the iconic superheroes of DC Entertainment to graphic novels for middle-grade and young adult readers.

    With world-class authors lending their expertise to brand-new standalone stories featuring the characters we know and love, these graphic novels will appeal to DC fans new and old.

DC Ink is for readers 13 and up, and features coming-of-age stories that encourage teens to ask themselves who they are and how they relate to others. DC Ink features storytelling that focuses on real-world situations and relatable characters who are not perfect, but are nuanced and complex—just like our readers.

MERA: TIDEBREAKER

From *New York Times* best-selling author Danielle Paige comes a Mera-and-Aquaman origin story that explores Mera's first steps on land and as a hero ... or a villain.

Writer: Danielle Paige | Artist: Stephen Byrne | ISBN: 9781401283391
Diamond Code: JUN188690 | Price: $16.99/$22.99 CAN | Format: TP | On sale: 4/2/2019

UNDER THE MOON: A CATWOMAN TALE

When 14-year-old Selina Kyle, the future Catwoman, becomes homeless, she must confront questions of who she is and who she will become. From Lauren Myracle, the *New York Times* best-selling author of *ttfn* and *ttyl*.

Writer: Lauren Myracle | Artist: Isaac Goodhart | ISBN: 9781401285913
Diamond Code: JUN188706 | Price: $16.99/$22.99 CAN | Format: TP | On sale: 5/7/2019

HARLEY QUINN: BREAKING GLASS

Harley Quinn: Breaking Glass is a coming-of-age story about choices, consequences, justice, fairness and progress, and how a weird kid from Gotham's poorest part of town goes about defining her world for herself. From Mariko Tamaki, author of Caldecott Honor-winning *This One Summer*.

Writer: Mariko Tamaki | Artist: Steve Pugh | ISBN: 9781401283292
Diamond Code: JUN188682 | Price: $16.99/$22.99 CAN | Format: TP | On sale: 6/4/2019

TEEN TITANS: RAVEN

After a fatal accident takes her memory, 16-year-old Raven is sent to New Orleans to start over. But she soon discovers that she can hear the thoughts of others ... and another disturbing voice in her head. From the *New York Times* best-selling author of *Beautiful Creatures*, Kami Garcia.

Writer: Kami Garcia | Artist: Gabriel Picolo
ISBN: 9781401286231 | Diamond Code: JUN188834 | Price: : $16.99/$22.99 CAN | Format: TP | On sale: 7/2/2019

BATMAN: NIGHTWALKER

Before he was Batman, he was Bruce Wayne—a reckless boy willing to break the rules for a girl who just might be his worst enemy. This is the highly-anticipated graphic novel adaptation of Marie Lu's instant *New York Times* best-selling novel!

Writer: Stuart Moore | Artist: Christian Wildgoose
ISBN: 9781401280048 | Diamond Code: JUN188671 | Price: $16.99/$22.99 CAN | Format: TP | On sale: 8/6/2019

SUPER SONS: THE POLARSHIELD PROJECT

Earth is facing its greatest crisis—and Superman and Batman are nowhere to be found. From *New York Times* best-selling author Ridley Pearson (*Kingdom Keepers*) and artist Ile Gonzalez comes the first book in an epic new series that follows the Super Sons of Superman and Batman as they struggle to find their place in a rapidly changing world!

Writer: Ridley Pearson | Artist: Ile Gonzalez | ISBN: 9781401286392 | Diamond Code: JUN188694 | Price: $9.99/$13.50 CAN | Format: TP | On sale: 4/2/2019

DC SUPER HERO GIRLS: SPACED OUT

There's a new student at Super Hero High, and she's about to take some of her new friends on an out-of-this-world mission!

Writer: Shea Fontana | Artist: Agnes Garbowska | ISBN: 9781401282561
Diamond Code: JUN188673
Price: $9.99/$13.50 CAN Format: TP
On Sale: 5/7/2019

SUPERMAN OF SMALLVILLE

Acts of awesomeness are happening all around town. People are being saved, runaway tractors stopped, and fires extinguished. Who is this super-man of Smallville? Thirteen-year-old Clark Kent knows. He has a super-secret—one his parents are constantly worried will get out.

Writers/Artists: Art Baltazar and Franco Aureliani
ISBN: 9781401283926 | Diamond Code: JUN188832
Price: $9.99/$13.50 CAN | Format: TP | On sale: 6/4/2019

DEAR JUSTICE LEAGUE

Dear Justice League showcases the correspondence between members of the Justice League and their young fans. The questions are direct—and sometimes inappropriate, in the way that kids' questions often are—and stir up humorous memories from the heroes own youthful experiences and blunders!

Writer: Michael Northrop | Artist: Gustavo Duarte | ISBN: 9781401284138
Diamond Code: JUN188833 | Price: $9.99/$13.50 CAN
Format: TP | On sale: 7/2/2019

BATMAN: OVERDRIVE

Driven to solve the mystery of his parents' murders, teenage loner Bruce Wayne hones his detective and combat skills as he scours Gotham City's underbelly looking for clues. From Shea Fontana, author of the best-selling *DC Super Hero Girls* series!

Writer: Shea Fontana | Artist: Marcelo Di Chiara
ISBN: 9781401283568 | Diamond Code: JUN188835
Price: $9.99/$13.50 CAN | Format: TP | On sale: 8/6/2019

The *DC Super Hero Girls* line of original graphic novels introduces an exciting universe of heroic storytelling, featuring DC Comics' most powerful and diverse lineup of female characters.

More than 300,000 copies in print!

DC SUPER HERO GIRLS: FINALS CRISIS
Written by Shea Fontana
Art by Yancey Labat
9781401262471 • TP
$9.99 • APR160322
Now Available

DC SUPER HERO GIRLS: HITS AND MYTHS
Written by Shea Fontana
Art by Yancey Labat
9781401267612 • TP
$9.99 • AUG160270
Now Available

DC SUPER HERO GIRLS: SUMMER OLYMPUS
Written by Shea Fontana
Art by Yancey Labat
9781401272357 • TP
$9.99 • MAR170353
Now Available

DC SUPER HERO GIRLS: PAST TIMES AT SUPER HERO HIGH
Written by Shea Fontana
Art by Yancey Labat
9781401273835 • TP
$9.99 • JUN170333
Now Available

DC SUPER HERO GIRLS: DATE WITH DISASTER!
Written by Shea Fontana
Art by Yancey Labat
9781401278786 • TP
$9.99 • NOV170216
Now Available

DC SUPER HERO GIRLS: OUT OF THE BOTTLE
Written by Shea Fontana Art by Marcelo Di Chiara & Agnes Garbowska
9781401274832 • TP
$9.99 • FEB180156
Now Available

"A neat entry point into the world of comic books for new audiences."
—io9

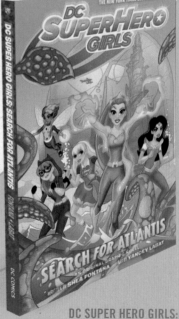

"Perfect for younger readers."
—A.V. Club

"A youthful twist on popular characters."
—Los Angeles Times

DC SUPER HERO GIRLS: SEARCH FOR ATLANTIS
Written by Shea Fontana • Illustrated by Yancey Labat
9781401283537 • JUN180439 • TR • $9.99/$13.50 CAN • Ages 6–12 • Grades 3–7 • On Sale: October 2, 2018

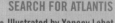

GENRE DEFINERS

Watchmen, Batman: The Killing Joke, Justice League Vol. 1: Origin. These graphic novels are now embedded into the very fabric of the comics industry, heralded as the best the medium has to offer. But all classics must have their beginnings. The following graphic novels are the next in line at DC, as top creators of recent years deliver innovative, poignant stories, with subject matter ranging from superheroes to love stories to autobiographical true crime. Pushing the boundaries of their respective genres and using the comics medium to maximum effect, each of these titles is a contemporary masterpiece in its own way.

AQUAMAN VOL. 1: THE TRENCH

Superstar writer Geoff Johns teams with artist Ivan Reis to relaunch Aquaman as one of the most powerful and important heroes of the DC Universe. As the King of the Seven Seas, Aquaman has sworn to protect his ocean home and there's been no greater threat to date than what's to come. They are called the Trench. And they are hungry.

"THIS MIGHT BE [GEOFF JOHNS'] MOST IMPRESSIVE FEAT TO DATE. GENIUS!" –USA TODAY

"FRESH." –ENTERTAINMENT WEEKLY

Writer: Geoff Johns | Artist: Ivan Reis | ISBN: 9781401237103 | Diamond Code: FEB130206
Price: $14.99/$17.99 CAN | Format: TP

BATGIRL VOL. 1: BATGIRL OF BURNSIDE

"THIS IS A MUST-BUY SERIES." –THE NEW YORK TIMES

Smart, savvy, chic and resourceful, Barbara Gordon is ready for a fresh start. But when Batgirl starts trending as Gotham's first viral vigilante, she also attracts a new wave of enemies looking to steal her social-media spotlight. Cameron Stewart, Brenden Fletcher and Babs Tarr revolutionize one of the most iconic female superheroes of all time in this incredibly relatable, socially relevant graphic novel.

Writers: Cameron Stewart & Brenden Fletcher | Artist: Babs Tarr | ISBN: 9781401257989 | Diamond Code: DEC148636
Price: $14.99/$17.99 CAN | Format: TP

BATMAN: THE DARK KNIGHT: MASTER RACE

The highly anticipated third installment of Frank Miller's futuristic saga, co-written by Brian Azzarello (100 Bullets) and illustrated by Andy Kubert (Flashpoint)!

"BATMAN, SUPERMAN, WONDER WOMAN AND OTHER HEROES ARE BACK ON THE PAGE SHOWCASING MILLER'S DISTINCTIVE FLAVOR." –USA TODAY

Writers: Frank Miller & Brian Azzarello | Artists: Andy Kubert, Klaus Janson, Frank Miller et al.
ISBN: 9781401284312 | Diamond Code: JUN180575 | Price: $24.99/$33.99 CAN | Format: TP

"FRANK MILLER'S RETURN TO THE DARK KNIGHT UNIVERSE IS NOT ONLY AN ALL-STAR COLLABORATION, BUT ALSO THE RARE COMIC-BOOK "EVENT" THAT LIVES UP TO ITS OWN HYPE." –WASHINGTON POST

BLACKEST NIGHT

"IF YOU'VE READ A SUPERHERO COMIC BOOK PUBLISHED BY DC COMICS WITHIN THE LAST FEW YEARS, AND WERE COMPLETELY BLOWN AWAY BY IT, THERE'S A GOOD CHANCE THAT IT WAS SOMETHING WRITTEN BY GEOFF JOHNS." –WASHINGTON EXAMINER

The Black Lanterns are the scourge of the universe—and they won't stop at gravedigging to secure dominance. Standing in their way? The Green Lantern Corps and the heroes of Earth. Geoff Johns and Ivan Reis craft an unforgettable ensemble of undead superheroes in this shockingly stylized blockbuster brawl.

Writer: Geoff Johns | Artist: Ivan Reis | ISBN: 9781401229535 | Diamond Code: APR110192
Price: $19.99/$23.99 CAN | Format: TP

DAYTRIPPER

In Daytripper, the Eisner Award-winning twin brothers Fábio Moon and Gabriel Bá tell a magical, mysterious and moving story about life itself—a hauntingly lyrical journey that uses the quiet moments to ask the big questions. Truly one of the most original and compelling graphic novels of the last decade, Daytripper is an affecting, memorable story that will stay with readers long after they've finished reading.

"MIXED WITH THE EXPERT CRAFTSMANSHIP OF TWO ARTISTS IN THEIR PRIME TELLING A UNIQUE STORY IN A REMARKABLE WAY, THE INDUSTRY MAY HAVE JUST CRAFTED ITS LATEST WATCHMEN." –POPMATTERS

Writers: Gabriel Bá & Fabio Moon | Artists: Gabriel Bá & Fábio Moon | ISBN: 9781401229696
Diamond Code: NOV100268 | Price: $19.99/$23.99 CAN | Format: TP FOR MATURE READERS

DARK NIGHT: A TRUE BATMAN STORY

In this autobiographical true story, *Batman: The Animated Series* co-creator Paul Dini recounts a harrowing near-death beating and subsequent road to recovery. While most know the Caped Crusader as the icon of justice and authority, in this surprising story, we see Batman not as the dark avenger, but the savior who helped a discouraged man recover mentally from a brutal attack that left him unable to face the world.

"PAUL DINI HAS TURNED A TRAGIC NIGHT OF FEAR INTO AN INSTANTLY-CLASSIC GRAPHIC NOVEL."
—WASHINGTON POST

Writer: Paul Dini | Artist: Eduardo Risso | ISBN: 9781401271367 | Diamond Code: MAR170445
Price: $16.99/$22.99 CAN | Format: TP

"THE CARTOONIST DARWYN COOKE IS AN EXTRAORDINARY TALENT ... [NEW FRONTIER] IS AN AUDACIOUS REVISIONIST LOOK AT THE FORMATION OF THE JUSTICE LEAGUE."
—THE NEW YORK TIMES

DC: THE NEW FRONTIER

Welcome to 1950s America—a land where heroes have been outlawed. Those icons who do still fight on—Superman, Wonder Woman, Batman—must operate under hidden agendas and dueling ideologies. This Eisner, Harvey and Shuster award-winning series takes readers on an epic journey from the end of the Golden Age of heroes to the beginnings of the legendary Justice League of America.

Writer: Darwyn Cooke | Artist: Darwyn Cooke | ISBN: 9781401263782
Diamond Code: MAR160267 | Price: $34.99/$41.99 CAN | Format: TP

FINAL CRISIS

Evil has finally won. Darkseid and his legion have claimed a devastating victory in a time-bending war between light and dark, forcing Batman, Superman and the Justice League to face the fallout and adjust to a new, apocalyptic reality. Experimental, vivid and relentless, Grant Morrison's epic explores what happens when the world's most imposing superheroes are stripped of their powers—and their hope.

"THE FERTILE MIND OF WRITER GRANT MORRISON.... THIS [IS] THE EVENT TO TRUMP ALL EVENTS."
—ENTERTAINMENT WEEKLY

Writer: Grant Morrison | Artists: J.G. Jones, Doug Mahnke & Carlos Pacheco | ISBN: 9781401245177
Diamond Code: JAN140352 | Price: $19.99/$23.99 CAN | Format: TP

"AN INVITINGLY BITING BOOK THAT SPIKES THE NARRATIVE WITH SHARP ONE-LINERS AND SLY ASIDES."
—WASHINGTON POST

THE FLINTSTONES VOL. 1

It's the Flintstones as you've never seen them before! This Eisner Award-nominated collection starring the first family of Bedrock tells the story of the dawn of civilization through the eyes of Fred, Wilma, Barney, Betty, Pebbles and Bamm-Bamm. This biting social-satirical commentary touches on concepts like religion, materialism, love, sex and war in one of the most surprisingly profound graphic novels in years.

Writer: Mark Russell | Artists: Steve Pugh and Rick Leonardi | ISBN: 9781401268374
Diamond Code: DEC160395 | Price: $16.99/$22.99 CAN | Format: TP

FOREVER EVIL

The Crime Syndicate—twisted, villainous versions of the Justice League—has taken over the world in search of new recruits. With the Justice League eliminated, it's up to Lex Luthor, Batman and a legion of super-villains to protect the planet from falling to an even greater evil in this giant crossover event!

"GEOFF JOHNS' BEST WORK SINCE THE NEW 52 BEGAN ... A BLAST TO READ." —NERDIST

Writer: Geoff Johns | Artist: David Finch | ISBN: 9781401253387 | Diamond Code: FEB150254
Price: $19.99/$23.99 CAN | Format: TP

GOTHAM ACADEMY VOL. 1: WELCOME TO GOTHAM ACADEMY

Welcome to Gotham Academy, the most prestigious school in Gotham City. Mixing in the mythology of Batman with high school drama, *Gotham Academy Vol. 1* is one of the most unique books DC has ever produced and one of its most inviting to audiences of all ages.

Writers: Becky Cloonan and Brenden Fletcher | Artist: Karl Kerschl | ISBN: 9781401254728
Diamond Code: MAR150269 | Price: $14.99/$17.99 CAN | Format: TP

> "A LITTLE BIT CW TELEVISION SERIES AND A LITTLE BIT HARRY POTTER, WITH A WEE TOUCH OF MANGA-INSPIRED STORYTELLING … A REALLY FUN AND CHARMING BOOK."
> —NERDIST

IDENTITY CRISIS

> "THE IDENTITY CRISIS MYSTERY INVOLVES THE BIGGEST DC HEROES AND WILL USE ALL OF MR. MELTZER'S SKILLS AS A THRILLER NOVELIST."
> —THE NEW YORK TIMES

After a grisly murder rocks the DC Universe, the entire superhero community searches for the killer. But before the mystery is solved, a number of long-buried secrets will threaten to divide the Justice League. *New York Times* best-selling novelist Brad Meltzer delivers one of the most intimate and heartbreaking graphic novels of all time.

Writer: Brad Meltzer | Artist: Rags Morales | ISBN: 9781401263133
Diamond Code: NOV150278 | Price: $19.99/$23.99 CAN | Format: TP

INJUSTICE: GODS AMONG US YEAR ONE: THE COMPLETE COLLECTION

Forget everything you think you know about the DC Universe. This graphic novel, inspired by the video game phenomenon, collects the initial year of the best-selling series in its entirety for the first time!

> "THIS IS A COMIC WELL WORTH READING." —IGN

Writer: Tom Taylor | Artists: Jheremy Raapack & Mike S. Miller | ISBN: 9781401262792
Diamond Code: DEC150338 | Price: $24.99/$33.99 CAN | Format: TP

KINGDOM COME

> "WAID'S CHARGED DIALOGUE AND ROSS' STUNNING VISUAL REALISM EXPOSE THE GENIUS, PRIDE, FEARS AND FOIBLES OF DC'S HEROES AND VILLAINS."
> —WASHINGTON POST

In the not-so-distant future, the DC Universe is spinning inexorably out of control. The new generation of heroes has lost its moral compass, becoming just as reckless and violent as the villains its members fight. The previous regime of heroes—the Justice League—returns under the direst of circumstances, setting up a battle of the old guard against these uncompromising protectors in a battle that will define what heroism truly is.

Writer: Mark Waid | Artist: Alex Ross | ISBN: 9781401220341 | Diamond Code: SEP138294
Price: $19.99/$25.99 CAN | Format: TP

THE MULTIVERSITY

Travel beyond the familiar DC Universe and come face to face with the Vampire League of Earth-43, the Justice Riders of Earth-18, Superdemon, Doc Fate, the Super Sons of Superman and Batman, the rampaging Retaliators of Earth-8, the Atomic Knights of Justice, Dino-Cop and more. This is Grant Morrison's expansive introduction to the alternate Earths of the DC Multiverse!

> "DOING 'BIG' AND 'GRAND' IS MORRISON'S GREATEST STRENGTH AS A WRITER, AND THE MULTIVERSITY IS THE OPUS HE'S BEEN WORKING ON NOW FOR OVER FIVE YEARS."
> —NERDIST

Writer: Grant Morrison | Artists: Frank Quitely, Ivan Reis, Jim Lee, et al. | ISBN: 9781401265250
Diamond Code: AUG160336 | Price: $29.99/$39.99 CAN | Format: TP

OMEGA MEN: THE END IS HERE

The Omega Men, an alleged terrorist cell, have killed Kyle Rayner, the White Lantern. But are they really the universe's biggest threat? Or are they the only hope for freedom this godforsaken sector of the universe has? The truth is much more complicated than it seems in this true definition of a modern classic.

"KING HAS TAKEN AN OBSCURE SUPER-TEAM AND REINVENTED THEM IN A BOLD, EXCITING WAY." –IGN

Writer: Tom King | Artist: Barnaby Bagenda | ISBN: 9781401261535 | Diamond Code: MAY160316 | Price: $24.99/$29.99 CAN | Format: TP

PREACHER BOOK ONE

"JUST ABOUT THE BEST THING TO COME ALONG SINCE COMICS STARTED FINDING THEIR WAY INTO BOOKS." –WASHINGTON POST

Jesse Custer, a wayward preacher, begins a violent journey to find God (literally), joined by his girlfriend, Tulip, and the hard-drinking Irish vampire Cassidy. The powerhouse creative team of Garth Ennis and Steve Dillon bring readers on a violent and riotous journey across the country in this award-winning Vertigo series.

Writer: Garth Ennis | Artist: Steve Dillon | ISBN: 9781401240455 | Diamond Code: MAR130303 | Price: $19.99/$23.99 CAN | Format: TP | FOR MATURE READERS

PUNK ROCK JESUS

Written and illustrated by award-winning creator Sean Murphy, *Punk Rock Jesus* brilliantly deconstructs modern society, embraces the punk aesthetic and takes readers on an epic, emotional ride, three chords at a time. J2 has created the ultimate reality-show stunt: create a human clone from DNA lifted off the Shroud of Turin and watch the boy who could be the second coming of Jesus Christ Himself.

"*PUNK ROCK JESUS* IS AMAZING. THE SERIES HAS BEEN INCREDIBLE RIGHT FROM THE BEGINNING AND IT ENDS IN A SPECTACULAR FASHION. IT'S BRILLIANT AND HEARTBREAKING, EPIC AND EMOTIONAL.... THIS IS A BOOK THAT MAKES YOU THINK." –IGN

Writer: Sean Murphy | Artist: Sean Murphy | ISBN: 9781401237684 | Diamond Code: JAN130330 | Price: $16.99/$19.99 CAN | Format: TP | FOR MATURE READERS

THE SANDMAN: OVERTURE

"A SWEEPING AND EXTRAVAGANT PREQUEL." –ENTERTAINMENT WEEKLY

"AS WEIRD AND MAGIC AND DREAMY AS EVER." –TIME

Twenty-five years after *The Sandman* changed the landscape of modern comics, Neil Gaiman returns to his monumental series and answers lingering questions about the origins of Morpheus and his siblings: Death, Desire, Despair, Delirium, Destruction and Destiny. All of it leads up to the events of *The Sandman Vol. 1: Preludes and Nocturnes*, in which Dream has been imprisoned for decades.

Writer: Neil Gaiman | Artist: J.H. Williams III | ISBN: 9781401265199 | Diamond Code: AUG160359 | Price: $19.99/$25.99 CAN | Format: TP | FOR MATURE READERS

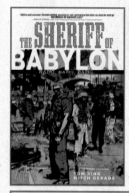

THE SHERIFF OF BABYLON VOL. 1: BANG. BANG. BANG.

Baghdad, 2003. The reign of Saddam Hussein is over. The Americans are in command. And no one is in control. Christopher Henry is in the country to train up a new Iraqi police force, and one of his recruits has just been murdered. Inspired by his real-life experiences as a CIA operations officer in Iraq, Tom King delivers a wartime crime thriller like no other.

"IT'S A VISUALLY STRIKING BOOK WITH AN EQUALLY ENGAGING STORY, CHANNELING THE SPIRIT OF CLASSIC VERTIGO WHILE STILL DELIVERING SOMETHING FRESH AND EXCITING."
—A.V. CLUB/THE ONION

Writer: Tom King | Artist: Mitch Gerads | ISBN: 9781401264666 | Diamond Code: APR160424 | Price: $14.99/$17.99 CAN | Format: TP | FOR MATURE READERS

"RED SON IS ONE OF THOSE RARE PROJECTS THAT BRIDGES THE GAP BETWEEN GENERATIONS AND ILLUSTRATES WHY COMICS—AND THE MOVIES BASED ON THEM—ARE STILL FRESH AND FULL OF SURPRISES FOR NEW AND OLD FANS ALIKE." —IFC

SUPERMAN: RED SON

In this startling twist on a familiar tale, a certain Kryptonian rocket ship crash-lands on Earth carrying an infant who will one day become the most powerful being on the planet. But his ship doesn't land in America. Instead, he makes his new home on a collective farm in the Soviet Union. As the young alien becomes a symbol to the Soviet people, the world changes drastically from what we know.

Writer: Mark Millar | Artists: Dave Johnson & Kilian Plunkett | ISBN: 9781401247119 | Diamond Code: JAN140353 | Price: $17.99/$21.99 CAN | Format: TP

Y: THE LAST MAN BOOK ONE

"COMPLETE AND UTTER GOLD."
—PUBLISHERS WEEKLY

"THIS YEAR'S BEST MOVIE IS A COMIC BOOK." —NPR

Brian K. Vaughan's epic series that made him a comics legend poses the question, "What would you do if you were the last man on Earth?" The winner of three Eisner Awards and one of the most critically acclaimed, best-selling comic book series of the last decade, *Y: The Last Man* is that rare example of a page-turner that is at once humorous, socially relevant and endlessly surprising.

Writer: Brian K. Vaughan | Artist: Pia Guerra
ISBN: 9781401251512 | Diamond Code: JUN140312
Price: $19.99/$23.99 CAN | Format: TP
FOR MATURE READERS

BATMAN

Dark Knight. Caped Crusader. World's Greatest Detective. Whatever you know him as, Batman shows us that you don't need superpowers to be a superhero—a point he proves again when he holds his own as a key member of the Justice League. As a child, Bruce Wayne watched helplessly as his parents were brutally murdered in front of him. From that day forth, he vowed to wage a one-man war on crime, donning the cape and the cowl to become Batman and redeem Gotham City. The Dark Knight made his debut in the pages of *Detective Comics* #27 and now dominates as one of the world's most iconic figures in popular culture.

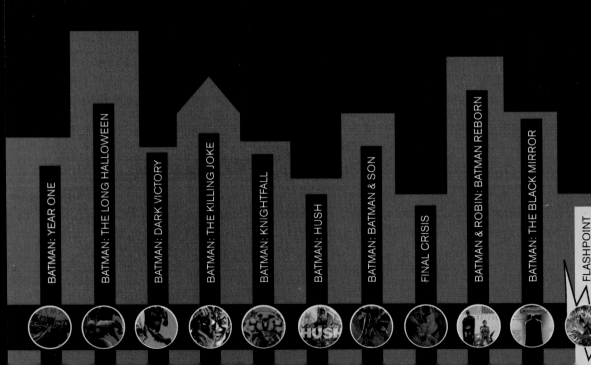

BATMAN: YEAR ONE

BATMAN: THE LONG HALLOWEEN

BATMAN: DARK VICTORY

BATMAN: THE KILLING JOKE

BATMAN: KNIGHTFALL

BATMAN: HUSH

BATMAN: BATMAN & SON

FINAL CRISIS

BATMAN & ROBIN: BATMAN REBORN

BATMAN: THE BLACK MIRROR

FLASHPOINT

BATMAN: THE GOLDEN AGE VOL. 1

The original adventures of the Dark Knight that made the character a pop icon the world over.

Writer: Bill Finger | Artist: Bob Kane | ISBN: 9781401263331 | Diamond Code: MAY160305
Price: $24.99/$29.99 CAN | Format: TP

BATMAN: YEAR ONE

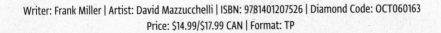

Frank Miller's genre-defining graphic novel details a rookie Dark Knight's first year in Gotham City.

Writer: Frank Miller | Artist: David Mazzucchelli | ISBN: 9781401207526 | Diamond Code: OCT060163
Price: $14.99/$17.99 CAN | Format: TP

BATMAN: THE LONG HALLOWEEN

A Batman murder mystery written by Jeph Loeb with art by Tim Sale, set during the Dark Knight's early days as he must race against the calendar to discover the identity of the serial killer Holiday.

Writer: Jeph Loeb | Artist: Tim Sale | ISBN: 9781401232597 | Diamond Code: JUL110251
Price: $24.99/$28.99 CAN | Format: TP

BATMAN: DARK VICTORY

In this sequel to *Batman: The Long Halloween*, Batman faces another seemingly unsolvable mystery, as the Hangman runs through a murder spree in Gotham City.

Writer: Jeph Loeb | Artist: Tim Sale | ISBN: 9781401244019 | Diamond Code: NOV130237
Price: $24.99/$29.99 CAN | Format: TP

BATMAN: ARKHAM ASYLUM 25TH ANNIVERSARY EDITION

Grant Morrison and Dave McKean's psychological horror story from Arkham Asylum, home to Gotham City's most deranged super-criminals.

Writer: Grant Morrison | Artist: Dave McKean | ISBN: 9781401251246 | Diamond Code: JUN140278
Price: $19.99/$23.99 CAN | Format: TP

BATMAN: THE KILLING JOKE

The Joker, Batman's greatest adversary, in his definitive origin story by Alan Moore with breathtaking art by Brian Bolland.

Writer: Alan Moore | Artist: Brian Bolland | ISBN: 9781401216672 | Diamond Code: NOV070226
Price: $17.99/$20.99 CAN | Format: HC | FOR MATURE READERS

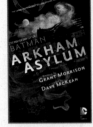

BATMAN: HUSH

The all-star team of Jeph Loeb and Jim Lee traces the tale of Batman as he seeks to stop a new and deadly villain who seems to know more about Batman than anyone—Hush!

Writer: Jeph Loeb | Artist: Jim Lee
ISBN: 9781401223175 | Diamond Code: MAY090178
Price: $24.99/$28.99 CAN | Format: TP

BATMAN AND SON

In Grant Morrison's epic Batman run, Bruce discovers that he's sired a son, Damian Wayne. Also included is *Batman: The Black Glove* by Morrison with art by J.H. Williams III.

Writer: Grant Morrison Artists: Andy Kubert,
J.H. Williams III & Tony S. Daniel
ISBN: 9781401244026 | Diamond Code: OCT130238
Price: $19.99/$23.99 CAN Format: TP

BATMAN & ROBIN VOL. 1: BATMAN REBORN

The dynamic duo is reborn, with Dick Grayson donning the cape and cowl along with new Robin Damian Wayne.

Writer: Grant Morrison | Artist: Frank Quitely
ISBN: 9781401229870 | Diamond Code: DEC100246
Price: $14.99/$17.99 CAN | Format: TP

EXPLORE THESE GRAPHIC NOVELS BY SCOTT SNYDER

BATMAN: THE BLACK MIRROR

The past comes back to haunt Commissioner Gordon and Batman by way of a diabolical murder mystery in this dark graphic novel that launched writer Scott Snyder into superstardom.

Writer: Scott Snyder | Artists: Jock & Francesco Francavilla
ISBN: 9781401232078 | Diamond Code: NOV120268
Price: $16.99/$19.99 CAN | Format: TP

BATMAN: THE COURT OF OWLS SAGA (DC ESSENTIAL EDITION)

Hidden for years, the mysterious Court of Owls surfaces in Gotham City—what must Batman do to defeat them, and what deadly connection do they have to his past? Scott Snyder and Greg Capullo's masterpiece epic is collected in its entirety in this DC Essential Edition!

Writer: Scott Snyder | Artist: Greg Capullo | ISBN: 9781401284336
Diamond Code: JUN180569 | Price: $24.99/$33.99 CAN | Format: TP

BATMAN VOL. 3: DEATH OF THE FAMILY

After having his face sliced off one year ago, the Joker makes his horrifying return to Gotham City! How can Batman protect his city and those he's closest to?

Writer: Scott Snyder | Artists: Greg Capullo & Jock
ISBN: 9781401246020 | Diamond Code: FEB140248
Price: $16.99/$19.99 CAN | Format: TP

BATMAN VOL. 7: ENDGAME

The Joker is out to finally destroy Batman for good as Scott Snyder and Greg Capullo tell their definitive Joker story with an ending you have to see to believe!

Writer: Scott Snyder | Artist: Greg Capullo
ISBN: 9781401261160 | Diamond Code: DEC150331
Price: $16.99/$19.99 CAN | Format: TP

ALL-STAR BATMAN VOL. 1: MY OWN WORST ENEMY

The #1 *New York Times* best-selling author of *Batman*, Scott Snyder returns to the Dark Knight, this time with legendary artist John Romita Jr., as Two-Face unleashes his greatest attack ever.

Writer: Scott Snyder | Artists: John Romita Jr. & Declan Shalvey | ISBN: 9781401274429 | Diamond Code: JUN170378
Price: $16.99/$22.99 CAN | Format: TP

ALSO AVAILABLE: ALL-STAR BATMAN VOLS. 2-3

DARK DAYS: THE ROAD TO METAL

For years, Batman has been tracking a mystery. Now, in an epic story spanning generations, the heroes and villains of the DC Universe are about to find out what he's discovered—and it could threaten the very existence of the Multiverse!

Writer: Scott Snyder | Artists: Jim Lee, Andy Kubert,
John Romita Jr. | ISBN: 9781401287627 | Diamond code: JUN188675
Price: $19.99/$25.99 CAN | Format: TP | On sale: 1/8/2019

DARK NIGHTS: METAL

The Dark Multiverse is coming, and nothing will ever be the same! One of the biggest events in DC history is here in the shocking, action-packed thrill ride from critically acclaimed duo Scott Snyder and Greg Capullo!

Writer: Scott Snyder | Artist: Greg Capullo | ISBN: 9781401288587
Diamond Code: JUN188676 | Price: $19.99/$25.99 CAN
Format: TP | On sale: 1/29/2019

EXPLORE THESE GRAPHIC NOVELS BY SCOTT SNYDER

DARK NIGHTS: METAL: DARK KNIGHTS RISING

Seven nightmarish versions of Batman from seven dying alternate realities threaten life across the Multiverse, and the Justice League may be powerless to stop them!

Writers: Grant Morrison, Scott Snyder and Peter J. Tomasi | ISBN: 9781401289072
Diamond Code: JUN188677 | Price: $24.99/$33.99 CAN | Format: TP | On sale: 3/26/2019

DARK NIGHTS: METAL: THE RESISTANCE

The Nightmare Batmen have descended to Earth! Against an army of evil Dark Knights, can the members of the Justice League, Teen Titans and Suicide Squad come together to form a resistance to stop them?

Writer: Joshua Williamson | Artists: Ethan Van Sciver, Liam Sharp | ISBN: ISBN: 9781401282981
Diamond Code: JAN180381 | Price: $24.99/$33.99 CAN | Format: TP

EXPLORE THESE GRAPHIC NOVELS BY TOM KING

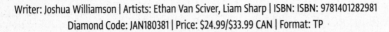

BATMAN/THE FLASH: THE BUTTON DELUXE EDITION

The Watchmen begin their invasion of the DC Universe here in this deluxe graphic novel *Batman/The Flash: The Button* by red-hot writers Tom King and Joshua Williamson.

Writers: Tom King & Joshua Williamson | Artists: Jason Fabok & Howard Porter | ISBN: 9781401276447 | Diamond Code: JUN170380 Price: $19.99/$25.99 CAN | Format: HC

BATMAN VOL. 3: I AM BANE

The man who has physically tested the Dark Knight like no one before is back to finally break the Bat for good. Can a battered, exhausted Batman fend off one of his greatest foes?

Writer: Tom King | Artist: David Finch
ISBN: 9781401271312 | Diamond Code: MAY170321
Price: $16.99/$22.99 CAN | Format: TP

BATMAN VOL. 1: I AM GOTHAM

Batman is back in an all-new series from rising star Tom King! The Dark Knight Detective must save Gotham from its newest threat ... another vigilante hero!

Writer: Tom King | Artists: David Finch & Mikel Janín
ISBN: 9781401267773 | Diamond Code: OCT160291
Price: $16.99/$22.99 CAN | Format: TP

BATMAN VOL. 4: THE WAR OF JOKES AND RIDDLES

In the aftermath of Zero Year? War. The Joker vs. the Riddler. They called it the War of Jokes and Riddles and its story has been untold ... until now.

BATMAN VOL. 2: I AM SUICIDE

Batman's brand-new solo series continues as he battles larger-than-life monsters, and a villain who's stolen something that the Caped Crusader will do anything to get back!

Writer: Tom King | Artists: David Finch & Mikel Janín
ISBN: 9781401268541 | Diamond Code: JAN170376
Price: $16.99/$22.99 CAN | Format: TP

Writer: Tom King | Artist: Mikel Janín
ISBN: 9781401273613 | Diamond Code: SEP170400
Price: $19.99/$25.99 CAN | Format: TP

It's the wedding of Batman and Catwoman—or is it?

BATMAN: PRELUDES TO THE WEDDING

Wedding bells are ringing in Gotham City ... and the criminal underworld is determined to silence them!

Writer: Tim Seeley | Artists: Various
ISBN: 9781401286545 | Diamond Code: JUN180571
Price: $16.99/$22.99 CAN | Format: TP

BATMAN/CATWOMAN: THE WEDDING ALBUM: THE DELUXE EDITION

The wedding of the century is commemorated in this special collector's item featuring never-before-seen photos from the wedding, behind-the-scenes design sketches and variant covers.

Writer: Tom King | Artist: Mikel Janín
ISBN: 9781401286538 | Diamond Code: JUN180572
Price: $17.99/$23.99 CAN | Format: HC

BATMAN VOL. 7: THE WEDDING

It's the marriage of Batman and Catwoman—or is it? Bruce Wayne and Selina Kyle are going to face even more trials before they can walk down the aisle in the wedding of the century.

Writer: Tom King | Artist: Mikel Janín | ISBN: 9781401283384
Diamond Code: JUL180717 | Price: $16.99/$22.99 CAN | Format: TP | On sale: 10/30/2019

ALSO AVAILABLE: BATMAN VOLS. 1-10

READ THESE STANDALONE BATMAN GRAPHIC NOVELS

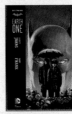

BATMAN: EARTH ONE VOL. 1

Geoff Johns reimagines the Dark Knight's origin story in this #1 *New York Times* bestseller.

Writer: Geoff Johns | Artist: Gary Frank
ISBN: 9781401232092 | Diamond Code: JUL158202
Price: $14.99/$17.99 CAN | Format: TP

BATMAN: THE DARK KNIGHT RETURNS

Frank Miller's classic and gritty take on the return of Gotham's hero.

Writer: Frank Miller | Artist: Frank Miller
ISBN: 9781401263119 | Diamond Code: NOV150279
Price: $19.99/$25.99 CAN | Format: TP

THE DARK KNIGHT RETURNS: THE LAST CRUSADE DELUXE EDITION

The prequel tale to one of the greatest graphic novels ever written, with art from the legendary John Romita Jr.

Writers: Frank Miller & Brian Azzarello | Artist: John Romita Jr. | ISBN: 9781401265069
Diamond Code: AUG160319
Price: $17.99/$23.99 CAN | Format: HC

BATMAN: THE DARK KNIGHT STRIKES AGAIN

The sequel to *Batman: The Dark Knight Returns*, in which Batman must come back once more to save a rapidly decaying world.

Writer: Frank Miller | Artist: Frank Miller
ISBN: 9781563899294 | Diamond Code: FEB058404
Price: $19.99/$23.99 CAN | Format: TP

BATMAN: THE DARK KNIGHT: MASTER RACE

The highly anticipated third installment of Frank Miller's futuristic saga, co-written by Brian Azzarello (*100 bullets*) and illustrated by Andy Kubert (*Flashpoint*)!

Writers: Frank Miller & Brian Azzarello
Artists: Andy Kubert, Klaus Janson, Frank Miller, et al.
ISBN: 9781401265137 | Diamond Code: JUN170390
Price: $29.99/$39.99 CAN | Format: HC

EXPLORE ALL CORNERS OF GOTHAM WITH THESE GRAPHIC NOVELS!

BATGIRL VOL. 1: BATGIRL OF BURNSIDE

It's a reinvention of Batgirl from the boots up, by the incredible creative team of Cameron Stewart, Brenden Fletcher and rising star Babs Tarr.

Writers: Cameron Stewart & Brenden Fletcher
Artist: Babs Tarr
ISBN: 9781401257989 | Diamond Code: DEC148636
Price: $14.99/$17.99 CAN | Format: TP

ALSO AVAILABLE: BATGIRL VOLS. 2-5

BATWOMAN VOL. 1: THE MANY ARMS OF DEATH

Batwoman's past transgressions are quickly catching up to her, and if she can't figure out whom to trust, it's going to cost her life!

Writers: Marguerite Bennett & James Tynion IV
Artist: Steve Epting | ISBN: 9781401274306
Diamond Code: AUG170318
Price: $16.99/$22.99 CAN | Format: TP

ALSO AVAILABLE: BATWOMAN VOLS. 2-3

BATGIRL VOL. 1: BEYOND BURNSIDE

Barbara Gordon (a.k.a. Batgirl) is leaving Burnside and hitting the road to find herself. Eisner winners Hope Larson and Rafael Albuquerque pair up to usher in a new era for our beloved Babs.

Writer: Hope Larson | Artist: Rafael Albuquerque
ISBN: 9781401268404 | Diamond Code: DEC160370
Price: $16.99/$22.99 CAN | Format: TP

ALSO AVAILABLE: BATGIRL VOLS. 2-3

NIGHTWING VOL. 1: TRAPS AND TRAPEZES

Dick Grayson, once Batman's sidekick Robin, has grown up and become the high-flying Nightwing. Every bit the hero his Caped Crusader mentor is, he pursues justice on his own path.

Writer: Kyle Higgins | Artist: Eddy Barrows
ISBN: 9781401237059 | Diamond Code: JUL120214
Price: $14.99/$17.99 CAN | Format: TP

ALSO AVAILABLE: NIGHTWING VOLS. 2-5

BATGIRL AND THE BIRDS OF PREY VOL. 1: WHO IS ORACLE?

Batgirl, Black Canary and Huntress reunite to hunt down Gotham's all-seeing enemy, who goes by a familiar name: Oracle!

Writers: Shawna Benson & Julie Benson | Artist: Claire Roe
ISBN: 9781401268671 | Diamond Code: MAY160212
Price: $16.99/$22.99 CAN | Format: TP

ALSO AVAILABLE: BATGIRL AND THE BIRDS OF PREY VOLS. 2-3

NIGHTWING VOL. 1: BETTER THAN BATMAN

Nightwing is back! Boy Wonder turned vigilante turned super-spy Dick Grayson returns to take down the international Parliament of Owls!

Writer: Tim Seeley | Artist: Javier Fernandez
ISBN: 9781401268039 | Diamond Code: OCT160296
Price: $16.99/$19.99 CAN | Format: TP

ALSO AVAILABLE: NIGHTWING VOLS. 2-5

EXPLORE ALL CORNERS OF GOTHAM WITH THESE GRAPHIC NOVELS!

NIGHTWING VOL. 1

It's a new beginning for Dick Grayson, as novelist Benjamin Percy takes the vigilante on a high-octane, adrenaline-fueled adventure in *Nightwing Vol. 1*, a great jumping on point for new readers!

Writer: Ben Percy | Artists: Chris Mooneyham
ISBN: 9781401285593 | Price: $16.99/$22.99 CAN
Format: TP | On sale: 1/1/2019 | COVER NOT FINAL

RED HOOD & THE OUTLAWS VOL. 1: DARK TRINITY

Red Hood embraces his bad side and looks to take down the crime lord Black Mask with the help of his new Outsiders: Bizarro and Artemis.

Writer: Scott Lobdell | Artist: Dexter Soy
ISBN: 9781401268756 | Diamond Code: JAN170381
Price: $16.99/$22.99 CAN | Format: TP

ALSO AVAILABLE: RED HOOD & THE OUTLAWS VOLS. 2-3

BATMAN: DETECTIVE COMICS VOL. 1: RISE OF THE BATMEN

Gotham needs more than just the Bat! Cousins Batman and Batwoman pair up to train new and familiar vigilante recruits in the fight against an army of mysterious foes!

Writer: James Tynion IV
Artists: Eddy Barrows and Alvaro Martinez
ISBN: 9781401267995 | Diamond Code: NOV160317
Price: $16.99/$22.99 CAN | Format: TP

ALSO AVAILABLE: BATMAN: DETECTIVE COMICS VOLS. 2-8

CATWOMAN VOL. 1

Coming off of the wedding of the century to Batman, Selina Kyle stars in an all-new solo series written and illustrated by Eisner Award nominee Joëlle Jones!

Writer: Joëlle Jones | Artist: Joëlle Jones
ISBN: 9781401288891 | Diamond code: JUN188707
Price: $16.99/$22.99 CAN | Format: TP | On sale: 4/16/2019

DETECTIVE COMICS: 80 YEARS OF BATMAN DELUXE EDITION

Join the Dark Knight and DC Comics to commemorate the 80th anniversary and 1,000th issue of one of the most iconic publications ever: *Detective Comics*!

Writers: Various | Artists: Various
ISBN: 9781401285388 | Price: $29.99/$39.99 CAN
Format: HC | On sale: 3/19/2019

BATMAN VS. DEATHSTROKE

When Batman discovers a mysterious package containing DNA test results proving that he is not Damian Wayne's biological father, the Dark Knight sets his sights on his son's true father—Deathstroke!

Writer: Christopher Priest | Artist: Diogenes Neves
ISBN: 9781401285890 | Price: $24.99/$33.99 | On sale: 3/19/2019 | Format: HC

SUPERMAN

Since his earth-shattering debut in 1938's *Action Comics* #1, Superman has achieved mythic folk-hero status. Rocketed to Earth from the dying planet Krypton, baby Kal-El was raised on Earth by a kindhearted farming couple. Clark Kent, as he was renamed, discovered that he had extraordinary and unmatched powers. Combining these abilities with the strong moral values his adoptive parents instilled in him, he became Superman. The Man of Steel soon became one of the most recognized and popular superheroes in all of pop culture, pushing past the printed page and emerging as an icon in all forms of media.

SUPERMAN: THE GOLDEN AGE VOL. 1

SUPERMAN: FOR ALL SEASONS

SUPERMAN: THE DEATH OF SUPERMAN

SUPERMAN/BATMAN VOL. 1

SUPERMAN: FOR TOMORROW

INFINITE CRISIS

SUPERMAN: LAST SON OF KRYPTON

FLASHPOINT

SUPERMAN: THE GOLDEN AGE VOL. 1

Back to where it all began: Superman's very first historic stories are now collected in one place, including the Man of Tomorrow's origin story and first battles against evil!

Writers: Jerry Siegel & Joe Shuster | Artists: Various
ISBN: 9781401261092 | Diamond Code: DEC150348
Price: $19.99/$23.99 CAN | Format: TP

SUPERMAN/BATMAN VOL. 1

The iconic superheroes must unite to stop longtime Superman enemy Lex Luthor in this team-up tale from superstar writer Jeph Loeb (*Batman: The Long Halloween*).

Writer: Jeph Loeb | Artists: Ed McGuinness & Michael Turner
ISBN: 9781401248185 | Diamond Code: JAN140354
Price: $19.99/$23.99 CAN | Format: TP

SUPERMAN: FOR ALL SEASONS

The tale of Clark Kent's transformation from country boy to Metropolis Superman as told by the acclaimed duo of Jeph Loeb and Tim Sale.

Writer: Jeph Loeb | Artist: Tim Sale
ISBN: 9781401281090 | Diamond Code: APR180280
Price: $19.99/$25.99 CAN | Format: TP

LUTHOR

The all-star team of Brian Azzarello and Lee Bermejo explores the mind of Superman's greatest villain, Lex Luthor.

Writer: Brian Azzarello | Artist: Lee Bermejo
ISBN: 9781401258184 | Diamond Code: AUG150269
Price: $14.99/$17.99 | Format: TP

THE DEATH OF SUPERMAN

The story that shocked the world! Superman pays the ultimate price to stop the killing machine Doomsday.

Writers: Dan Jurgens, Jerry Ordway, Louise Simonson & Roger Stern | Artists: Dan Jurgens, Jon Bogdanove, Tom Grummett & Jackson Guice
ISBN: 9781401266653 | Diamond Code: JAN168880
Price: $17.99/$21.99 CAN | Format: TP

SUPERMAN: FOR TOMORROW

A cataclysmic event has made half the Earth's population disappear, and no one is left unaffected, including Superman, in this graphic novel by the superstar team of Jim Lee and Brian Azzarello.

Writer: Brian Azzarello | Artist: Jim Lee
ISBN: 9781401237806 | Diamond Code: NOV120270
Price: $24.99/$28.99 CAN | Format: TP

SUPERMAN: LAST SON OF KRYPTON

Film director Richard Donner and Geoff Johns pit the Man of Steel against General Zod and Brainiac in these stories illustrated by Adam Kubert and Gary Frank.

Writers: Geoff Johns & Richard Donner | Artists: Adam Kubert & Gary Frank | ISBN: 9781401237790
Diamond Code: OCT120270 | Price: $19.99/$23.99 CAN | Format: TP

SUPERMAN UNCHAINED

All-star creators Scott Snyder and Jim Lee unite for the first time to take on the Man of Steel in this graphic novel blockbuster!

Writer: Scott Snyder | Artists: Jim Lee & Dustin Nguyen
ISBN: 9781401250935 | Diamond Code: DEC150346
Price: $24.99/$29.99 CAN | Format: TP

SUPERMAN: THE MEN OF TOMORROW

Comics legends Geoff Johns and John Romita Jr. team up to launch an all-new era of Superman!

Writer: Geoff Johns | Artist: John Romita Jr.
ISBN: 9781401258689 | Diamond Code: JAN160315
Price: $16.99/$19.99 CAN | Format: TP

SUPERMAN: THE FINAL DAYS OF SUPERMAN

It's a new chapter in the Man of Steel's life that will change everything you know about Superman, as the superhero faces his own last moments.

Writer: Peter J. Tomasi | Artists: Various
ISBN: 9781401269142 | Diamond Code: FEB170317
Price: $19.99/$25.99 CAN | Format: TP

SUPERMAN: ACTION COMICS VOL. 1: PATH OF DOOM

Following the events of DC Rebirth, a new beginning includes an unlikely figure as the protector of Metropolis: Lex Luthor!

Writer: Dan Jurgens | Artists: Patrick Zircher & Tyler Kirkham
ISBN: 9781401268046 | Diamond Code: NOV160319
Price: $16.99/$22.99 CAN | Format: TP

SUPERMAN VOL. 1
SON OF SUPERMAN

A new Superman appears to protect the world while raising a super-son with his wife, Lois Lane.

Writers: Peter J. Tomasi & Patrick Gleason
Artists: Patrick Gleason & Doug Mahnke
ISBN: 9781401267766 | Diamond Code: OCT160297
Price: $16.99/$22.99 CAN | Format: TP

SUPERMAN REBORN

The creative talent behind *Superman: Action Comics* and *Superman* present the first monumental Superman crossover event following DC Rebirth, answering lingering questions from the beginning of the New 52!

Writer: Peter J. Tomasi, Patrick Gleason & Dan Jurgens
Artists: Patrick Gleason & Doug Mahnke | ISBN: 9781401278625
Diamond Code: FEB180289 | Price: $16.99/$22.99 | Format: TP

ACTION COMICS #1000: THE DELUXE EDITION

The monumental, best-selling *Action Comics #1000* is now available in this deluxe hardcover edition.

Writers: Brian Michael Bendis, Geoff Johns, Scott Snyder & Tom King | Artists: Olivier Coipel et al. | ISBN: 9781401285975
Diamond Code: JUN180558 | Price: $19.99/$25.99 | Format: HC

EXPLORE BRIAN MICHAEL BENDIS'S SUPERMAN

THE MAN OF STEEL

A new era begins for Superman as a threat from his earliest origins reemerges to destroy the Last Son of Krypton.

Writer: Brian Michael Bendis | Artists: Ivan Reis, Jason Fabok, Adam Hughes & Ryan Sook
ISBN: 9781401283483 | Diamond Code: JUL180765
Price: $24.99/$33.99 CAN | Format: HC | On sale: 11/6/2018

SUPERMAN VOL. 1

Clark Kent is looking at the world through new eyes ... with new ideas about what Superman can and should do for the city of Metropolis and the planet Earth. Brian Michael Bendis begins his run on the all-new *Superman*!

Writer: Brian Michael Bendis | Artist: Ivan Reis
ISBN: 9781401288198 | Diamond Code: JUN188697
Price: $24.99/$33.99 CAN | Format: HC | On sale: 3/5/2019

SUPERMAN: ACTION COMICS VOL. 1

The devastating repercussions from *The Man of Steel* reverberate in Metropolis! *The Daily Planet* teeters on the brink of disaster while a new criminal element has made its way onto the streets of Superman's hometown!

Writer: Brian Michael Bendis | Artist: Patrick Gleason
ISBN: 9781401288723 | Price: $24.99/$33.99 CAN | Format: HC
Diamond Code: JUN188698 | On sale: 4/9/2019

READ THESE STANDALONE SUPERMAN GRAPHIC NOVELS

SUPERMAN: EARTH ONE VOL. 1

The #1 *New York Times* best-selling original graphic novel that reimagines Superman as a brooding, reluctant hero in modern-day Metropolis.

Writer: J. Michael Straczynski | Artist: Shane Davis
ISBN: 9781401224691 | Diamond Code: FEB130226
Price: $14.99/$17.99 CAN | Format: TP

ALSO AVAILABLE: SUPERMAN: EARTH ONE VOLS. 2-3

SUPERMAN: AMERICAN ALIEN

Hollywood screenwriter and Eisner Award nominee Max Landis joins forces with top comics illustrators to create a new epic that chronicles the life of Clark Kent.

Writer: Max Landis
Artists: Francis Manapul, Jae Lee, Nick Dragotta, Jock, et al. | ISBN: 9781401274467
Diamond Code: AUG170342
Price: $19.99/$25.99 | Format: HC

SUPERMAN: BIRTHRIGHT

Superstar writer Mark Waid updates the origin of the Man of Steel in this classic tale.

Writer: Mark Waid | Artist: Leinil Francis Yu
ISBN: 9781401202521 | Diamond Code: JUL050214
Price: $19.99/$23.99 CAN | Format: TP

ALL-STAR SUPERMAN

The critically acclaimed series that hearkens back to the Golden Age of Superman by superstar writer Grant Morrison and artist Frank Quitely.

Writer: Grant Morrison | Artist: Frank Quitely
ISBN: 9781401232054 | Diamond Code: JUL110247
Price: $29.99/$35.00 CAN | Format: TP

SUPERMAN: RED SON

In this alternate take on the Man of Steel's origin, the ship carrying the infant who would grow up to become Superman lands in the midst of the 1950s Soviet Union.

Writer: Mark Millar | Artists: Dave Johnson & Kilian Plunkett | ISBN: 9781401247119
Diamond Code: JAN140353
Price: $17.99/$21.99 CAN | Format: TP

CHECK OUT THE ADVENTURES OF THE MAN OF STEEL'S ALLIES

SUPERGIRL: LAST DAUGHTER (DC ESSENTIAL EDITION)

Superman's teenage cousin mysteriously crash-lands on earth decades after the destruction of Krypton.

Writer: Michael Green | Artist: Mike Johnson
ISBN: 9781401288358 | Price: $24.99/$33.99 CAN | Format: TP
Diamond Code: JUN188696 | On sale: 3/19/2019

NEW SUPER-MAN & THE JLC VOL. 1: JUSTICE LEAGUE CHINA

Through a series of government experiments, Kong Kenan has become China's New Super-Man! And now by his side is the mighty Justice League of China!

Writer: Gene Luen Yang | Artist: Brent Peeples
ISBN: 9781401288297 | Price: $16.99/$22.99 CAN | Format: TP
On sale: 2/12/2019 | COVER NOT FINAL

SUPERGIRL VOL. 1: REIGN OF THE CYBORG SUPERMEN

Supergirl moves to National City in this new series that's perfect for fans of the hit TV show, now on The CW.

Writer: Steve Orlando | Artist: Brian Ching
ISBN: 9781401268466 | Diamond Code: FEB170296
Price: $16.99/$19.99 CAN | Format: TP

ALSO AVAILABLE: SUPERGIRL VOLS. 2-4

SUPER SONS VOL. 1: WHEN I GROW UP

The offspring of Superman and Batman, Superboy (a.k.a. Jonathan Kent) and Robin (a.k.a. Damian Wayne), make their super-hero duo debut in this all-new series.

Writer: Peter J. Tomasi | Artist: Jorge Jimenez
ISBN: 9781401274016 | Diamond Code: JUL170465
Price: $12.99/$17.50 CAN | Format: TP

ALSO AVAILABLE: SUPER SONS VOLS. 2-3

SUPERGIRL VOL. 1

Supergirl's understanding of herself and her origins has been rattled to the core following the events of *The Man Of Steel*! Her plan? To find out the truth and punish whoever is behind it.

Writer: Marc Andreyko | Artist: Kevin Maguire
ISBN: 9781401289188 | Price: $16.99/$22.99 CAN | Format: TP
Diamond Code: JUN188695 | On sale 4/30/2019 | COVER NOT FINAL

SUPER SONS OF TOMORROW

Jonathan Kent is just a kid, and one of the most powerful beings on the planet. But what if he has the potential to hurt people without even meaning to? An epic crossover between the Super Sons, Superman and the Teen Titans!

Writer: Peter J. Tomasi | Artists: Patrick Gleason, Jorge Jimenez & Doug Mahnke | ISBN: 9781401282394
Diamond Code: MAR180354 | Price: $14.99/$19.99 CAN | Format: TP

NEW SUPER-MAN VOL. 1: MADE IN CHINA

The #1 *New York Times* best-selling author Gene Luen Yang introduces a new Man of Steel, created by the Chinese government. But the government may have chosen the wrong person for the job.

Writer: Gene Luen Yang | Artist: Viktor Bogdanovic
ISBN: 9781401270933 | Diamond Code: MAR170405
Price: $16.99/$22.99 CAN | Format: TP

ALSO AVAILABLE: NEW SUPER-MAN VOLS. 2-3

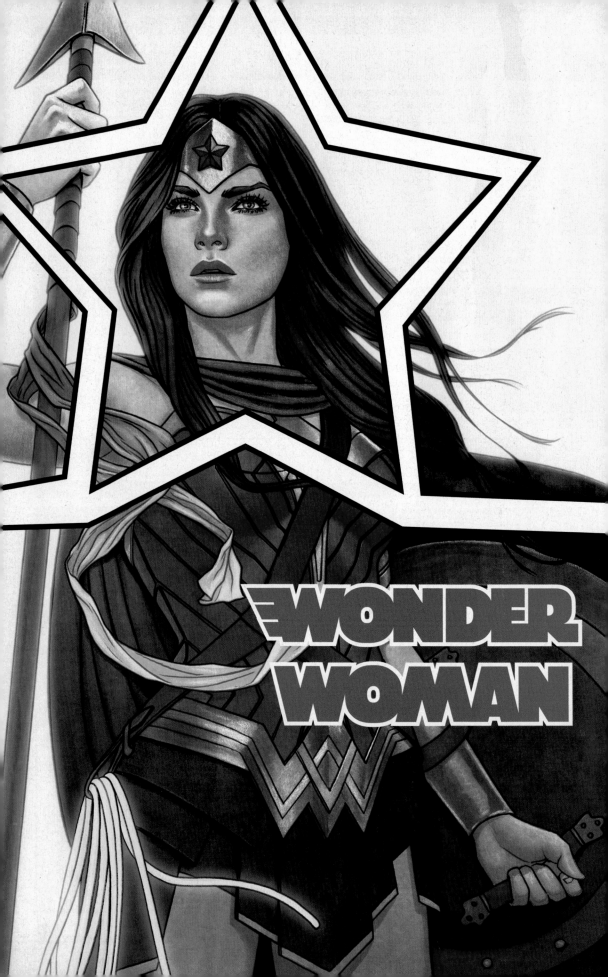

Diana, princess of the immortal Amazons from Greek mythology, equipped with powers granted by the gods of Olympus and an arsenal of iconic weapons, has come to the world of man to spread her message of love and justice. Over seven formative decades, Wonder Woman has become an essential figure in the DC Universe, and through it all, an icon of female empowerment. With a critically acclaimed film under her belt, the Amazon Warrior is getting her just due worthy of her status as a pop culture icon.

WONDER WOMAN: THE GOLDEN AGE VOL. 1

In these Golden Age stories, the world is introduced to the Amazon Warrior, as Wonder Woman travels from Paradise Island to Man's World, where she serves as an emissary of peace, using her bracelets and Lasso of Truth to stop injustice!

Writers: Various | Artists: Various
ISBN: 9781401274443 | Diamond Code: AUG170345
Price: $24.99/$33.99 | Format: TP

WONDER WOMAN BY GEORGE PÉREZ VOL. 1

George Pérez's revolutionary series gives a new life to the legend of the original warrior princess, and it's a must-read for any Wonder Woman fan.

Writer: George Pérez | Artist: George Pérez
ISBN: 9781401263751 | Diamond Code: MAY160328
Price: $24.99/$29.99 CAN | Format: TP

WONDER WOMAN BY GREG RUCKA VOL. 1

Greg Rucka's first and now-legendary run on the Amazon Warrior begins as Diana is the new Themysciran ambassador to the United Nations.

Writer: Greg Rucka | Artist: Various
ISBN: 9781401263324 | Diamond Code: APR160406
Price: $29.99/$39.99 CAN | Format: TP

WONDER WOMAN VOL. 1: BLOOD

Superheroics meet ancient myth as critically acclaimed writer Brian Azzarello teams with Cliff Chiang and Tony Akins to begin a new chapter for the Amazon Princess.

Writer: Brian Azzarello | Artists: Cliff Chiang & Tony Akins
ISBN: 9781401235628 | Diamond Code: OCT120256
Price: $14.99/$17.99 CAN | Format: TP

ALSO AVAILABLE: WONDER WOMAN VOLS. 2-8

WONDER WOMAN VOL. 1: THE LIES

New York Times best-selling writer Greg Rucka returns to Wonder Woman with a tale that will forever alter the DC icon.

Writer: Greg Rucka | Artist: Liam Sharp
ISBN: 9781401267780 | Diamond Code: NOV160320
Price: $16.99/$22.99 CAN | Format: TP

WONDER WOMAN VOL. 2: YEAR ONE

New York Times best-selling writer Greg Rucka continues his return to *Wonder Woman*! The team of Rucka and artist Nicola Scott weave the definitive and shocking tale of Diana's first year as Earth's protector.

Writer: Greg Rucka | Artist: Nicola Scott
ISBN: 9781401268800 | Diamond Code: FEB170298
Price: $16.99/$22.99 CAN | Format: TP

WONDER WOMAN VOL. 3: THE TRUTH

Diana's search for the truth about herself, her history and her home, Themyscira, takes her on a journey into darkness. But the price of understanding may be one sacrifice too many for Wonder Woman.

Writer: Greg Rucka | Artist: Liam Sharp
ISBN: 9781401271411 | Diamond Code: MAY170328
Price: $16.99/$22.99 | Format: TP

ALSO AVAILABLE: WONDER WOMAN REBIRTH VOL. 4-8

READ THESE STANDALONE WONDER WOMAN GRAPHIC NOVELS

WONDER WOMAN: EARTH ONE VOL. 1

Comics masters Grant Morrison and Yanick Paquette continue the best-selling Earth One series with a provocative take on Wonder Woman for the modern world.

Writer: Grant Morrison | Artist: Yanick Paquette
ISBN: 9781401268633 | Diamond Code: JAN170402
Price: $16.99/$22.99 CAN | Format: TP

THE LEGEND OF WONDER WOMAN: ORIGINS

This unique new retelling of Wonder Woman's origin follows a young Diana as she learns the lessons that will eventually help her become the Amazon Warrior!

Writer: Renae De Liz | Artist: Renae De Liz
ISBN: 9781401274252 | Diamond Code: AUG170338
Price: $19.99/$25.99 CAN | Format: TP

WONDER WOMAN: THE TRUE AMAZON

In this original graphic novel from writer/artist Jill Thompson (*The Little Endless Storybook*), a spoiled young princess, Diana—the future Wonder Woman—must learn to take responsibility for her actions.

Writer: Jill Thompson | Artist: Jill Thompson
ISBN: 9781401274504 | Diamond Code: AUG170346
Price: $16.99/$22.99 CAN | Format: TP

WONDER WOMAN: EARTH ONE VOL. 2

For years Diana of Paradise Island yearned to leave the only home she knew behind for adventures that lay beyond its shores. Now, after a fateful meeting with Air Force pilot Steve Trevor, the Amazon Warrior finds herself in Man's World. And she is ready for anything that it may throw at her.

Writer: Grant Morrison | Artist: Yanick Paquette | ISBN: 9781401281175
Diamond Code: JUL180591 | Price: $24.99/$33.99 CAN | Format: HC | On sale: 10/2/2018

Greater than the sum of their awe-inspiring parts, the Justice League handles threats too massive for any single hero. Made up of the World's Greatest Super Heroes, the core lineup is known as the Big Seven: Superman, Batman, Wonder Woman, the Flash, Green Lantern, Aquaman and Cyborg. These graphic novels featuring this super-team stand out as not only great Justice League reads, but as some of the most important works in DC history.

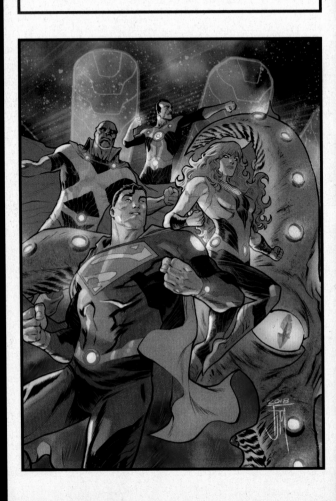

JUSTICE LEAGUE OF AMERICA:
THE SILVER AGE VOL. 1

For the first time, the JLA's first 20 adventures are collected in a single volume, spanning 1960-1964.

Writers: Various | Artists: Various
ISBN: 9781401261115 | Diamond Code: NOV150283
Price: $19.99/$23.99 CAN | Format: TP

ALSO AVAILABLE: JUSTICE LEAGUE OF AMERICA: THE SILVER AGE VOLS. 2-4

CRISIS ON INFINITE EARTHS

Worlds will live and worlds will die in comics' original epic event story-line by the legendary creative team of Marv Wolfman and George Pérez.

Writer: Marv Wolfman | Artist: George Pérez
ISBN: 9781563897504 | Diamond Code: AUG058162
Price: $29.99/$39.99 CAN | Format: TP

ZERO HOUR

The time-shattering follow-up events to *Crisis on Infinite Earths* are now collected in a brand-new hard-cover.

Writer: Dan Jurgens | Artists: Dan Jurgens & Jerry Ordway
ISBN: 9781401278519 | Diamond Code: FEB180317
Price: $24.99.99/$33.99 CAN | Format: HC

JLA VOL. 1

Grant Morrison relaunches the greatest team in the DC Universe—returning the powerhouse lineup of Superman, Batman, Wonder Woman, the Flash, Green Lantern, Aquaman and Martian Manhunter!

Writer: Grant Morrison | Artist: Howard Porter
ISBN: 9781401233143 | Diamond Code: JUN110276
Price: $19.99/$23.99 CAN | Format: TP

ALSO AVAILABLE: JLA VOLS. 2-9

INFINITE CRISIS

It's the DCU's darkest day, and long-lost heroes from the past return to make things right in this epic sequel to *Crisis on Infinite Earths*.

Writer: Geoff Johns | Artists: Phil Jimenez, Jerry Ordway & George Pérez | ISBN: 9781401210601
Diamond Code: FEB118149 | Price: $17.99/$21.99 | Format: TP

IDENTITY CRISIS

Uncover the DC Universe's deadliest secret in this acclaimed miniseries from *New York Times* best-selling novelist Brad Meltzer.

Writer: Brad Meltzer | Artist: Rags Morales
ISBN: 9781401263133 | Diamond Code: NOV150278
Price: $19.99/$25.99 CAN | Format: TP

FINAL CRISIS

Grant Morrison takes the DC Universe on a battle through the Multiverse that will leave both heroes and villains changed forever.

Writer: Grant Morrison | Artists: J.G. Jones, Doug Mahnke & Carlos Pacheco | ISBN: 9781401245177
Diamond Code: JAN140352 | Price: $19.99/$25.99 CAN | Format: TP

JUSTICE LEAGUE VOL. 1:
ORIGIN

In one of the most game-changing titles in comics industry history, Geoff Johns and Jim Lee reimagine the Justice League for the 21st century.

Writer: Geoff Johns | Artist: Jim Lee
ISBN: 9781401237882 | Diamond Code: OCT120252
Price: $16.99/$19.99 CAN | Format: TP

DC UNIVERSE: REBIRTH DELUXE EDITION

The monumental, best-selling *DC Universe: Rebirth* #1 is presented in a Deluxe Edition hardcover, featuring expansive bonus material including concept sketches and variant covers!

Writer: Geoff Johns | Artists: Gary Frank, Ivan Reis, Ethan Van Sciver and Phil Jimenez | ISBN: 9781401270728 | Diamond Code: AUG160316
Price: $17.99/23.99 CAN | Format: HC

JUSTICE LEAGUE VOL. 1: THE EXTINCTION MACHINES

Following DC Rebirth, the World's Greatest Super Heroes—the Justice League—come together again to face new, more devastating threats!

Writer: Bryan Hitch | Artist: Tony S. Daniel
ISBN: 9781401267797 | Diamond Code: OCT160295
Price: $16.99/$19.99 CAN | Format: TP

AQUAMAN: WAR FOR THE THRONE

Six years ago he was a surface dweller, raised as the son of a lighthouse keeper. Then tragedy struck, destiny was revealed, and young Arthur Curry claimed his birthright: the Throne of Atlantis.

Writer: Geoff Johns | Artist: Ivan Reis| ISBN: 9781401283582
Diamond Code: AUG180587 | Price: $12.99/$17.50 CAN
Format: TP | On sale: 11/27/2018 | COVER NOT FINAL

JUSTICE LEAGUE: NO JUSTICE

The balance of power in the DC Universe has snapped, and there's a threat coming to destroy Earth, one that the heroes are ill-equipped to handle. DC heroes and villains unite to stop one of the gravest dangers ever.

Writers: Scott Snyder, Joshua Williamson, James Tynion IV
Artists: Francis Manapul, Marcus To | ISBN: 9781401283346
Diamond Code: JUN180583 | Price: $16.99/$22.99 CAN | Format: TP

FOREVER EVIL

The Justice League is dead! An evil version of the Justice League takes over the DC Universe, and no one stands in the way ... no one except for Lex Luthor.

Writer: Geoff Johns | Artist: David Finch
ISBN: 9781401253387 | Diamond Code: FEB150254
Price: $19.99/$23.99 CAN | Format: TP

JUSTICE LEAGUE VOL. 1:

Comics legends Scott Snyder and Jim Cheung launch the Justice League into a cosmos-shaking mystery that will draw out their most terrible foes. The core members of the Justice League—Superman, Batman, Wonder Woman, Aquaman, the Flash and more—are finally reunited in an adventure for the ages!

Writers: Scott Snyder, James Tynion IV
Artists: Jim Cheung, Jorge Jimenez | ISBN: 9781401284992
Diamond Code: AUG180630 | Price: $17.99/$23.99 CAN
Format: TP | On sale: 11/13/2019 | COVER NOT FINAL

JUSTICE LEAGUE: THE DARKSEID WAR (DC ESSENTIAL EDITION)

Darkseid and the Anti-Monitor—two of the most powerful beings in the universe—face off in one of the biggest Justice League storylines ever!

Writer: Geoff Johns | Artist: Jason Fabok
ISBN: 9781401284558 | Diamond Code: JUNE180763
Price $29.99/$39.99 CAN | Format: TP | On sale: 10/9/2018

JUSTICE LEAGUE VOL. 2

The Justice League clashes with the Legion of Doom! Superstar writer Scott Snyder continues his run with the World's Greatest Super Heroes.

Writers: Scott Snyder | Artists: Jim Cheung & Jorge Jimenez
ISBN: 9781401288495 | Price: $16.99/$22.99 CAN
Format: TP | On sale: 3/26/2019 | COVER NOT FINAL

DEATHSTROKE VOL. 1: THE PROFESSIONAL

Slade Wilson, a.k.a. Deathstroke, just got a new contract. The trouble is, the people on his hit list are his closest family and confidants!

Writer: Christopher Priest | Artist: Carlo Pagulayan
ISBN: 9781401268237 | Diamond Code: DEC160372
Price: $16.99/$22.99 CAN | Format: TP

ALSO AVAILABLE: DEATHSTROKE VOLS. 2-5

JUSTICE LEAGUE DARK VOL. 1

Earth's magic once belonged to them. Now they want the magic back. But who exactly are they? It's up to the new Justice League Dark to find out and stop this nightmarish new threat at all costs!

Writer: James Tynion IV | Artists: Alvaro Martinez
ISBN: 9781401288112 | Diamond Code: JUN188686
Price: $16.99/$22.99 CAN | Format: TP | On sale: 3/12/2019
COVER NOT FINAL

DARK NIGHTS: METAL

The Dark Knight has uncovered one of the lost mysteries of the universe … one that could destroy the very fabric of the DC Universe!

Writer: Scott Snyder | Artist: Greg Capullo
ISBN: 9781401288587 | Price: $19.99/$29.99 CAN
Diamond Code: JUN188676 | Format: TP | On sale: 1/29/2019

JUSTICE LEAGUE ODYSSEY VOL. 1

When a cosmic menace threatens worlds beyond our own in the Ghost Sector, it falls to a new Justice League team to answer the call to battle!

Writer: Joshua Williamson | Artist: Stjepan Sejic
ISBN: 9781401289492 | Diamond Code: JUN188687
Price: $16.99/$22.99 CAN | Format: TP | On sale: 5/21/2019
COVER NOT FINAL

HEROES IN CRISIS

There's a crisis headed toward DC's greatest heroes, but it isn't coming from outer space or another dimension—this time, the threat is homegrown.

Writer: Tom King | Artists: Clay Mann
and Tomeu Morey | Diamond Code: JUN188683
ISBN: 9781401288587 | Price: $19.99 / $29.99 CAN | Format: TP
On sale: 8/3/2019 | COVER NOT FINAL

BATMAN & THE JUSTICE LEAGUE VOL. 1

The Justice League begins a new mission in these manga tales newly translated for an American audience.

Writer: Shiori Teshirogi | Artist: Shiori Teshirogi
ISBN: 9781401284695 | Diamond Code: JUN180436
Price: $12.99/$17.50 CAN | Format: TP | On sale: 10/23/2018

FOLLOW THE ADVENTURES OF THE MEMBERS OF THE JUSTICE LEAGUE!

AQUAMAN VOL. 1: THE TRENCH

Superstar writer Geoff Johns reteams with artist Ivan Reis to relaunch Aquaman as one of the most powerful and important heroes of the DC Universe.

Writer: Geoff Johns | Artist: Ivan Reis
ISBN: 9781401237103 | Diamond Code: FEB130206
Price: $14.99/$17.99 CAN | Format: TP

GREEN LANTERN: REBIRTH

A jaw-dropping epic that reintro-duces the quintessential Green Lantern, Hal Jordan!

Writer: Geoff Johns | Artist: Ethan Van Sciver
ISBN: 9781401227555 | Diamond Code: FEB100185
Price: $14.99/$17.99 CAN | Format: TP

CYBORG VOL. 1: THE IMITATION OF LIFE

Justice League member Cyborg, in his own series, begins his greatest quest to date: to find his soul ... if he has one!

Writer: John Semper Jr. | Artists: Will Conrad & Paul Pelletier
ISBN: 9781401267926 | Diamond Code: DEC160371
Price: $16.99/$22.99 CAN | Format: TP

ALSO AVAILABLE: CYBORG VOLS. 2-3

GREEN LANTERNS VOL. 1: RAGE PLANET

Rookie Green Lanterns Jessica Cruz and Simon Baz must overcome their clashing personalities and tackle the universe's toughest beat: Earth!

Writers: Sam Humphries | Artist: Rocha Robson
ISBN: 9781401267759 | Diamond Code: OCT 160294
Price: $16.99/$22.99 CAN | Format: TP

ALSO AVAILABLE: GREEN LANTERNS VOLS. 2-7

GREEN ARROW: WAR OF THE CLANS (DC ESSENTIAL EDITION)

As Green Arrow, Oliver Queen found a sense of purpose and belonging. But now he's not even sure where he came from ... or whom he came from. Jeff Lemire's entire run is now collected in one iconic edition!

Writer: Jeff Lemire | Artist: Andrea Sorrentino | ISBN: 9781401285623
Diamond Code: JUN188681 | Price: $29.99/$39.99 CAN | Format: TP
On sale: 1/1/2018 | COVER NOT FINAL

HAL JORDAN & THE GREEN LANTERN CORPS VOL. 1: SINESTRO'S LAW

Robert Venditti launches a new era as Hal Jordan and the Corps must rise up against the new force of order in the universe: the Sinestro Corps!

Writer: Robert Venditti | Artists: Ethan Van Sciver & Rafa Sandoval
ISBN: 9781401268008 | Diamond Code: NOV160318
Price: $16.99/$23.99 CAN | Format: TP

ALSO AVAILABLE: HAL JORDAN AND THE GREEN LANTERN CORPS VOLS. 2-7

GREEN ARROW VOL. 1: THE DEATH AND LIFE OF OLIVER QUEEN

Oliver Queen is back in Seattle to uncover an illegal human-trafficking operation when he comes face to face with a familiar yet mysterious woman—Black Canary!

Writer: Benjamin Percy | Artists:Otto Schmidt and Juan Ferreyra
ISBN: 9781401267810 | Diamond Code: OCT160293
Price $16.99/$22.99 CAN | Format: TP

ALSO AVAILABLE: GREEN ARROW VOLS. 2-7

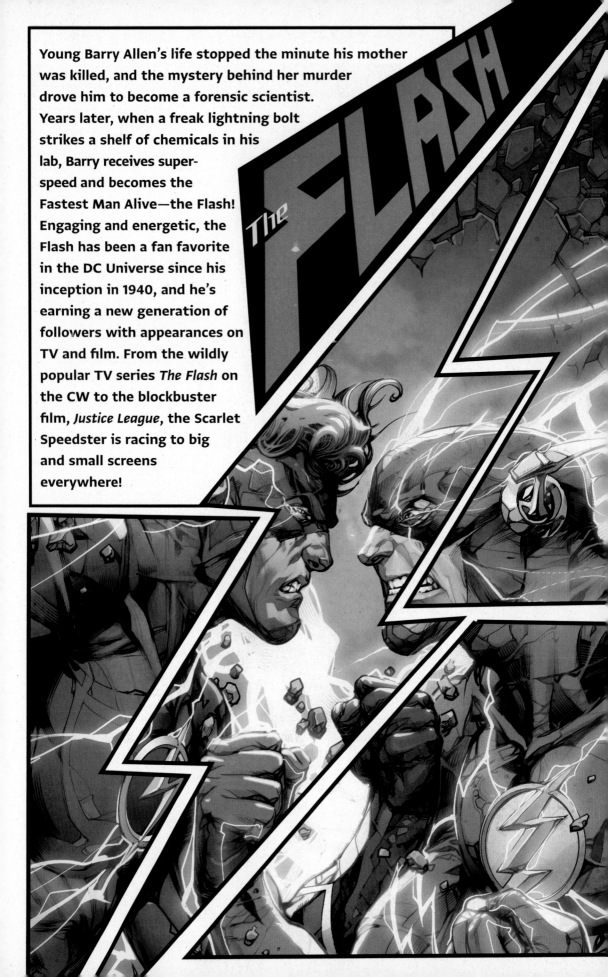

Young Barry Allen's life stopped the minute his mother was killed, and the mystery behind her murder drove him to become a forensic scientist. Years later, when a freak lightning bolt strikes a shelf of chemicals in his lab, Barry receives super-speed and becomes the Fastest Man Alive—the Flash! Engaging and energetic, the Flash has been a fan favorite in the DC Universe since his inception in 1940, and he's earning a new generation of followers with appearances on TV and film. From the wildly popular TV series *The Flash* on the CW to the blockbuster film, *Justice League*, the Scarlet Speedster is racing to big and small screens everywhere!

THE FLASH: THE SILVER AGE VOL. 1

These classic stories from the 1950s tell the origin of the Flash, his discovery of his incredible super-speed, and the introductions of the first of his "Rogues Gallery" of super-villains.

Writer: Robert Kanigher | Artist: Various
ISBN: 9781401261108 | Diamond Code: MAR160261
Price: $24.99/$33.99 | Format: TP

ALSO AVAILABLE: THE FLASH: THE SILVER AGE VOLS. 2-4

THE FLASH: STARTING LINE (ESSENTIAL EDITION)

The Fastest Man Alive returns as Central City's greatest protector. This stunning graphic novel is one of the fastest and easiest entry points in all of DC Comics' vast library.

Writer: Brian Buccellato | Artist: Francis Manapul
ISBN: 9781401284763 | Diamond Code: JUL180755 | Price: $24.99/$33.99 CAN
Format: TP | On sale: 10/30/2018 | COVER NOT FINAL

THE FLASH BY GEOFF JOHNS BOOK ONE

The critically acclaimed and best-selling adventures of Wally West, the Fastest Man Alive, as written by Geoff Johns.

Writer: Geoff Johns | Artist: Scott Kolins
ISBN: 9781401258733 | Diamond Code: AUG150268
Price: $24.99/$29.99 CAN | Format: TP

ALSO AVAILABLE: THE FLASH BY GEOFF JOHNS BOOKS 2-5

THE FLASH VOL. 1: LIGHTNING STRIKES TWICE

Rising-star writer Joshua Williamson ushers in a new era for the Flash, who finds himself in a city of speedsters after a familiar lightning storm.

Writer: Joshua Williamson | Artists: Carmine Di Giandomenico & Neil Googe
ISBN: 9781401267841 | Diamond Code: OCT160292
Price: $17.99/$23.99 CAN | Format: TP

THE FLASH: REBIRTH

The explosive epic that reintroduces the newly returned Barry Allen as the Flash!

Writer: Geoff Johns | Artist: Ethan Van Sciver
ISBN: 9781401230012 | Diamond Code: JAN110329
Price: $14.99/$17.99 CAN | Format: TP

THE FLASH VOL. 2: SPEED OF DARKNESS

Spinning directly out of the epic events of *DC Universe: Rebirth*, the Fastest Man Alive finds himself at the center of a DC Universe at a crossroads.

Writer: Joshua Williamson | Artist: Carmine Di Giandomenico
ISBN: 9781401268930 | Diamond Code: FEB170294
Price: $14.99/$19.99 CAN | Format: TP

FLASHPOINT

Heroes become villains in an alternate-universe tale that changed the DC Universe forever!

Writer: Geoff Johns | Artist: Andy Kubert
ISBN: 9781401233389 | Diamond Code: OCT138324
Price: $16.99/$19.99 CAN | Format: TP

THE FLASH VOL. 3: ROGUES RELOADED

The Rogues have ripped off the wrong guy. The only man who can save them? The Flash!

Writer: Joshua Williamson | Artist: Carmine Di Giandomenico
ISBN: 9781401271572 | Diamond Code: APR170413
Price: $16.99/$22.99 CAN | Format: TP

THE FLASH VOL. 7: PERFECT STORM

Gorilla Grodd is after Central City's Speed Force, but the one thing Barry Allen can't outrun is the truth, and his nemesis knows a terrible secret about the Fastest Man Alive.

Writer: Joshua Williamson
Artists: Carmine Di Giandomenico and Carlos D'Anda
ISBN: 9781401284527
Price: $16.99/$22.99 CAN | Format: TP

BATMAN/THE FLASH: THE BUTTON DELUXE EDITION

The *Watchmen* characters begin their invasion of the DC Universe here in the deluxe graphic novel *Batman/The Flash: The Button* by red-hot writers Tom King and Joshua Williamson.

Writers: Tom King & Joshua Williamson
Artists: Jason Fabok & Howard Porter | ISBN: 9781401276447
Diamond Code: JUN170380 | Price: $19.99/$25.99 CAN | Format: HC

THE FLASH VOL. 8: FLASH WAR

One of the greatest Flash adventures starts here, with a special story starring the classic Wally West, who's conflicted over whether to let Iris West know he is alive—and he'll need the help of Barry Allen to figure out what to do!

Writer: Joshua Williamson
Artists: Howard Porter and Scott Kolins
ISBN: 9781401283506 | Price: $16.99/$22.99 CAN
Format: TP | COVER NOT FINAL

HARLEY QUINN

SUICIDE SQUAD

Harley Quinn, Deadshot, Killer Croc, Captain Boomerang, El Diablo and the Enchantress—six of the deadliest and most unpredictable metahumans on the planet are finally being put to good use. Government agent Amanda Waller has sanctioned them to be part of Task Force X, led by Rick Flag and Katana, in which these villainous prisoners will complete dangerous missions in exchange for freedom. Conceptualized in 1959 and revived in modern form by John Ostrander in 1987, the Suicide Squad are the stars of the blockbuster film from DC.

SUICIDE SQUAD VOL. 1: KICKED IN THE TEETH

Former super-villains are recruited by a shadowy government agency for missions so dangerous, they're suicide.

Writer: Adam Glass | Artists: Federico Dallocchio & Clayton Henry
ISBN: 9781401235444 | Diamond Code: APR120250
Price: $14.99/$17.99 CAN | Format: TP

ALSO AVAILABLE: SUICIDE SQUAD VOLS. 2-5

NEW SUICIDE SQUAD VOL. 1: PURE INSANITY

Deadshot. Harley Quinn. The Joker's Daughter. Black Manta. Deathstroke. The world's most dangerous incarcerated super-villains are sent to carry out impossible missions on foreign soil in exchange for a commuted prison sentence.

Writer: Sean Ryan | Artists: Jeremy Roberts, Tom Derenick & Rob Hunter | ISBN: 9781401252380 | Diamond Code: APR150302
Price: $16.99/$19.99 CAN | Format: TP

ALSO AVAILABLE: NEW SUICIDE SQUAD VOLS. 2-4

SUICIDE SQUAD VOL. 1: THE BLACK VAULT

From Rob Williams, superstar artist Jim Lee and Philip Tan comes the new Suicide Squad—Harley Quinn, Deadshot, Captain Boomerang, Katana and Killer Croc!

Writer: Rob Williams | Artists: Jim Lee & Philip Tan
ISBN: 9781401269814 | Diamond Code: DEC160375
Price: $16.99/$22.99 CAN | Format: TP

ALSO AVAILABLE: SUICIDE SQUAD VOLS. 2-8

BATMAN: THE KILLING JOKE

The definitive Joker origin story from the mind of legendary writer Alan Moore.

Writer: Alan Moore | Artist: Brian Bolland
ISBN: 9781401216672 | Diamond Code: NOV070226
Price: $17.99/$20.99 CAN | Format: HC
FOR MATURE READERS

BATMAN ADVENTURES: MAD LOVE DELUXE EDITION

Collects the comics debut of Harley Quinn, one of the most popular—and controversial—characters in the DC Universe. Now in a deluxe format with exclusive extras and bonus material, this new collection is a must-have for Harley fans everywhere!

Writer: Paul Dini | Artist: Bruce Timm
ISBN: 9781401255121 | Diamond Code: NOV140306
Price:24.99/$29.99 | Format: HC

SUGGESTED READING ORDER

HARLEY QUINN BY KARL KESEL AND TERRY DODSON: THE DELUXE EDITION BOOK ONE

Harley's original solo series is finally recollected, as she is driven to astounding lengths to free her loony lover from his prison.

Writer: Karl Kesel | Artist: Terry Dodson
ISBN: 9781401276423 | Diamond Code: MAY170342
Price: $29.99/$39.99 | Format: HC

HARLEY QUINN VOL. 1: HOT IN THE CITY

The Cupid of Crime returns in her smash-hit solo series! Jimmy Palmiotti and Amanda Conner unleash Harley on an unsuspecting DC Universe, leaving no one unscathed in her wake.

Writers: Jimmy Palmiotti & Amanda Conner | Artist: Chad Hardin
ISBN: 9781401254155 | Diamond Code: JAN150369
Price: $16.99/$19.99 CAN | Format: TP

ALSO AVAILABLE: HARLEY QUINN VOLS. 2-6

HARLEY QUINN VOL. 1: DIE LAUGHING

Jimmy Palmiotti and Amanda Conner spearhead Harley's return in the wake of DC Rebirth as her crazy world gets even crazier.

Writers: Jimmy Palmiotti & Amanda Conner
Artists: Chard Hardin & John Timms
ISBN: 9781401268312 | Diamond Code: DEC160373
Price: $16.99/$22.99 CAN | Format: TP

ALSO AVAILABLE: HARLEY QUINN VOLS. 2-6

HARLEY QUINN VOL. 1: HARLEY VS. APOKOLIPS

Harley Quinn's story starts anew as an explosion at her favorite bodega turns out to be a mysterious assassination attempt on Harley!

Writer: Sam Humphries | Artist: Mirka Andolfo
ISBN: 9781401285074 | Price: $16.99/$22.99 CAN
Format: TP | On sale: 12/11/2018
COVER NOT FINAL

Originally a team composed of comics' most famous sidekicks, the Teen Titans have evolved over the years to become one of the most powerful teams in the DC Universe. Robin, Wonder Girl, Aqualad and Speedy—now Nightwing, Donna Troy, Tempest and Arsenal—have stepped out of their mentor's shadows and come into their own. But now taking up the mantle are a new group of Teen Titans—Kid Flash, Starfire, Raven, Beast Boy and a new Robin, Damian Wayne. These Titans and Teen Titans graphic novels epitomize the generational nature of the DC Universe, steeped in history yet incredibly accessible to the new reader!

TEEN TITANS: THE SILVER AGE VOL. 1

The sidekicks of DC's greatest heroes—including Robin, Aqualad, Kid Flash, Speedy and Wonder Girl—formed their own team in these lighthearted tales from the 1960s.

Writer: Bob Haney | Artists: Various
ISBN: 9781401275082 | Diamond Code: SEP170431
Price: $34.99/$45.99 CAN | Format: TP

THE NEW TEEN TITANS VOL. 1

The first eight issues of *New Teen Titans* by Marv Wolfman and George Pérez are presented in this graphic novel collection of the groundbreaking 1980s classic.

Writer: Marv Wolfman | Artist: George Pérez
ISBN: 9781401251437 | Diamond Code: JUN140283
Price: $19.99/$23.99 CAN | Format: TP

ALSO AVAILABLE: THE NEW TEEN TITANS VOL. 2-10

NEW TEEN TITANS:
THE JUDAS CONTRACT DELUXE EDITION

One of the greatest stories in DC history. They were Earth's teenage defenders—unbeatable and unstoppable. Riding high, they took an eighth member—a young girl—into their ranks. And she would be their downfall.

Writer: Marv Wolfman | Artist: George Pérez
ISBN: 9781401275778 | Diamond Code: SEP170420
Price: $29.99/$39.99 CAN | Format: HC

TEEN TITANS BY GEOFF JOHNS BOOK ONE

After years of dormancy, original Titans Cyborg, Beast Boy, Raven and Starfire aim to re-create the team for a new generation of heroes.

Writer: Geoff Johns | Artist: Mike McKone
ISBN: 9781401265984 | Diamond Code: DEC160383
Price: $24.99/$33.99 CAN | Format: TP

TEEN TITANS VOL. 1:
IT'S OUR RIGHT TO FIGHT

Tim Drake, Batman's former sidekick, is back in action when an international organization called Project N.O.W.H.E.R.E. seeks to capture, kill or co-opt super-powered teenagers.

Writer: Scott Lobdell | Artist: Brett Booth | ISBN: 9781401236984
Diamond Code: JUN120239 | Price: $14.99/$17.99 CAN | Format: TP

ALSO AVAILABLE: TEEN TITANS VOLS. 2-5

TITANS VOL. 1:
THE RETURN OF WALLY WEST

The classic Kid Flash, Wally West, returns after the events of DC Universe Rebirth! But will the rest of the Titans—Nightwing, Donna Troy, Tempest, Arsenal and Omen—recognize their ally who's been erased from time?

Writer: Dan Abnett | Artist: Brett Booth
ISBN: 9781401268176 | Diamond Code: DEC160376
Price: $16.99/$19.99 CAN | Format: TP

TEEN TITANS VOL. 1:
DAMIAN KNOWS BEST

His father is the World's Greatest Detective. His grandfather is the world's deadliest terrorist. He is Damian Wayne, a.k.a. Robin, Son of Batman—and he now commands the Teen Titans.

Writer: Benjamin Percy | Artists: Jonboy Myers & Khoi Pham
ISBN: 9781401270773 | Diamond Code: MAR170410
Price: $16.99/$22.99 CAN | Format: TP

TITANS: THE LAZARUS CONTRACT

Titans past, present and future collide with their eternal enemy Deathstroke in this monumental crossover from DC Rebirth!

Writers: Christopher Priest, Benjamin Percy & Dan Abnett | Artists: Brett Booth,
Paul Pelletier, Khoi Pham & Carlo Pagulayan | ISBN: 9781401276508
Diamond Code: AUG170327 | Price: $24.99/$33.99 CAN | Format: HC

TITANS BOOK 1:
TOGETHER FOREVER

A new team of Titans is forged when old friends must reunite to uncover a new mystery that threatens the lives of all Titans … past and present!

Writer: Judd Winick | Artist: Ian Churchill
ISBN: 9781401284282 | Diamond Code: JUN180590
Price: $24.99/$33.99 CAN | Format: TP | COVER NOT FINAL

TEEN TITANS GO! VOL. 1: PARTY PARTY

From the hit Cartoon Network series to the printed page, join Robin, Starfire, Beast Boy, Cyborg and Raven as they display their unique brand of hijinks, mayhem and justice!

Writer: Sholly Fisch | Artist: Lea Hernandez
ISBN: 9781401252427 | Diamond Code: DEC140400
Price: $12.99/$17.50 CAN | Format: TP

ALSO AVAILABLE: TEEN TITANS GO! VOL. 2-6

BATMAN: THE COURT OF OWLS SAGA (DC ESSENTIAL EDITION)

An epic tale from critically acclaimed author Scott Snyder. Hidden for years, the mysterious Court of Owls surfaces in Gotham City—what must Batman do to defeat them, and what deadly connection do they have to his past?

Writer: Scott Snyder | Artist: Greg Capullo
ISBN: 9781401284336 | Diamond Code: JUN180569
Price: $24.99/$33.99 CAN | Format: TP

JUSTICE LEAGUE: DARKSEID WAR (DC ESSENTIAL EDITION)

Darkseid and the Anti-Monitor—two of the most powerful beings in the universe—face off in one of the biggest Justice League storylines ever!

Writer: Geoff Johns | Artists: Jason Fabok & Francis Manapul
ISBN: 9781401284558 | Diamond Code: JUL180763
Price: $29.99/$39.99 CAN | Format: TP | On sale: 10/9/2018

BATMAN AND ROBIN: BAD BLOOD (DC ESSENTIAL EDITION)

As Batman and Robin try to adjust to their new partnership, a figure emerges from Bruce Wayne's past—one not happy that Batman Incorporated is shining a light on his own shadowy war against evil.

Writer: Peter J. Tomasi | Artist: Patrick Gleason
ISBN: 9781401289331 | Diamond Code: AUG180607
Price: $24.99/$33.99 CAN | Format: TP | On sale: 11/13/2018

SUPERGIRL: LAST DAUGHTER (DC ESSENTIAL EDITION)

Superman's teenage cousin mysteriously crash-lands on Earth decades after the destruction of Krypton.

Writers: Michael Green | Artist: Mike Johnson
ISBN: 9781401288358 | Diamond Code: JUN188696
Price: $24.99/$33.99 CAN | Format: TP | On sale: 3/19/2019

THE FLASH: STARTING LINE (DC ESSENTIAL EDITION)

The Fastest Man Alive returns as Central City's greatest protector. This stunning graphic novel is one of the fastest and easiest entry points in all of DC Comics' vast library.

Writer: Brian Buccellato | Artist: Francis Manapul
ISBN: 9781401284763 | Diamond Code: JUL180755
Price: $24.99/$33.99 CAN | Format: TP | On sale: 10/30/2018

FINAL CRISIS (DC ESSENTIAL EDITION)

From the mind of genre-defining writer Grant Morrison comes *Final Crisis*, one of the most epic sagas ever to hit the DC Universe! *Final Crisis* is a deconstruction of superhero comics and a challenging, thought-provoking take on the modern, four-color icons.

Writer: Grant Morrison | Artist: Doug Mahnke and J.G. Jones
ISBN: 9781401290955 | Diamond Code: JUN188678
Price: $24.99/$33.99 CAN | Format: TP | On sale: 4/9/2019

GREEN ARROW: WAR OF THE CLANS (DC ESSENTIAL EDITION)

As Green Arrow, Oliver Queen found a sense of purpose and belonging. But now he's not even sure where he came from … or whom he came from. Jeff Lemire's entire run is now collected in one iconic edition!

Writer: Jeff Lemire | Artist: Andrea Sorrentino
ISBN: 9781401285623 | Diamond Code: JUN188681
Price: $29.99/$39.99 CAN | Format: TP | On sale: 1/1/2019

79

DC MODERN CLASSICS

DC Modern Classics features the most highly regarded graphic novels from the world's foremost authority on graphic literature. These groundbreaking, genre-defining works are presented in new unique hardcover editions, each fitting into a beautifully designed exclusive slipcase, perfect for display. DC Modern Classics are a must-have for any collector, as well as any new fan just beginning to build their graphic novel library.

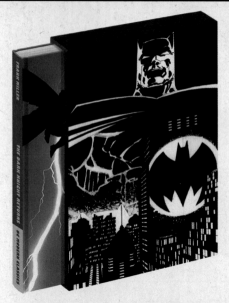

BATMAN: THE DARK KNIGHT RETURNS (DC MODERN CLASSICS EDITION)

Frank Miller's undisputed masterwork of a broken-down, veteran crime-fighter trying to bring Gotham City back from the brink of destruction is now joining this elite line of new hardcover editions. Miller's story is not only the greatest Dark Knight tale ever told, but one of the very finest in popular fiction. With nuanced storytelling and stunning artwork that still stands up today, *Batman: The Dark Knight Returns* is the very essence of DC Modern Classics.

Writer: Frank Miller | Artist: Frank Miller | ISBN: 9781401285319
Diamond code: STL089379 | Price: $49.99/$65.99 CAN
Format: HC | On sale: 5/4/2019

WATCHMEN (DC MODERN CLASSICS EDITION)

Widely considered the greatest graphic novel ever written, Alan Moore's dystopian masterpiece *Watchmen* is now presented in a new hardcover edition with an exclusive slipcase, as a part of DC Modern Classics. Alan Moore and Dave Gibbons created *Watchmen* and changed the course of comics history, essentially remaking how popular culture perceived the medium.

Writer: Alan Moore | Artist: Dave Gibbons | ISBN: 9781401284718
Diamond code: AUG180662 | Price: $49.99/$65.99 CAN | Format: HC
On sale: 3/26/2019

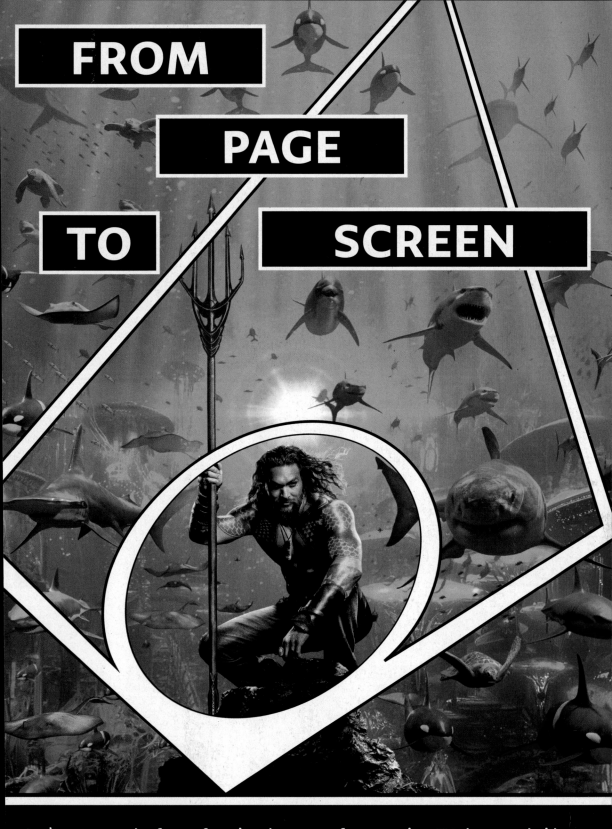

FROM PAGE TO SCREEN

Can't get enough of your favorite characters from movies, TV shows and video games? Get even more of the heroes and villains you can't stop watching with this guide to the comics and graphic novels that take them on their wildest adventures. Between prequels to hit video games, continuations of classic and modern TV shows, storylines familiar from movies and more, there are plenty of ways to be a comics fan.

The magnetic Jason Momoa returns to the character he portrayed in *Justice League* with the highly anticipated *Aquaman* film, coming December 2018. Learn more about Aquaman, Mera, Ocean Master and Black Manta in these starting-point graphic novels.

AQUAMAN: WAR FOR THE THRONE

Six years ago he was a surface dweller, raised as the son of a lighthouse keeper. Then tragedy struck, destiny was revealed, and young Arthur Curry claimed his birthright: the Throne of Atlantis. From the superstar duo of Geoff Johns and Ivan Reis comes the ultimate Aquaman tale of conflict and conquest!

Writer: Geoff Johns | Artist: Ivan Reis | ISBN: 9781401283582
Diamond Code: AUG180587 | Price: $12.99/$17.50 CAN
Format: TP | On sale: 11/27/2018 | COVER NOT FINAL

MERA: QUEEN OF ATLANTIS

In her first solo series ever, Mera must keep the peace between the surface world and Atlantis as its newly anointed queen in exile, as the brutal Atlantean Civil War rages.

Writer: Dan Abnett | Artist: Lan Medina | ISBN: 9781401285302
Price: $16.99/$22.99 CAN | Format: TP | On sale: 12/11/2018

AQUAMAN VOL. 1: THE TRENCH

Writer: Geoff Johns
Artist: Ivan Reis
ISBN: 9781401237103
Diamond Code: FEB130206
Price: $14.99/$17.99 CAN
Format: TP

AQUAMAN VOL. 1: THE DROWNING

Writer: Dan Abnett
Artists: Brad Walker &
Philippe Briones
ISBN: 9781401267827
Diamond Code: OCT160290
Price: $16.99/$22.99 CAN
Format: TP

AQUAMAN VOL. 2: THE OTHERS

Writer: Geoff Johns
Artist: Ivan Reis
ISBN: 9781401242954
Diamond Code: AUG130295
Price: $14.99/$17.99 CAN
Format: TP

AQUAMAN VOL. 3: THRONE OF ATLANTIS

Writer: Geoff Johns
Artists: Paul Pelletier &
Ivan Reis
ISBN: 9781401246952
Diamond Code: FEB140252
Price: $16.99/$19.99 CAN
Format: TP

AQUAMAN VOL. 4: DEATH OF A KING

Writer: Geoff Johns
Artist: Paul Pelletier
ISBN: 9781401249953
Diamond Code: AUG140327
Price: $16.99/$19.99 CAN
Format: TP

AQUAMAN VOL. 2: BLACK MANTA RISING

Writer: Dan Abnett
Artist: Brad Walker &
Philippe Briones
ISBN: 9781401272272
Diamond Code: APR160388
Price: $19.99/$25.99 CAN
Format: TP

AQUAMAN BY PETER DAVID BOOK ONE

Writer: Peter David
Artists: Various
ISBN: 9781401277468
Diamond Code: NOV170357
Price: $29.99/$39.99 CAN
Format: TP

JUSTICE LEAGUE VOL. 1: ORIGIN

Writer: Geoff Johns
Artist: Jim Lee
ISBN: 9781401237882
Diamond Code: OCT120252
Price: $16.99/$19.99 CAN
Format: TP

DC SUPER HERO GIRLS: SEARCH FOR ATLANTIS

Writer: Shea Fontana
Artist: Yancey Labat
ISBN: 9781401283537
Diamond Code: JUN180439
Price: $9.99/$13.50 CAN
Format: TP

SHAZAM!

We all have a superhero inside us, it just takes a bit of magic to bring it out. In Billy Baston's case, by shouting one word—SHAZAM!—this streetwise 14-year-old foster kid can turn into the adult Super Hero Shazam, courtesy of an ancient wizard.

LEARN MORE ABOUT BILLY'S JOURNEY IN THESE GREAT GRAPHIC NOVELS AND GET READY FOR THE HIGHLY ANTICIPATED FEATURE FILM STARRING ZACHARY LEVI, COMING APRIL 2019.

SHAZAM!: POWER OF HOPE

Shazam!: Power of Hope is a story of a superhero using his powers in the most human of ways, to instill hope in the hearts of children. Paul Dini and Alex Ross's critically acclaimed, classic tale is now back in this hardcover deluxe edition!

Writer: Paul Dini | Artist: Alex Ross | ISBN: 9781401288228
Price: $17.99/$23.99 CAN | Format: HC | On sale: 4/23/2019

SHAZAM! VOL. 1 (THE NEW 52)

Young orphan Billy Batson has bounced from foster home to foster home, but he's far from the ideal child. Brash and rude, Billy is a troubled teen that just can't seem to find a calling. But after a fateful night on a subway car, that all will change.

Writer: Geoff Johns | Artist: Gary Frank | ISBN: 9781401246990
Diamond Code: MAY130219 | Price: $16.99/$19.99 CAN | Format: TP

SHAZAM!: A CELEBRATION OF 75 YEARS

This hardcover anthology collects some of the greatest Shazam's stories ever told. Get caught up on the charming and entertaining history of DC's most fun-loving hero with *Shazam!: A Celebration of 75 Years*.

Writer: Bill Parker | Artist: C.C. Beck | ISBN: 9781401255381
Diamond Code: NOV140315 | Price: $39.99/$47.99 CAN | Format: HC

SUPERMAN/SHAZAM!: FIRST THUNDER DELUXE EDITION

Witness the thunderous first meeting of the Last Son of Krypton, Superman, and Earth's Mightiest Mortal, Shazam, in the acclaimed *Superman/Shazam!: First Thunder*, now collected in this hardcover deluxe edition.

Writer: Judd Winick | Artist: Joshua Middleton | ISBN: 9781401285371
Price: $29.99/$39.99 CAN | Format: HC | On sale: 12/18/2018

DC ON TV: FROM PAGE TO SCREEN

Whether it's the Girl of Steel or the Scarlet Speedster, the heroes and villains from the page of your favorite DC and Vertigo graphic novels are hitting the small screen almost every day of the week! Check out these amazing books featuring these unforgettable characters

SUPERGIRL: LAST DAUGHTER (DC ESSENTIAL EDITION)

Writer: Michael Green
Artist: Mike Johnson
ISBN: 9781401288358
On sale: 3/19/2019
Diamond code: JUN188696
Price: $24.99/$33.99 CAN
Format: TP

SUN 8/7c

THE CW DARE TO DEFY

MON 8/7c THE CW DARE TO DEFY

GREEN ARROW: WAR OF THE CLANS (DC ESSENTIAL EDITION)

Writer: Jeff Lemire
Artist: Andrea Sorrentino
ISBN: 9781401285623
Diamond Code: JUN188681
Price: $29.99/$39.99 CAN
Format: TP
On sale: 1/1/2019

THE FLASH: STARTING LINE (ESSENTIAL EDITION)

Writer: Brian Buccellato
Artist: Francis Manapul
ISBN: 9781401284763
Diamond Code: JUL180755
Price: $24.99/$33.99 CAN
Format: TP
On sale: 10/30/2018

TUES 8/7c

THE CW DARE TO DEFY

COVERS NOT FINAL

iZOMBIE VOL. 1: DEAD TO THE WORLD

Writer: Chris Roberson
Artist: Mike Allred
ISBN: 9781401229658
Diamond Code: DEC100299
Price: $14.99/$17.99 CAN
Format: TP

MIDSEASON 2019

PREACHER BOOK ONE

Writer: Garth Ennis
Artist: Steve Dillon
ISBN: 9781401240455
Diamond Code: MAR130303
Price: $19.99/$23.99 CAN
Format: TP

aMC **SUN 10/9c**

LUCIFER BOOK ONE

Writer: Mike Carey
Artists: Peter Gross &
Scott Hampton
ISBN: 9781401240264
Diamond Code: FEB130247
Price: $29.99/$35.00 CAN
Format: TP

Season 4 premieres on
NETFLIX

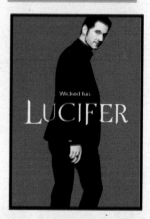

BLACK LIGHTNING: YEAR ONE (NEW EDITION)

Writer: Jan Van Meter
Artist: Cully Hamner
ISBN: 9781401279646
Diamond Code: OCT170366
Price: $14.99/$19.99 CAN
Format: TP

TUES 9/8c THE **CW** DARE TO DEFY

NEW AGE OF HEROES

DC introduces a bold new line of graphic novels starring a thrilling array of heroes, illustrated by world-class artists, including Jim Lee, Andy Kubert, John Romita Jr., Ivan Reis and Tony S. Daniel. These books are great entry points for new readers and a welcome addition for longtime fans of the DC library!

NEW CHALLENGERS

A group of fearless explorers uncovers the worst—and weirdest—the DC Universe has to offer.

Writers: Scott Snyder & Aaron Gillespie
Artist: Andy Kubert
ISBN: 9781401283445
Price: $16.99/$22.99 CAN
Format: TP
On sale: 12/24/2018

THE IMMORTAL MEN

The superstar creative team of comics legend Jim Lee and James Tynion IV unite to tell the tale of the secret history of heroes who have protected humanity from the shadows since the dawn of time ... and who can live forever.

Writer: James Tynion IV | Artist: Jim Lee
ISBN: 9781401283308| Price: $16.99/$22.99 CAN
Format: TP | On sale: 12/4/2018

DAMAGE VOL. 1

Ethan "Elvis" Avery just wanted to serve his country. Instead, he's been turned into the government's own living, breathing, ticking time bomb. Cheaper than a nuclear warhead and twice as effective, Ethan fights to rein in the damage he unleashes when the beast inside him springs free for one hour a day. His first challenge? The Suicide Squad.

Writer: Jeff Lemire | Artist: Evan "Doc" Shaner & Ivan Reis
ISBN: 9781401283339 | Diamond Code: JUL180800
Price: $16.99/$22.99 CAN | Format: TP

THE TERRIFICS VOL. 1

When Mr. Terrific, Metamorpho, Plastic Man and Phantom Girl find themselves bound together by a tragic accident, the team of unlikely allies must rely on one another to make their way back home.

Writer: Jeff Lemire | Artist:s Evan "Doc" Shaner & Ivan Reis
ISBN: 9781401283360 | Diamond Code: JUL180800
Price: $16.99/$22.99 CAN | Format: TP | On sale: 10/16/2018

THE SILENCER VOL. 1

The Silencer is one of the DC Universe's deadliest assassins ... and you've never heard of her. Inhumanly strong, highly trained, armed with devastating and stealthy metahuman abilities, the Silencer is virtually invincible. Or at least she was....

Writer: Dan Abnett
Artists: John Romita Jr. & Viktor Bogdanovic
ISBN: 9781401283353 | Diamond Code: JUL180787
Price: $16.99/$22.99 CAN | Format: TP

SIDEWAYS VOL. 1

High school junior Derek James accidentally fell through a rift into the Dark Multiverse. Now, as Sideways, he can create rifts in midair to leap through dimensions at will! But with that much power comes great liability—and cracks are starting to form in the fabric of the space-time continuum.

Writers: Dan DiDio & Justin Jordan | Artist: Kenneth Rocafort
ISBN: 9781401283377 | Price: $16.99/$22.99 CAN
Format: TP | On sale: 10/23/2018

COVERS NOT FINAL

BRIAN MICHAEL BENDIS'S JINXWORLD

Brian Michael Bendis's critically acclaimed Jinxworld library now comes to DC! These beloved, hard-to-find Jinxworld titles are accompanied by new stories from continuing series as well as new series. Catch up on the vast library of graphic novels from one of the greatest comics creators ever!

"Bendis is the funny pages descendent of Sam Fuller, Martin Scorsese and Quentin Tarantino." —Entertainment Weekly

POWERS BOOK ONE

In a world where heroes soar through the sky on bolts of lightning and fire, detectives Christian Walker and Deena Pilgrim deal with special cases that involve … powers.

Writer: Brian Michael Bendis
Artist: Michael Avon Oeming
ISBN: 9781401287450
Diamond Code: JUL180773
Price: $29.99/$39.99 CAN
Format: TP | On sale: 10/16/18

SCARLET BOOK ONE

A no-holds-barred series that tackles some of the most prevalent issues in modern American society. A young woman is pushed to the edge by a world filled with police brutality, government corruption and unspeakable crimes.

Writer: Brian Michael Bendis
Artist: Alex Maleev
ISBN: 9781401287443
Diamond Code:JUL180782
Price: $14.99/$19.99 CAN
Format: TP | On sale: 10/30/18

COVER VOL. 1

A very well-known comics creator is recruited by the agency to live a double life as a spy. And convention season is upon us. Based on a true story!

Writer: Brian Michael Bendis
Artist: David Mack
ISBN: 9781401291044
Price: $16.99/$22.99
Format: TP
On sale: 5/28/2019

SCARLET VOL. 1

Scarlet is back! In this great jumping-on point graphic novel any new fan, you'll see what happens when one young woman is pushed too far—and what one country will do to stop her.

Writer:Brian Michael Bendis
Artist: Alex Maleev
ISBN: 9781401290627
Diamond Code: JUN188831
Price: $16.99/$22.99
Format: TP | On sale: 4/30/2019
COVER NOT FINAL

GOLDFISH

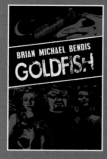

After years away, con man David Gold returns to the city he once called home and finds that nothing is as it once was.

Writer: Brian Michael Bendis
Artist: Brian Michael Bendis
ISBN: 9781401287498
Diamond Code: JUN188680
Price: $24.99/$33.99 CAN
Format: TP | On sale: 12/11/2018

JINX

A classic crime-noir tale of deceit, murder and passion. When bounty hunter Jinx Alameda met con-man David "Goldfish" Gold, she thought he was too good to be true. He was.

Writer: Brian Michael Bendis
Artist: Brian Michael Bendis
ISBN: 9781401287504
Diamond Code: JUN188685
Price: $24.99/$33.99 CAN
Format: TP | On sale: 12/24/2018

THE UNITED STATES OF MURDER INC. VOL. 1: TRUTH

Welcome to a world where the influence of organized crime has risen to a place where parts of the United States are fully controlled by the mafia.

Writer: Brian Michael Bendis
Artist: Michael Avon Oeming
ISBN: 9781401287467
Price: $16.99/$22.99 CAN
Format: TP
On sale: 10/16/2018

PEARL VOL. 1

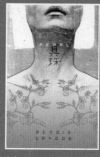

Pearl is an exceptional tattoo artist … and an accidental assassin for one of the modern-day San Francisco Yakuza. She was born into one life, but another is calling to her.

Writer: Brian Michael Bendis
Artist: Michael Gaydos
ISBN: 9781401290610
Diamond Code: JUN188691
Price: $16.99/$22.99 CAN
Format: TP | On sale: 5/14/2019

New York Times best-selling author Neil Gaiman's transcendent series *The Sandman* is often hailed as the definitive DC Vertigo title and one of the finest achievements in graphic storytelling. Gaiman created an unforgettable tale of the forces that exist beyond life and death by weaving ancient mythology, folklore and fairy tales with his own distinct narrative vision. Now *The Sandman* celebrates its 30th anniversary with all-new editions of this classic series.

THE SANDMAN UNIVERSE

A new line of books curated by Neil Gaiman conjures epic storytelling, immersing readers into the evolving world of the Dreaming. The Sandman Universe begins with four new series, existing in a shared universe, all building upon Gaiman's *New York Times* best-selling series that lyrically weaved together stories of dreams and magic.

THE DREAMING VOL. 1

Writer:
Si Spurrier
Artist: Bilquis Evely
ISBN: 9781401291174
Diamond Code:
JUN188700
Price:
$16.99/$22.99 CAN
Format: TP
On sale: 6/11/2019

LUCIFER VOL. 1

Writer:
Dan Watters
Artist:
Sebastian Fiumara
ISBN: 9781401291334
Diamond Code:
JUN188689
Price
$16.99/$22.99 CAN
Format: TP
On sale: 6/25/2019

BOOKS OF MAGIC VOL. 1

Writer:
Kat Howard
Artist: Tom Fowler
ISBN: 9781401291341
Diamond Code:
JUN188672
Price:
$16.99/$22.99 CAN
Format: TP
On sale: 7/16/2019

HOUSE OF WHISPERS VOL. 1

Writer:
Nalo Hopkinson
Artist: Dominike
"Domo" Stanton
ISBN: 9781401291358
Diamond Code:
JUN188684
Price
$16.99/$22.99 CAN
Format: TP
On sale: 7/30/2019

THE SANDMAN VOL. 1: PRELUDES & NOCTURNES 30TH ANNIVERSARY EDITION

Writer: Neil Gaiman
Artist: Sam Kieth
ISBN: 9781401284770 | On sale: 10/30/2018
Diamond Code: JUL180774
Price: $19.99/$25.99 CAN | Format: TP

THE SANDMAN VOL. 2: THE DOLL'S HOUSE 30TH ANNIVERSARY EDITION

Writer: Neil Gaiman
Artist: Mike Dringenberg
ISBN: 9781401285067 | On sale: 11/20/2018
Diamond Code: AUG180642
Price: $19.99/$25.99 CAN | Format: TP

THE SANDMAN VOL. 3: DREAM COUNTRY 30TH ANNIVERSARY EDITION

Writer: Neil Gaiman
Artist: Kelley Jones
ISBN: 9781401285487
Price: $19.99/$25.99 CAN | Format: TP
On sale: 12/18/2018

THE SANDMAN VOL. 4: SEASON OF MISTS 30TH ANNIVERSARY EDITION

Writer: Neil Gaiman
Artist: Kelley Jones
ISBN: 9781401285814 | On sale: 1/29/2019
Diamond Code: JUN188701
Price: $19.99/$25.99 CAN | Format: TP

THE SANDMAN VOL. 5: A GAME OF YOU 30TH ANNIVERSARY EDITION

Writer: Neil Gaiman
Artists: Shawn McManus & Dick Giordano
ISBN: 9781401288075
Diamond Code: JUN188702 | On sale: 3/5/2019
Price: $19.99/$25.99 CAN | Format: TP

THE SANDMAN VOL. 6: FABLES & REFLECTIONS 30TH ANNIVERSARY EDITION

Writer: Neil Gaiman
Artist: P. Craig Russell
ISBN: 9781401288464 | On sale: 3/26/2019
Diamond Code: JUN188703
Price: $19.99/$25.99 CAN | Format: TP

THE SANDMAN VOL. 7: BRIEF LIVES 30TH ANNIVERSARY EDITION

Writer: Neil Gaiman
Artist: Jill Thompson
ISBN: 9781401289089 | On sale: 4/23/2019
Diamond Code: JUN188704
Price: $19.99/$25.99 CAN | Format: TP

THE SANDMAN VOL. 8: WORLDS' END 30TH ANNIVERSARY EDITION

Writer: Neil Gaiman
Artist: Bryan Talbot
ISBN: 9781401289591 | On sale: 5/28/2019
Diamond Code: JUN188705
Price: $19.99/$25.99 CAN | Format: TP

COVERS NOT FINAL

100 BULLETS BOOK ONE

If guaranteed full immunity, what would you do? Vertigo's seminal crime series features ordinary citizens who are given the opportunity to exact revenge on a person who has wronged them.

Writer: Brian Azzarello | Artist: Eduardo Risso
ISBN: 9781401250560 | Diamond Code: JUL140274
Price: $24.99/$28.99 CAN | Format: TP

ALSO AVAILABLE: 100 BULLETS BOOKS 2-5

DARK NIGHT: A TRUE BATMAN STORY

In this autobiographical true story, *Batman: The Animated Series* co-creator Paul Dini recounts a harrowing near-death beating and subsequent road to recovery, through the lens of the Dark Knight.

Writer: Paul Dini | Artist: Eduardo Risso
ISBN: 9781401271367 | Diamond Code: MAR170445
Price: $16.99/$22.99 CAN | Format: TP

AMERICAN VAMPIRE VOL. 1

Scott Snyder and legendary novelist Stephen King offer a stirring take on the vampire mythology.

Writers: Stephen King & Scott Snyder | Artist: Rafael Albuquerque
ISBN: 9781401229740 | Diamond Code: JUL110284
Price: $19.99/$23.99 CAN | Format: TP

ALSO AVAILABLE: AMERICAN VAMPIRE VOL. 2-8

DAYTRIPPER

This award-winning graphic novel follows Bras de Oliva Domingo during different periods in his life, each with the same ending: his death.

Writers: Gabriel Bá & Fábio Moon | Artists: Gabriel Bá & Fábio Moon
ISBN: 9781401229696 | Diamond Code: NOV100268
Price: $19.99/$23.99 CAN | Format: TP

AMERICAN WAY: THOSE ABOVE AND THOSE BELOW

It's been a decade since the Civil Defense Corps was exposed as a fraud created for propaganda purposes. While most of the heroes who survived have receded, the New American carries on, trying to keep communities safe amid the social turmoil of the 1970s.

Writer: John Ridley | Artist: Georges Jeanty
ISBN: 9781401278359 | Diamond Code: JAN180417
Price: $16.99/$22.99 CAN | Format: TP

ALSO AVAILABLE: AMERICAN WAY 10TH ANNIVERSARY EDITION

DOOM PATROL BOOK ONE

Grant Morrison reinvents the Silver Age super-team as only he can, as the Doom Patrol investigates the surreal corners of the DC Universe.

Writer: Grant Morrison | Artist: Richard Case
ISBN: 9781401263126 | Diamond Code: NOV150304
Price: $29.99/39.99 CAN | Format: TP

ALSO AVAILABLE: DOOM PATROL BOOKS TWO AND THREE

BORDER TOWN

When a crack in the border between worlds releases an army of monsters from Mexican folklore into the small town of Devil's Fork, Arizona, the residents blame the ensuing weirdness—the shared nightmares, the otherworldly radio transmissions, the mysterious goat mutilations—on "God-dang illegals."

Writer: Eric. M. Esquivel | Artist: Ramon Villalobos
ISBN: 9781401291365 | Price:$16.99/$22.99 CAN
Format: TP | On sale: 7/30/2019

FABLES VOL. 1: LEGENDS IN EXILE

Folklore comes to life as these real-life fairy tale characters are exiled in modern-day New York City.

Writer: Bill Willingham | Artist: Lan Medina
ISBN: 9781401237554 | Diamond Code: FEB120285
Price: $12.99/$15.99 CAN | Format: TP

ALSO AVAILABLE: FABLES VOLS. 2-22

THE INVISIBLES BOOK ONE

Throughout history, a secret society called the Invisibles has worked against dark forces conspiring to end mankind.

Writer: Grant Morrison | Artists: Steve Yeowell & Jill Thompson
ISBN: 9781401267957 | Diamond Code: NOV160356
Price: $19.99/$23.99 CAN | Format: TP

ALSO AVAILABLE: THE INVISIBLES BOOKS TWO-FOUR

PREACHER BOOK ONE

Jesse Custer, a wayward preacher, begins a violent journey to find God (literally), joined by his girlfriend, Tulip, and the hard-drinking Irish vampire Cassidy.

Writer: Garth Ennis | Artist: Steve Dillon
ISBN: 9781401240455 | Diamond Code: MAR130303
Price: $19.99/$23.99 CAN | Format: TP

ALSO AVAILABLE: PREACHER BOOKS TWO-SIX

JOHN CONSTANTINE, HELLBLAZER VOL. 1: ORIGINAL SINS

In the longest-running Vertigo series ever, Earth's resident exorcist, demonologist and master of the dark arts, John Constantine, is on the side of the angels—but he's willing to make a deal with a demon to prevail.

Writer: Jamie Delano | Artists: John Ridgway, Alfredo Alcala, Rick Veitch & Tom Mandrake | ISBN: 9781401230067
Diamond Code: DEC100302 | Price: $19.99/$23.99 CAN | Format: TP

ALSO AVAILABLE: JOHN CONSTANTINE, HELLBLAZER VOLS. 2-19

PRIDE OF BAGHDAD DELUXE EDITION

Inspired by true events, acclaimed writer Brian K. Vaughan brings readers a startlingly original look at life on the streets of Baghdad during the Iraq War.

Writer: Brian K. Vaughan | Artist: Niko Henrichon
ISBN: 9781401248949 | Diamond Code: AUG140360
Price: $24.99/$28.99 CAN | Format: HC

THE LEAGUE OF EXTRAORDINARY GENTLEMEN VOL. 1

The best-known characters of 19th-century literature band together in Alan Moore's award-winning graphic novel.

Writer: Alan Moore | Artist: Kevin O'Neill
ISBN: 9781563898587 | Diamond Code: MAY118167
Price: $16.99/$19.99 CAN | Format: TP

LUCIFER BOOK ONE

In this inspiration behind the Fox TV show, the king of Hell abdicates his throne for a life on Earth.

Writer: Mike Carey | Artists: Peter Gross & Scott Hampton
ISBN: 9781401240264 | Diamond Code: FEB130247
Price: $29.99/$35.00 CAN | Format: TP

ALSO AVAILABLE: LUCIFER BOOKS TWO-FIVE

SAGA OF THE SWAMP THING BOOK ONE

Alan Moore's take on the classic monster stretched the creative boundaries of the medium and became one of the most spectacular series in comic book history.

Writer: Alan Moore | Artist: Stephen Bissette
ISBN: 9781401220839 | Diamond Code: JAN120343
Price: $19.99/$23.99 CAN | Format: TP

ALSO AVAILABLE: SAGA OF THE SWAMP THING BOOKS TWO-SIX

DC VERTIGO

SCALPED BOOK ONE

Fifteen years ago, Dashiell "Dash" Bad Horse ran away from a life of abject poverty and utter hopelessness on the Prairie Rose Indian Reservation searching for something better. Now he's come back.

Writer: Jason Aaron | Artist: R.M. Guéra
ISBN: 9781401271268 | Diamond Code: APR170454
Price: $24.99/$33.99 CAN | Format: TP

ALSO AVAILABLE: SCALPED BOOKS TWO-FIVE

SIX DAYS

This original graphic novel from DC Vertigo is the true story of an obscure World War II battle that took place in the small village of Graignes, France for six days and the men who survived to tell the tale. *Six Days* is a true story of survival, loyalty, the brutality of war and a triumph of the human spirit.

Writer: Robert Venditti | Artist: Kevin Maurer
ISBN: 9781401290719 | Diamond Code: APR170454
Price: $24.99/$33.99 CAN | Format: HC | On sale: 5/14/2019
COVER NOT FINAL

THE SHERIFF OF BABYLON VOL. 1: BANG. BANG. BANG.

Inspired by his real-life experiences as a CIA operations officer in Iraq, Tom King delivers a wartime crime thriller like no other.

Writer: Tom King | Artist: Mitch Gerads
ISBN: 9781401264666 | Diamond Code: APR160424
Price: $14.99/$17.99 CAN | Format: TP

ALSO AVAILABLE: SHERIFF OF BABYLON VOL. 2

TRANSMETROPOLITAN VOL. 1: BACK ON THE STREET

Mastermind writer Warren Ellis delivers this sharp, manic, anything-goes exploration of urban life about journalist/cult author Spider Jerusalem.

Writer: Warren Ellis | Artist: Darick Robertson
ISBN: 9781401220846 | Diamond Code: DEC080220
Price: $14.99/$17.99 CAN | Format: TP

ALSO AVAILABLE: TRANSMETROPOLITAN VOLS. 2-10

TRILLIUM

Two disparate souls are separated by thousands of years and hundreds of millions of miles. Yet they will fall in love and, as a result, bring about the end of the universe. Even though reality is unraveling all around them, nothing can pull them apart. Eisner Award-nominated writer/artist Jeff Lemire reinvents the concept of a love story in the comics medium in this visually innovative and mind-expanding tale.

Writer: Jeff Lemire | Artist: Jeff Lemire | ISBN: 9781401249007
Diamond Code: MAY140407 | Price: $16.99/$19.99 CAN
Format: TP | FOR MATURE READERS

VERTIGO: A CELEBRATION OF 25 YEARS

One of the most influential imprints in comics history celebrates its 25th anniversary in this anthology graphic novel! This deluxe hardcover relives the history of the innovative imprint as told by the people who lived it. A luxurious hybrid of oral history and retrospective art book, *Vertigo: A Celebration of 25 Years* features a comprehensive timeline of every Vertigo project ever released.

Writer: Neil Gaiman, Garth Ennis and Warren Ellis
Artist: Jock | ISBN: 9781401282011 | Diamond Code: AUG180495
Price: $49.99/$65.99 CAN | Format: HC | On sale: 11/13/2018

Y: THE LAST MAN BOOK ONE

Brian K. Vaughan's epic series that made him a comics legend poses the question "What would you do if you were the last man on Earth?"

Writer: Brian K. Vaughan | Artist: Pia Guerra
ISBN: 9781401251512 | Diamond Code: JUN140312
Price: $19.99/$23.99 CAN | Format: TP

ALSO AVAILABLE: Y: THE LAST MAN BOOKS TWO-FIVE

DC's YOUNG ANIMAL

DC's Young Animal is a grassroots mature-reader pop-up imprint, creatively spearheaded by Eisner Award-winning writer and rock icon Gerard Way! This avant-garde imprint bridges the gap between the DCU and Vertigo, focusing on the collision of visual and thematic storytelling. These are comics for dangerous humans.

DC/YOUNG ANIMAL: MILK WARS

A history-making meeting of the World's Greatest Heroes and the motley misfits of the Doom Patrol!

Writer: Gerard Way | Artist: Nick Derington
ISBN: 9781401277338 | Diamond Code: MAR180321
Price: $19.99/$25.99 CAN | Format: TP

SHADE, THE CHANGING GIRL VOL. 1: EARTH GIRL MADE EASY

An alien girl from a faraway planet takes up residence in the body of a young Earth girl and chaos ensues in this reimagining of the classic *Shade, The Changing Man.*

Writer: Cecil Castellucci | Artist: Marley Zarcone
ISBN: 9781401270995 | Diamond Code: APR170410
Price: $16.99/$22.99 CAN | Format: TP | COVER NOT FINAL

DOOM PATROL VOL. 1: BRICK BY BRICK

Grant Morrison's classic misfit team—the Doom Patrol—is reintroduced by Eisner Award-winning writer and rock star Gerard Way in a bombastic new series.

Writer: Gerard Way | Artist: Nick Derington
ISBN: 9781401269791 | Diamond Code: FEB170287
Price: $16.99/$22.99 CAN | Format: TP

SHADE, THE CHANGING WOMAN

Shade has shed her alien identity. She's stepped out of her original Earth body and into another one. Now free of the burdens of any past life, and finally on her own, she sets out to see more of her new home.

Writer: Cecil Castellucci | Arist: Marley Zarcone
ISBN: 9781401285708 | Price: $16.99/$22.99 CAN
Format: TP | On sale: 1/15/2019

CAVE CARSON HAS A CYBERNETIC EYE VOL. 1: GOING UNDERGROUND

From deep within the DC mythology, Cave Carson—everyone's favorite spelunker—is back for a whole new adventure as Gerard Way takes readers on an absurd journey through a world that can only be understood when looking through a cybernetic eye.

Writers: Gerard Way & Jon Rivera | Artist: Michael Avon Oeming
ISBN: 9781401270827 | Diamond Code: MAR170396
Price: $16.99/$22.99 CAN | Format: TP

MOTHER PANIC VOL. 1: A WORK IN PROGRESS

If Batman has taught the world anything, it's that Gotham City needs its vigilantes! Enter Mother Panic! Motivated by her traumatic youth, celebutante Violet Paige seeks to exact vengeance on her privileged peers as she disguises herself as the terrifying new vigilante known only as Mother Panic.

Writer: Jody Houser | Artist: Tommy Lee Edwards & Shawn Crystal | ISBN: 9781401271114 | Diamond Code: APR170407
Price: $16.99/$22.99 CAN | Format: TP

CAVE CARSON HAS AN INTERSTELLAR EYE

After a year of Multiverse-hopping and fighting in the Milk Wars, returning to a normal life of digging and cave-diving just isn't the same for explorer Cave Carson.

Writer: Jon Rivera | Artist: Michael Avon Oeming
ISBN: 9781401285401 | Price: $16.99/$22.99 CAN
Format: TP | On sale: 12/18/2018 | COVER NOT FINAL

MOTHER PANIC: GOTHAM A.D

After the fallout of *Milk Wars,* Violet Paige finds herself in a Gotham City unlike any we have seen before.

Writer: Jody Houser | Artist: Shawn Crystal| ISBN: 9781401281007
Diamond Code: MAR180351 | Price: $16.99/$22.99 CAN
Format: TP | On sale: 11/13/2018 | COVER NOT FINAL

MAD

For over six decades, *MAD* has been a part of the American humor landscape, for better or worse, but mostly for worse. Armed with irreverence and a sense of duty to satirize and parody anything and everything in pop culture, *MAD* has been a staple in bedrooms, living rooms, dorm rooms and recycling bins.

SUPERMAN AND THE MISERABLE, ROTTEN, NO FUN, REALLY BAD DAY

Superman and the citizens of Metropolis are featured in this parody of the bestselling children's book *Alexander and the Terrible, Horrible, No Good, Very Bad Day* from the minds of MAD Magazine.

Writer: Dave Croatto | Artist: Tom Richmond | ISBN: 9781401276119
Diamond Code: JUN170359 Price: $14.99/$19.99 CAN | Format: HC

DON'T LET THE PENGUIN DRIVE THE BATMOBILE

While Batman is busy fighting crime on the mean streets of Gotham, it's up to us to keep an eye on the Batmobile. The only problem? The Penguin really, REALLY wants to drive it! The best-selling children's book is parodied with the heroes and villains from the world of DC Comics' *Batman*!

Writer: Jacob Lambert | Artist: Tom Richmond
ISBN: 9781401277246 | Diamond Code: JUN180440
Price: $14.99/$19.99 CAN | Format: HC | On sale: 10/16/2018

MAD ABOUT TRUMP: A BRILLIANT LOOK AT OUR BRAINLESS PRESIDENT

MAD's best reprinted material with the sharpest satiric shots at "the Donald," comically chronicling his rise from obnoxious businessman to really obnoxious reality show host to uber-obnoxious "Commander-in-Tweet."

Writers: Various | Artists: Various | ISBN: 9781401277703
Diamond Code: FEB178711 | Price: $12.99/$17.50 CAN | Format: TP

GOODNIGHT BATCAVE

A *Goodnight Moon* parody featuring Batman as only the world-famous MAD Magazine can do it!

Writer: Dave Croatto | Artist: Tom Richmond
ISBN: 9781401270100 | Diamond Code: JUL160389
Price: $14.99/$17.99 CAN | Format: HC

ISBN	DIAMOND CODE	TITLE	AUTHOR	ARTIST	US$/$CAN	FORMAT

BATMAN BACKLIST AND SUGGESTED READING ORDER

#	ISBN	DIAMOND CODE	TITLE	AUTHOR | ARTIST	US$/$CAN | FORMAT
1.	9781401260095	JUL150308	BATMAN: THE GOLDEN AGE OMNIBUS VOL. 1	FINGER, BILL | KANE, BOB	$75.00/$85.00 | HC
2.	9781401263768	MAR160262	BATMAN: THE GOLDEN AGE OMNIBUS VOL. 2	KANE, BOB | VARIOUS	$75.00/$85.00 | HC
3.	9781401269029	NOV160324	BATMAN: THE GOLDEN AGE OMNIBUS VOL. 3	VARIOUS | VARIOUS	$75.00/$99.00 | HC
4.	9781401273590	JUN170396	BATMAN: THE GOLDEN AGE OMNIBUS VOL. 4	VARIOUS | VARIOUS	$75.00/$99.00 | HC
5.	9781401278700	NOV170360	BATMAN: THE GOLDEN AGE OMNIBUS VOL. 5	VARIOUS | VARIOUS	$99.99/$130.99 | HC
6.	9781401284381	MAY180571	BATMAN: THE GOLDEN AGE OMNIBUS VOL. 6	VARIOUS | VARIOUS	$125.00/$163.00 | HC
7.	9781401263331	MAY160305	BATMAN: THE GOLDEN AGE VOL. 1	FINGER, BILL | VARIOUS	$24.99/$29.99 | TP
8.	9781401268084	NOV160325	BATMAN: THE GOLDEN AGE VOL. 2	VARIOUS | VARIOUS	$19.99/$25.99 | TP
9.	9781401271305	MAY170333	BATMAN: THE GOLDEN AGE VOL. 3	KANE, BOB | VARIOUS	$29.99/$39.99 | TP
10.	9781401277581	NOV170361	BATMAN: THE GOLDEN AGE VOL. 4	VARIOUS | VARIOUS	$29.99/$39.99 | TP
11.	9781401284619	JUN180565	BATMAN: THE GOLDEN AGE VOL. 5	VARIOUS | VARIOUS	$29.99/$39.99 | TP
12.	9781401261122	OCT150249	BATMAN & SUPERMAN IN WORLD'S FINEST: THE GOLDEN AGE OMNIBUS VOL. 1	VARIOUS | VARIOUS	$75.00/$85.00 | HC
13.	9781401289058	DEC170386	BATMAN & SUPERMAN IN WORLD'S FINEST: THE SILVER AGE OMNIBUS VOL. 2	VARIOUS | VARIOUS	$99.99/$130.99 | HC
14.	9781401277802	DEC170386	BATMAN & SUPERMAN IN WORLD'S FINEST: THE SILVER AGE VOL. 2	VARIOUS | VARIOUS	$24.99/$33.99 | TP
15.	9781401272944	JUN170392	BATMAN: YEAR ONE DELUXE EDITION	MILLER, FRANK | MAZZUCCHELLI, DAVID	$34.99/$45.99 | HC
16.	9781401243791	APR160378	ABSOLUTE BATMAN YEAR ONE	MILLER, FRANK | MAZZUCCHELLI, DAVID	$125.00/$163.00 | HC
17.	9781401274566	AUG170331	BATMAN: YEAR TWO 30TH ANNIVERSARY DELUXE EDITION	BARR, MIKE W. | DAVIS, ALAN; MCFARLANE, TODD	$29.99/$39.99 | HC
18.	9781401255183	APR150290	BATMAN: SECOND CHANCES	COLLINS, MAX ALLAN | COCKRUM, DAVE	$19.99/$23.99 | TP
19.	9781401216269	SEP080167	BATMAN: THE MAN WHO LAUGHS	BRUBAKER, ED | MAHNKE, DOUG	$14.99/$17.99 | TP
20.	9781401284862		BATMAN: HAUNTED KNIGHT (NEW EDITION)	LOEB, JEPH | SALE, TIM	$19.99/$25.99 | TP
21.	9781401251222	APR140278	ABSOLUTE BATMAN: HAUNTED KNIGHT	LOEB, JEPH | SALE, TIM	$99.99/$112.00 | HC
22.	9781401232597	JUL110251	BATMAN: THE LONG HALLOWEEN	LOEB, JEPH | SALE, TIM	$24.99/$33.99 | TP
23.	9781401248833	JUL140253	BATMAN NOIR: THE LONG HALLOWEEN	LOEB, JEPH | SALE, TIM	$49.99/$58.00 | HC
24.	9781401244019	NOV130237	BATMAN: DARK VICTORY	LOEB, JEPH | SALE, TIM	$24.99/$28.99 | TP
25.	9781401271060	APR170420	BATMAN NOIR: DARK VICTORY	LOEB, JEPH | SALE, TIM	$39.99/$53.99 | HC
26.	9781401284268	MAR180338	BATMAN BY JEPH LOEB & TIM SALE OMNIBUS	LOEB, JEPH | SALE, TIM	$125.00/$163.00 | HC
27.	9781401201876	APR050327	BATMAN/SUPERMAN/WONDER WOMAN: TRINITY	WAGNER, MATT | WAGNER, MATT	$17.99/$20.99 | TP
28.	9781401278458	DEC170389	BATMAN: GOTHIC (NEW EDITION)	MORRISON, GRANT | JANSON, KLAUS	$16.99/$22.99 | TP
29.	9781401251246	JUN140278	BATMAN ARKHAM ASYLUM 25TH ANNIVERSARY	MORRISON, GRANT | MCKEAN, DAVE	$19.99/$23.99 | TP
30.	9781401251253	JUN140277	BATMAN ARKHAM ASYLUM 25TH ANNIVERSARY DELUXE EDITION	MORRISON, GRANT | MCKEAN, DAVE	$29.99/$35.00 | HC
31.	9781401247515	FEB140259	BATMAN: ARKHAM ASYLUM LIVING HELL DELUXE EDITION	SLOTT, DAN | SOOK, RYAN	$22.99/$26.99 | HC
32.	9781401216672	NOV070226	BATMAN: THE KILLING JOKE	MOORE, ALAN | BOLLAND, BRIAN	$17.99/$20.99 | HC
33.	9781401263645	APR160379	BATMAN NOIR: THE KILLING JOKE	MOORE, ALAN | BOLLAND, BRIAN	$24.99/$29.99 | HC
34.	9781401284121	JAN180393	ABSOLUTE BATMAN: THE KILLING JOKE (30TH ANNIVERSARY EDITION)	MOORE, ALAN | BOLLAND, BRIAN	$49.99/$65.99 | HC
35.	9781401277826	DEC170387	BATMAN BY NEAL ADAMS BOOK ONE	VARIOUS | ADAMS, NEAL	$24.99/$33.99 | TP
36.	9781401285784		BATMAN BY NEAL ADAMS BOOK TWO	VARIOUS | ADAMS, NEAL	$24.99/$33.99 | TP
37.	9781401255510	SEP150292	BATMAN BY NEAL ADAMS OMNIBUS	O'NEIL, DENNY | ADAMS, NEAL	$99.99/$112.00 | HC
38.	9781401268121	NOV160328	BATMAN AND THE OUTSIDERS VOL. 1	BARR, MIKE W. | APARO, JIM	$39.99/$53.99 | HC
39.	9781401277536	NOV170358	BATMAN AND THE OUTSIDERS VOL. 2	BARR, MIKE W. | DAVIS, ALAN	$49.99/$65.99 | HC
40.	9781401287641		BATMAN AND THE OUTSIDERS VOL. 3	BARR, MIKE W. | DAVIS, ALAN	$49.99/$65.99 | HC
41.	9781401275174	SEP170411	BATMAN: THE BRAVE & THE BOLD: THE BRONZE AGE VOL. 1	HANEY, BOB | VARIOUS	$34.99/$45.99 | TP
42.	9781401285821		BATMAN: THE BRAVE & THE BOLD: THE BRONZE AGE VOL. 2	VARIOUS | VARIOUS	$34.99/$45.99 | TP
43.	9781401267186	AUG160340	BATMAN: THE BRAVE & THE BOLD BRONZE AGE OMNIBUS	HANEY, BOB | APARO, JIM	$125.00/$163.00 | HC
44.	9781401281670	FEB180298	BATMAN: THE BRAVE & THE BOLD THE BRONZE AGE OMNIBUS VOL. 2	HANEY, BOB | APARO, JIM	$99.99/$130.99 | HC
45.	9781401281366	MAY180570	BATMAN: THE CAPED CRUSADER VOL. 1	STARLIN, JIM | APARO, JIM	$29.99/$39.99 | TP
46.	9781401287825		BATMAN: THE CAPED CRUSADER VOL. 2	VARIOUS | VARIOUS	$29.99/$39.99 | TP
47.	9781401271084	JAN180395	BATMAN: THE DARK KNIGHT DETECTIVE VOL. 1	VARIOUS | VARIOUS	$29.99/$39.99 | TP
48.	9781401284688		BATMAN THE DARK KNIGHT DETECTIVE VOL. 2	VARIOUS | VARIOUS	$29.99/$39.99 | TP
49.	9781401232740	JUN110267	BATMAN: A DEATH IN THE FAMILY	STARLIN, JIM | APARO, JIM	$24.99/$28.99 | TP
50.	9781401288532		BATMAN: FAMILY	MOORE, JOHN FRANCIS | GAUDIANO, STEFANO	$19.99/$25.99 | TP
51.	9781401285739		BATMAN: SHAMAN	O'NEIL, DENNY | VARIOUS	$16.99/$22.99 | TP
52.	9781401233839	JAN120305	BATMAN: VENOM	O'NEIL, DENNIS J. | GARCIA-LOPEZ, JOSE LUIS	$14.99/$17.99 | TP
53.	9781401247645	NOV130238	BATMAN BY DOUG MOENCH AND KELLEY JONES VOL. 1	MOENCH, DOUG | JONES, KELLEY	$39.99/$47.99 | HC
54.	9781401281298	MAY180569	BATMAN BY DOUG MOENCH & KELLEY JONES VOL. 2	MOENCH, DOUG | JONES, KELLEY	$49.99/$65.99 | HC
55.	9781401242398	JUN130259	BATMAN: LEGENDS OF THE DARK KNIGHT VOL. 1	VARIOUS | VARIOUS	$14.99/$17.99 | TP
56.	9781401246006	FEB140254	BATMAN: LEGENDS OF THE DARK KNIGHT VOL. 2	VARIOUS | VARIOUS	$14.99/$17.99 | TP
57.	9781401248154	SEP140320	BATMAN: LEGENDS OF THE DARK KNIGHT VOL. 3	VARIOUS | VARIOUS	$16.99/$19.99 | TP
58.	9781401254674	FEB150259	BATMAN: LEGENDS OF THE DARK KNIGHT VOL. 4	SOULE, CHARLES | DAVIS, SHANE; CALERO, DENNIS	$16.99/$19.99 | TP
59.	9781401258146	AUG150264	BATMAN: LEGENDS OF THE DARK KNIGHT VOL. 5	MARZ, RON | WOODS, PETE	$16.99/$19.99 | TP
60.	9781401265885	MAY170331	BATMAN: SHADOW OF THE BAT VOL. 2	GRANT, ALAN | BLEVINS, BRET	$29.99/$39.99 | TP
61.	9781401275204	OCT170364	BATMAN: SHADOW OF THE BAT VOL. 3	GRANT, ALAN | BLEVINS, BRET	$24.99/$33.99 | TP
62.	9781401288051		BATMAN: SHADOW OF THE BAT VOL. 4	GRANT, ALAN | BLEVINS, BRET	$24.99/$33.99 | TP

	ISBN | DIAMOND CODE	TITLE	AUTHOR | ARTIST	US$/$CAN | FORMAT
63.	9781401284220 JUN180560	BATMAN: PRELUDE TO KNIGHTFALL	DIXON, CHUCK | VARIOUS	$19.99/$25.99 | TP
64.	9781401284299 JUN180561	BATMAN: KNIGHTFALL VOL. 1 (25TH ANNIVERSARY EDITION)	DIXON, CHUCK | VARIOUS	$19.99/$25.99 | TP
65.	9781401284398 JUN180562	BATMAN: KNIGHTFALL VOL. 2 (25TH ANNIVERSARY EDITION)	DIXON, CHUCK | VARIOUS	$19.99/$25.99 | TP
66.	9781401284503 JUN180563	BATMAN: KNIGHTQUEST: THE CRUSADE VOL. 1	DIXON, CHUCK | VARIOUS	$19.99/$25.99 | TP
67.	9781401284589	BATMAN: KNIGHTQUEST: THE CRUSADE VOL. 2	DIXON, CHUCK | VARIOUS	$19.99/$25.99 | TP
68.	9781401285012	BATMAN: KNIGHTQUEST: THE SEARCH	DIXON, CHUCK | VARIOUS	$19.99/$25.99 | TP
69.	9781401285180	BATMAN: KNIGHTSEND	DIXON, CHUCK | VARIOUS	$19.99/$25.99 | TP
70.	9781401285609	BATMAN: PRODIGAL	DIXON, CHUCK | VARIOUS	$24.99/$33.99 | TP
71.	9781401285876	BATMAN: TROIKA	DIXON, CHUCK | JONES, MICHAEL; KITSON, BARRY; NOLAN, GRAHAM	$19.99/$25.99 | TP
72.	9781401270421 NOV160327	BATMAN: KNIGHTFALL OMNIBUS VOL. 1	VARIOUS | VARIOUS	$99.99/$130.99 | HC
73.	9781401274368 MAY170332	BATMAN: KNIGHTFALL OMNIBUS VOL. 2: KNIGHTQUEST	DIXON, CHUCK | JONES, KELLEY; APARO, JIM	$99.99/$130.99 | HC
74.	9781401278496 NOV170359	BATMAN KNIGHTFALL OMNIBUS VOL. 3: KNIGHTSEND	DIXON, CHUCK | VARIOUS	$99.99/$130.99 | HC
75.	9781401280895 APR180262	BATMAN: DEATH & THE MAIDENS (NEW EDITION)	RUCKA, GREG | JANSON, KLAUS	$19.99/$25.99 | HC
76.	9781401260682 DEC150342	BATMAN: CONTAGION	DIXON, CHUCK | VARIOUS	$29.99/$35.00 | TP
77.	9781401255152 MAR150278	BATMAN: CATACLYSM (NEW EDITION)	DIXON, CHUCK | VARIOUS	$29.99/$35.00 | TP
78.	9781401272029 JAN170386	BATMAN: LEGACY VOL. 1	DIXON, CHUCK | VARIOUS	$29.99/$39.99 | TP
79.	9781401277611 NOV170362	BATMAN: LEGACY VOL. 2	DIXON, CHUCK | VARIOUS	$24.99/$33.99 | TP
80.	9781401258276 JUL150303	BATMAN: ROAD TO NO MAN'S LAND VOL. 1	DIXON, CHUCK | HAMNER, CULLY	$29.99/$35.00 | TP
81.	9781401260637 APR160387	BATMAN: ROAD TO NO MAN'S LAND VOL. 2	DIXON, CHUCK | VARIOUS	$34.99/$41.99 | TP
82.	9781401232283 AUG110242	BATMAN: NO MAN'S LAND VOL. 1	VARIOUS | VARIOUS	$29.99/$35.00 | TP
83.	9781401233808 APR148300	BATMAN: NO MAN'S LAND VOL. 2	VARIOUS | VARIOUS	$29.99/$41.99 | TP
84.	9781401234560 MAY120289	BATMAN: NO MAN'S LAND VOL. 3	VARIOUS | VARIOUS	$34.99/$41.99 | TP
85.	9781401235642 SEP120237	BATMAN: NO MAN'S LAND VOL. 4	VARIOUS | VARIOUS	$34.99/$41.99 | TP
86.	9781401263676 FEB170301	BATMAN: NEW GOTHAM VOL. 1	RUCKA, GREG | VARIOUS	$29.99/$39.99 | TP
87.	9781401277949 DEC170390	BATMAN: NEW GOTHAM VOL. 2	RUCKA, GREG | VARIOUS	$24.99/$33.99 | TP
88.	9781401251741 JUN140276	BATMAN: GORDON OF GOTHAM	O'NEIL, DENNIS | DIXON, CHUCK; JANSON, KLAUS	$19.99/$23.99 | TP
89.	9781401267278 FEB170305	BATMAN/WILDCAT	DIXON, CHUCK | VARIOUS	$16.99/$22.99 | TP
90.	9781401246822 APR140276	BATMAN: BRUCE WAYNE - FUGITIVE (NEW EDITION)	VARIOUS | VARIOUS	$29.99/$35.00 | TP
91.	9781401246839 FEB148212	BATMAN: BRUCE WAYNE - MURDERER? (NEW EDITION)	BRUBAKER, ED | MCDANIEL, SCOTT	$29.99/$35.00 | TP
92.	9781401260651 JUL160398	BATMAN BY ED BRUBAKER VOL. 1	BRUBAKER, ED | VARIOUS	$19.99/$23.99 | TP
93.	9781401264857 JUL160398	BATMAN BY ED BRUBAKER VOL. 2	BRUBAKER, ED | VARIOUS	$19.99/$23.99 | TP
94.	9781401223175 MAY090178	BATMAN: HUSH	LOEB, JEPH | LEE, JIM	$24.99/$33.99 | TP
95.	9781401276492 JUL170467	BATMAN HUSH: THE 15TH ANNIVERSARY DELUXE EDITION	LOEB, JEPH | LEE, JIM	$49.99/$65.99 | HC
96.	9781401290214 JUN180570	BATMAN: HUSH UNWRAPPED DELUXE EDITION (NEW EDITION)	LOEB, JEPH | LEE, JIM	$34.99/$45.99 | HC
97.	9781401258030 MAY150233	BATMAN NOIR: HUSH	LOEB, JEPH | LEE, JIM	$39.99/$48.99 | HC
98.	9781401290603	BATMAN: HUSH OMNIBUS	LOEB, JEPH; DINI, PAUL | LEE, JIM; NGUYEN, DUSTIN	$99.99/$130.99 | HC
99.	9781401271015 FEB170302	BATMAN BY AZZARELLO & RISSO DELUXE EDITION	AZZARELLO, BRIAN | RISSO, EDUARDO	$29.99/$39.99 | HC
100.	9781401238902 JAN130307	BATMAN NOIR: EDUARDO RISSO: THE DELUXE EDITION	RISSO, EDUARDO | AZZARELLO, BRIAN	$24.99/$28.99 | HC
101.	9781401258139 JUL150304	BATMAN: WAR GAMES BOOK ONE	GABRYCH, ANDERSEN | WOODS, PETE	$34.99/$41.99 | TP
102.	9781401260705 FEB160228	BATMAN: WAR GAMES BOOK TWO	BRUBAKER, ED; DIXON, CHUCK | VARIOUS	$34.99/$41.99 | TP
103.	9781401277727 NOV170363	BATMAN: SUPER POWERS	GUGGENHEIM, MARC | VARIOUS	$16.99/$22.99 | TP
104.	9781401231453 MAY110241	BATMAN: UNDER THE RED HOOD	WINICK, JUDD | MAHNKE, DOUG	$29.99/$35.00 | TP
105.	9781401231644 MAR110343	BATMAN: RED HOOD: LOST DAYS	WINICK, JUDD | VARIOUS	$14.99/$17.99 | TP
106.	9781401268381 DEC160380	BATMAN BY BRIAN K. VAUGHAN	VAUGHAN, BRIAN K. | VARIOUS	$16.99/$22.99 | TP
107.	9781401244026 OCT130238	BATMAN: BATMAN AND SON	MORRISON, GRANT | KUBERT, ANDY, WILLIAMS III, J.H.; DANIEL, TONY S.	$19.99/$23.99 | TP
108.	9781401242428 OCT130247	BATMAN UNWRAPPED BY ANDY KUBERT	MORRISON, GRANT | KUBERT, ANDY	$34.99/$41.99 | HC
109.	9781401225766 MAR100237	BATMAN: R.I.P.	MORRISON, GRANT | DANIEL, TONY S.	$14.99/$17.99 | TP
110.	9781401256883 MAY150235	BATMAN R.I.P. UNWRAPPED	MORRISON, GRANT | DANIEL, TONY S.	$34.99/$41.99 | HC
111.	9781401221249 DEC090202	BATMAN: HEART OF HUSH	DINI, PAUL | NGUYEN, DUSTIN	$14.99/$17.99 | TP
112.	9781401245177 JAN140352	FINAL CRISIS (NEW EDITION)	MORRISON, GRANT | JONES, J.G.; MAHNKE, DOUG	$19.99/$23.99 | TP
113.	9781401227241 APR100218	BATMAN: WHATEVER HAPPENED TO THE CAPED CRUSADER?	GAIMAN, NEIL | KUBERT, ANDY	$14.99/$17.99 | TP
114.	9781401224172 AUG100199	BATMAN: BATTLE FOR THE COWL	DANIEL, TONY S. | DANIEL, TONY S.	$14.99/$17.99 | TP
115.	9781401265724 JAN170387	BATMAN/TWO-FACE: FACE THE FACE DELUXE EDITION	ROBINSON, JAMES | KRAMER, DON; KIRK, LEONARD	$34.99/$45.99 | HC
116.	9781401229870 DEC100246	BATMAN & ROBIN VOL. 1: BATMAN REBORN	MORRISON, GRANT | QUITELY, FRANK	$14.99/$17.99 | TP
117.	9781401232719 AUG110241	BATMAN & ROBIN VOL. 2: BATMAN VS. ROBIN	MORRISON, GRANT | STEWART, CAMERON	$17.99/$20.99 | TP
118.	9781401235086 FEB120258	BATMAN & ROBIN VOL. 3: BATMAN & ROBIN MUST DIE!	MORRISON, GRANT | FRAZER, IRVING	$17.99/$20.99 | TP
119.	9781401233822 OCT110245	BATMAN: THE RETURN OF BRUCE WAYNE	MORRISON, GRANT | PAQUETTE, YANICK	$19.99/$23.99 | TP
120.	9781401229900 NOV110198	BATMAN: TIME AND THE BATMAN	VARIOUS | VARIOUS	$14.99/$17.99 | TP
121.	9781401238278 OCT120258	BATMAN, INCORPORATED	MORRISON, GRANT | PAQUETTE, YANICK	$19.99/$23.99 | TP
122.	9781401242633 AUG130293	BATMAN INCORPORATED VOL. 1: DEMON STAR	MORRISON, GRANT | BURNHAM, CHRIS	$16.99/$19.99 | TP
123.	9781401246976 MAY140369	BATMAN INCORPORATED VOL. 2: GOTHAM'S MOST WANTED	MORRISON, GRANT | BURNHAM, CHRIS	$16.99/$19.99 | TP
124.	9781401251215 MAY140382	ABSOLUTE BATMAN INCORPORATED	MORRISON, GRANT | BURNHAM, CHRIS	$125.00/$144.00 | HC
125.	9781401282998 FEB180294	BATMAN BY GRANT MORRISON OMNIBUS VOL. 1	MORRISON, GRANT | KUBERT, ANDY; DANIEL, TONY	$75.00/$99.00 | HC

DC COMICS READING ORDER

	ISBN | DIAMOND CODE	TITLE	AUTHOR | ARTIST	US$/$CAN | FORMAT
126.	9781401288839	BATMAN BY GRANT MORRISON OMNIBUS VOL. 2	MORRISON, GRANT | DANIEL, TONY S.; WILLIAMS III, J.H.	$75.00/$99.00 | HC
127.	9781401284206	BATMAN: GATES OF GOTHAM DELUXE EDITION	SNYDER, SCOTT | HIGGINS, KYLE	$29.99/$39.99 | HC
128.	9781401232078 NOV120268	BATMAN: THE BLACK MIRROR	SNYDER, SCOTT | JOCK; FRANCAVILLA, FRANCESCO	$16.99/$19.99 | TP
129.	9781401259686 MAY150233	BATMAN NOIR: BLACK MIRROR	SNYDER, SCOTT | JOCK; FRANCAVILLA, FRANCESCO	$34.99/$41.99 | HC
130.	9781401289553	ABSOLUTE BATMAN: THE BLACK MIRROR	SNYDER, SCOTT | JOCK; FRANCAVILLA, FRANCESCO	$99.99/$130.99 | HC
131.	9781401233389 OCT138324	FLASHPOINT	JOHNS, GEOFF | KUBERT, ANDY	$16.99/$19.99 | TP
132.	9781401234058 DEC110277	FLASHPOINT: WORLD OF FLASHPOINT FEATURING BATMAN	AZZARELLO, BRIAN | RISSO, EDUARDO	$17.99/$20.99 | TP
133.	9781401235420 DEC120323	BATMAN VOL. 1: THE COURT OF OWLS	SNYDER, SCOTT | CAPULLO, GREG	$16.99/$19.99 | TP
134.	9781401237783 JUL130235	BATMAN VOL. 2: THE CITY OF OWLS	SNYDER, SCOTT | CAPULLO, GREG; ALBUQUERQUE, RAFAEL	$16.99/$19.99 | TP
135.	9781401242527 AUG130291	BATMAN: NIGHT OF THE OWLS	SNYDER, SCOTT | CAPULLO, GREG	$19.99/$23.99 | TP
136.	9781401284336 JUN180569	BATMAN: THE COURT OF OWLS SAGA (DC ESSENTIAL EDITION)	SNYDER, SCOTT | CAPULLO, GREG	$24.99/$33.99 | TP
137.	9781401273958 JUN170397	BATMAN NOIR: THE COURT OF OWLS	SNYDER, SCOTT | CAPULLO, GREG	$34.99/$45.99 | HC
138.	9781401245078 APR140256	BATMAN UNWRAPPED: THE COURT OF OWLS	SNYDER, SCOTT | CAPULLO, GREG	$39.99/$47.99 | HC
139.	9781401246020 FEB140248	BATMAN VOL. 3: DEATH OF THE FAMILY	SNYDER, SCOTT | CAPULLO, GREG; JOCK	$16.99/$19.99 | TP
140.	9781401246464 JAN140340	THE JOKER: DEATH OF THE FAMILY	SNYDER, SCOTT | CAPULLO, GREG	$24.99/$28.99 | TP
141.	9781401249274 MAY140361	BATMAN: DEATH OF THE FAMILY BOOK AND JOKER MASK SET	SNYDER, SCOTT | CAPULLO, GREG	$39.99/$47.99 | TP
142.	9781401290931	BATMAN: DEATH OF THE FAMILY SAGA (DC ESSENTIAL EDITION)	SNYDER, SCOTT | CAPULLO, GREG	$24.99/$33.99 | TP
143.	9781401274887 JUL170468	BATMAN UNWRAPPED: DEATH OF THE FAMILY	SNYDER, SCOTT | CAPULLO, GREG	$29.99/$39.99 | HC
144.	9781401249335 FEB140248	BATMAN VOL. 4: ZERO YEAR-SECRET CITY	SNYDER, SCOTT | CAPULLO, GREG	$16.99/$19.99 | TP
145.	9781401253356 JUL140237	BATMAN VOL. 5: ZERO YEAR - DARK CITY	SNYDER, SCOTT | CAPULLO, GREG	$16.99/$19.99 | TP
146.	9781401253370 JAN150363	DC COMICS: ZERO YEAR	SNYDER, SCOTT | CAPULLO, GREG	$24.99/$28.99 | TP
147.	9781401257538 JUN150290	BATMAN VOL. 6: GRAVEYARD SHIFT	SNYDER, SCOTT | CAPULLO, GREG; KUBERT, ANDY	$16.99/$19.99 | TP
148.	9781401261160 DEC150331	BATMAN VOL. 7: ENDGAME	SNYDER, SCOTT | CAPULLO, GREG	$19.99/$23.99 | TP
149.	9781401261658 FEB160224	THE JOKER: ENDGAME	SNYDER, SCOTT | CAPULLO, GREG	$24.99/$29.99 | TP
150.	9781401266301 JUN160332	BATMAN VOL. 8: SUPERHEAVY	SNYDER, SCOTT | CAPULLO, GREG	$16.99/$22.99 | TP
151.	9781401269227 SEP160335	BATMAN VOL. 9: BLOOM	SNYDER, SCOTT | CAPULLO, GREG	$16.99/$22.99 | TP
152.	9781401268329 JAN170385	BATMAN VOL. 10: EPILOGUE	SNYDER, SCOTT; TYNION IV, JAMES | CAPULLO, GREG	$16.99/$22.99 | TP
153.	9781401267667 APR160382	BATMAN BY SCOTT SNYDER & GREG CAPULLO BOX SET 1	SNYDER, SCOTT | CAPULLO, GREG	$49.99/$65.99 | Boxed Set
154.	9781401271473 FEB170303	BATMAN BY SCOTT SNYDER & GREG CAPULLO BOX SET 2	SNYDER, SCOTT | CAPULLO, GREG	$49.99/$65.99 | Boxed Set
155.	9781401285982 FEB180296	BATMAN BY SCOTT SNYDER & GREG CAPULLO BOX SET 3	SNYDER, SCOTT | CAPULLO, GREG	$59.99/$78.99 | Boxed Set
156.	9781401251734 SEP140302	BATMAN ETERNAL VOL. 1	SNYDER, SCOTT; SEELEY, TIM; TYNION IV, JAMES; FAWKES, RAY | FABOK, JASON	$39.99/$47.99 | TP
157.	9781401252311 APR150286	BATMAN ETERNAL VOL. 2	SNYDER, SCOTT; SEELEY, TIM; TYNION IV, JAMES; FAWKES, RAY | FABOK, JASON	$39.99/$47.99 | TP
158.	9781401257521 AUG150261	BATMAN ETERNAL VOL. 3	SNYDER, SCOTT; SEELEY, TIM; TYNION IV, JAMES; FAWKES, RAY | QUINONES, JOE	$39.99/$48.99 | TP
159.	9781401259679 DEC150341	BATMAN AND ROBIN ETERNAL VOL. 1	SNYDER, SCOTT; TYNION IV, JAMES; SEELEY, TIM; ORLANDO, STEVE | DANIEL, TONY S.	$24.99/$29.99 | TP
160.	9781401262488 MAR160259	BATMAN AND ROBIN ETERNAL VOL. 2	SNYDER, SCOTT; TYNION IV, JAMES; SEELEY, TIM; ORLANDO, STEVE | VARIOUS	$29.99/$35.00 | TP
161.	9781401234676 JAN130296	BATMAN: DETECTIVE COMICS VOL. 1: FACES OF DEATH	DANIEL, TONY S. | DANIEL, TONY S.	$16.99/$19.99 | TP
162.	9781401290948	BATMAN: FACES OF DEATH (DC ESSENTIAL EDITION)	DANIEL, TONY S. | DANIEL, TONY S.; BENES, ED	$24.99/$33.99 | TP
163.	9781401242657 AUG130290	BATMAN: DETECTIVE COMICS VOL. 2: SCARE TACTICS	DANIEL, TONY S. | DANIEL, TONY S.; BENES, ED	$16.99/$19.99 | TP
164.	9781401246341 MAR140251	BATMAN: DETECTIVE COMICS VOL. 3: EMPEROR PENGUIN	LAYMAN, JOHN | FABOK, JASON	$16.99/$19.99 | TP
165.	9781401249977 AUG140329	BATMAN: DETECTIVE COMICS VOL. 4: THE WRATH	LAYMAN, JOHN | FABOK, JASON	$17.99/$20.99 | TP
166.	9781401254667 FEB150249	BATMAN: DETECTIVE COMICS VOL. 5: GOTHTOPIA	LAYMAN, JOHN | FABOK, JASON	$16.99/$19.99 | TP
167.	9781401258023 OCT150247	BATMAN: DETECTIVE COMICS VOL. 6: ICARUS	MANAPUL, FRANCIS; BUCCELLATO, BRIAN | MANAPUL, FRANCIS	$16.99/$19.99 | TP
168.	9781401263546 APR160381	BATMAN: DETECTIVE COMICS VOL. 7: ANARKY	BUCCELLATO, BRIAN; MANAPUL, FRANCIS | BLANCO, FERNANDO	$17.99/$21.99 | TP
169.	9781401284855	BATMAN BY FRANCIS MANAPUL & BRIAN BUCCELLATO DELUXE EDITION	BUCCELLATO, BRIAN | MANAPUL, FRANCIS	$49.99/$65.99 | HC
170.	9781401269241 AUG160318	BATMAN: DETECTIVE COMICS VOL. 8: BLOOD OF HEREOS	TOMASI, PETER J. | PASARIN, FERNANDO	$17.99/$23.99 | TP
171.	9781401274115 MAR170417	BATMAN: DETECTIVE COMICS VOL. 9: GORDON AT WAR	TOMASI, PETER J. | PASARIN, FERNANDO	$16.99/$22.99 | TP
172.	9781401237110 APR130221	BATMAN - THE DARK KNIGHT VOL. 1: KNIGHT TERRORS	JENKINS, PAUL; FINCH, DAVID | FINCH, DAVID	$16.99/$19.99 | TP
173.	9781401242824 OCT130236	BATMAN - THE DARK KNIGHT VOL. 2: CYCLE OF VIOLENCE	HURWITZ, GREGG | FINCH, DAVID	$14.99/$17.99 | TP
174.	9781401246198 APR140257	BATMAN - THE DARK KNIGHT VOL. 3: MAD	HURWITZ, GREGG | VAN SCIVER, ETHAN	$16.99/$19.99 | TP
175.	9781401249304 NOV140294	BATMAN - THE DARK KNIGHT VOL. 4: CLAY	HURWITZ, GREGG | MALEEV, ALEX; PONTICELLI, ALBERTO	$16.99/$19.99 | TP
176.	9781401238384 MAR130270	BATMAN AND ROBIN VOL. 1: BORN TO KILL	TOMASI, PETER J. | GLEASON, PATRICK	$16.99/$19.99 | TP
177.	9781401242671 FEB130207	BATMAN AND ROBIN VOL. 2: PEARL	TOMASI, PETER J. | GLEASON, PATRICK	$16.99/$19.99 | TP
178.	9781401246174 MAR140250	BATMAN AND ROBIN VOL. 3: DEATH OF THE FAMILY	TOMASI, PETER J. | GLEASON, PATRICK	$14.99/$17.99 | TP
179.	9781401250584 AUG140330	BATMAN AND ROBIN VOL. 4: REQUIEM FOR DAMIAN	TOMASI, PETER J. | GLEASON, PATRICK	$16.99/$19.99 | TP
180.	9781401253332 MAR150266	BATMAN AND ROBIN VOL. 5: THE BIG BURN	TOMASI, PETER J. | GLEASON, PATRICK	$16.99/$19.99 | TP
181.	9781401258009 AUG150262	BATMAN AND ROBIN VOL. 6: THE HUNT FOR ROBIN	TOMASI, PETER J. | GLEASON, PATRICK; KUBERT, ANDY	$16.99/$19.99 | TP
182.	9781401261146 FEB160226	BATMAN AND ROBIN VOL. 7: ROBIN RISES	TOMASI, PETER J. | GLEASON, PATRICK; KUBERT, ANDY	$16.99/$19.99 | TP
183.	9781401276836 JUN170395	BATMAN & ROBIN BY PETER J. TOMASI & PATRICK GLEASON OMNIBUS	TOMASI, PETER J. | GLEASON, PATRICK	$125.00/$163.00 | HC
184.	9781401249342 AUG140333	BATMAN/SUPERMAN VOL. 1: CROSS WORLD	PAK, GREG | LEE, JAE; OLIVER, BEN	$14.99/$17.99 | TP
185.	9781401254230 FEB150252	BATMAN/SUPERMAN VOL. 2: GAME OVER	PAK, GREG | LEE, JAE; BOOTH, BRETT	$16.99/$19.99 | TP
186.	9781401257545 SEP150290	BATMAN/SUPERMAN VOL. 3: SECOND CHANCE	PAK, GREG | LEE, JAE	$14.99/$17.99 | TP
187.	9781401263683 MAY160306	BATMAN/SUPERMAN VOL. 4: SIEGE	PAK, GREG | SYAF, ARDIAN	$16.99/$19.99 | TP
188.	9781401268183 JAN170388	BATMAN/SUPERMAN VOL. 5: TRUTH HURTS	PAK, GREG | SYAF, ARDIAN	$16.99/$22.99 | TP

	ISBN | DIAMOND CODE	TITLE	AUTHOR | ARTIST	US$/$CAN | FORMAT
189.	9781401271565 MAY170334	BATMAN/SUPERMAN VOL. 6: UNIVERSE'S FINEST	TOMASI, PETER J. | VARIOUS	$19.99/$25.99 | TP
190.	9781401267773 OCT160291	BATMAN VOL. 1: I AM GOTHAM (REBIRTH)	KING, TOM | FINCH, DAVID; JANIN, MIKEL	$16.99/$19.99 | TP
191.	9781401268541 JAN170376	BATMAN VOL. 2: I AM SUICIDE (REBIRTH)	KING, TOM | FINCH, DAVID; JANIN, MIKEL	$16.99/$19.99 | TP
192.	9781401271312 MAY170321	BATMAN VOL. 3: I AM BANE (REBIRTH)	KING, TOM | FINCH, DAVID	$16.99/$22.99 | TP
193.	9781401276447 JUN170380	BATMAN/THE FLASH: THE BUTTON DELUXE EDITION	KING, TOM: WILLIAMSON, JOSHUA | FABOK, JASON; PORTER, HOWARD	$19.99/$25.99 | HC
194.	9781401276799 JUN170381	BATMAN/THE FLASH: THE BUTTON DELUXE EDITION (INTERNATIONAL VERSION)	KING, TOM: WILLIAMSON, JOSHUA | FABOK, JASON; PORTER, HOWARD	$19.99/$0.00 | HC
195.	9781401273613 SEP170400	BATMAN VOL. 4: THE WAR OF JOKES AND RIDDLES (REBIRTH)	KING, TOM | JANIN, MIKEL	$19.99/$25.99 | TP
196.	9781401277314 JAN180382	BATMAN VOL. 5: RULES OF ENGAGEMENT (REBIRTH)	KING, TOM | JONES, JOELLE	$16.99/$22.99 | TP
197.	9781401280277 APR180261	BATMAN VOL. 6: BRIDE OR BURGLAR	KING, TOM | JANIN, MIKEL	$16.99/$22.99 | TP
198.	9781401286545 JUN180571	BATMAN: PRELUDES TO THE WEDDING	SEELEY, TIM | VARIOUS	$16.99/$22.99 | TP
199.	9781401286538 JUN180572	BATMAN/CATWOMAN: THE WEDDING ALBUM - THE DELUXE EDITION	KING, TOM | JANIN, MIKEL	$17.99/$23.99 | HC
200.	9781401283384 JUL180717	BATMAN VOL. 7: THE WEDDING	KING, TOM | JANIN, MIKEL	$16.99/$22.99 | TP
201.	9781401283520	BATMAN VOL. 8: COLD DAYS	KING, TOM | JONES, JOELLE	$16.99/$22.99 | TP
202.	9781401288440	BATMAN VOL. 9	KING, TOM |	$16.99/$22.99 | TP
203.	9781401271329 MAY170322	BATMAN: THE REBIRTH DELUXE EDITION BOOK 1	KING, TOM | FINCH, DAVID; JANIN, MIKEL	$34.99/$45.99 | HC
204.	9781401280352 MAR180335	BATMAN: THE REBIRTH DELUXE EDITION BOOK 2	KING, TOM | FINCH, DAVID; MANN, CLAY; GERADS, MITCH	$34.99/$45.99 | HC
205.	9781401285210	BATMAN: THE REBIRTH DELUXE EDITION BOOK 3	KING, TOM | JANIN, MIKEL; MANN, CLAY	$34.99/$45.99 | HC
206.	9781401267995 NOV160317	BATMAN: DETECTIVE COMICS VOL. 1: THE RISE OF THE BATMEN (REBIRTH)	TYNION IV, JAMES | BARROWS, EDDY; MARTINEZ, ALVARO	$16.99/$19.99 | TP
207.	9781401268916 FEB170293	BATMAN: DETECTIVE COMICS VOL. 2: THE VICTIM SYNDICATE (REBIRTH)	TYNION IV, JAMES | BARROWS, EDDY; MARTINEZ, ALVARO	$16.99/$19.99 | TP
208.	9781401274313 JUL170456	BATMAN: NIGHT OF THE MONSTER MEN (REBIRTH)	KING, TOM: ORLANDO, STEVE | ROSSMO, RILEY	$16.99/$22.99 | TP
209.	9781401276096 JUL170458	BATMAN: DETECTIVE COMICS VOL. 3: LEAGUE OF SHADOWS (REBIRTH)	TYNION IV, JAMES | TAKARA, MARCIO	$19.99/$25.99 | TP
210.	9781401274979 SEP170399	BATMAN: DETECTIVE COMICS VOL. 4: DEUS EX MACHINA (REBIRTH)	TYNION, IV, JAMES | MARTINEZ, ALVARO	$16.99/$22.99 | TP
211.	9781401278229 JAN180383	BATMAN: DETECTIVE COMICS VOL. 5: A LONELY PLACE OF LIVING (REBIRTH)	TYNION IV, JAMES | BARROWS, EDDY; MARTINEZ, ALVARO	$16.99/$22.99 | TP
212.	9781401281458 MAR180334	BATMAN: DETECTIVE COMICS VOL. 6: FALL OF THE BATMEN	TYNION IV, JAMES | BARROWS, EDDY	$19.99/$25.99 | TP
213.	9781401284213 JUN180566	BATMAN: DETECTIVE COMICS VOL. 7: BATMEN ETERNAL	TYNION IV, JAMES | BARROWS, EDDY; MARTINEZ, ALVARO	$16.99/$22.99 | TP
214.	9781401285289	BATMAN: DETECTIVE COMICS VOL. 8	HILL, BRYAN | VARIOUS	$14.99/$19.99 | TP
215.	9781401290641	BATMAN: DETECTIVE COMICS VOL. 9	ROBINSON, JAMES | VARIOUS	$16.99/$22.99 | TP
216.	9781401276089 AUG170319	BATMAN: DETECTIVE COMICS: THE REBIRTH DELUXE EDITION BOOK 1	TYNION IV, JAMES | BARROWS, EDDY; MARTINEZ, ALVARO	$34.99/$45.99 | HC
217.	9781401278571 FEB180281	BATMAN: DETECTIVE COMICS: THE REBIRTH DELUXE EDITION BOOK 2	TYNION IV, JAMES | BARROWS, EDDY; MARTINEZ, ALVARO	$34.99/$45.99 | HC
218.	9781401284817	BATMAN: DETECTIVE COMICS: THE REBIRTH DELUXE EDITION BOOK 3	TYNION IV, JAMES | FERNANDEZ, JAVIER	$34.99/$45.99 | HC
219.	9781401289102	BATMAN: DETECTIVE COMICS: THE REBIRTH DELUXE EDITION BOOK 4	TYNION IV, JAMES | BARROWS, EDDY	$34.99/$45.99 | HC
220.	9781401274429 JUN170378	ALL-STAR BATMAN VOL. 1: MY OWN WORST ENEMY (REBIRTH)	SNYDER, SCOTT | ROMITA JR., JOHN	$16.99/$22.99 | TP
221.	9781401277895 DEC170373	ALL STAR BATMAN VOL. 2: ENDS OF THE EARTH	SNYDER, SCOTT | JOCK	$14.99/$19.99 | TP
222.	9781401284305 DEC170374	ALL-STAR BATMAN VOL. 3: THE FIRST ALLY	SNYDER, SCOTT | ALBUQUERQUE, RAFAEL	$16.99/$22.99 | TP
223.	9781401279677 MAY180566	BATMAN & THE SIGNAL	SNYDER, SCOTT; PATRICK, TONY | HAMMER, CULLY	$19.99/$25.99 | TP
224.	9781401287627 JUN188675	DARK DAYS: THE ROAD TO METAL	SNYDER, SCOTT | LEE, JIM; KUBERT, ANDY; ROMITA JR., JOHN	$19.99/$25.99 | TP
225.	9781401288587 JUN188676	DARK NIGHTS: METAL	SNYDER, SCOTT | CAPULLO, GREG	$19.99/$25.99 | TP
226.	9781401289072 JUN188677	DARK NIGHTS: METAL: DARK KNIGHTS RISING	MORRISON, GRANT; SNYDER, SCOTT; TOMASI, PETER J. | MANAPUL, FRANCIS	$24.99/$33.99 | HC
227.	9781401282981 JAN180381	DARK NIGHTS: METAL: THE RESISTANCE	WILLIAMSON, JOSHUA; LEMIRE, JEFF; VAN SCIVER, ETHAN; SHARP, LIAM	$24.99/$33.99 | HC

BATMAN COMPILATION GRAPHIC NOVELS

	ISBN | DIAMOND CODE	TITLE	AUTHOR | ARTIST	US$/$CAN | FORMAT
1.	9781401247584 APR140254	BATMAN: A CELEBRATION OF 75 YEARS	VARIOUS | VARIOUS	$39.99/$47.99 | HC
2.	9781401247591 APR140255	THE JOKER: A CELEBRATION OF 75 YEARS	VARIOUS | VARIOUS	$39.99/$47.99 | HC
3.	9781401285388 JUN188670	DETECTIVE COMICS: 80 YEARS OF BATMAN DELUXE EDITION	VARIOUS | VARIOUS	$29.99/$39.99 | HC
4.	9781401271442 MAY170329	BATMAN ARKHAM: CLAYFACE	VARIOUS | VARIOUS	$19.99/$25.99 | TP
5.	9781401288815	BATMAN ARKHAM: RA'S AL GHUL	VARIOUS | VARIOUS	$19.99/$25.99 | TP
6.	9781401274702 JAN180394	BATMAN ARKHAM: HUGO STRANGE	VARIOUS | VARIOUS	$19.99/$25.99 | TP
7.	9781401275013 SEP170410	BATMAN ARKHAM: JOKER'S DAUGHTER	VARIOUS | VARIOUS	$19.99/$25.99 | TP
8.	9781401263454 MAR160260	BATMAN ARKHAM: KILLER CROC	VARIOUS | VARIOUS	$19.99/$23.99 | TP
9.	9781401265922 OCT160299	BATMAN ARKHAM: MAN-BAT	VARIOUS |·VARIOUS	$19.99/$25.99 | TP
10.	9781401268879 FEB170300	BATMAN ARKHAM: MISTER FREEZE	VARIOUS | VARIOUS	$19.99/$25.99 | TP
11.	9781401281731 MAY180565	BATMAN ARKHAM: PENGUIN	VARIOUS | VARIOUS	$19.99/$25.99 | TP
12.	9781401264451 JUN160331	BATMAN ARKHAM: POISON IVY	VARIOUS | VARIOUS	$19.99/$25.99 | TP
13.	9781401255138 FEB150251	BATMAN ARKHAM: RIDDLER	FOX, GARDNER | MOLDOFF, SHELDON	$19.99/$23.99 | TP
14.	9781401260620 NOV150277	BATMAN ARKHAM: SCARECROW	VARIOUS | VARIOUS	$19.99/$23.99 | TP
15.	9781401258153 FEB150251	BATMAN ARKHAM: TWO-FACE	DINI, PAUL | BACHS, RAMON; RISSO, EDUARDO	$19.99/$23.99 | TP
16.	9781401255176 APR150289	BATMAN: HARLEY QUINN	DINI, PAUL | GOOGE, NEIL	$19.99/$23.99 | TP
17.	9781401276935 JUN170398	BATMAN: HIS GREATEST ADVENTURES	VARIOUS | VARIOUS	$9.99/$13.50 | TP
18.	9781401256982 SEP150285	BATMAN VS. SUPERMAN: THE GREATEST BATTLES	VARIOUS | VARIOUS	$9.99/$11.99 | TP
19.	9781401275099	TALES OF THE BATMAN: ALAN BRENNERT	BRENNERT, ALAN | VARIOUS	$19.99/$25.99 | TP
20.	9781401277697 OCT170381	TALES OF THE BATMAN: GENE COLAN VOL. 2	VARIOUS | COLAN, GENE	$39.99/$53.99 | HC
21.	9781401281632 MAY180593	TALES OF THE BATMAN: GERRY CONWAY VOL. 2	CONWAY, GERRY | VARIOUS	$49.99/$65.99 | HC
22.	9781401247621 MAR140263	TALES OF THE BATMAN: J.H. WILLIAMS III	VARIOUS | WILLIAMS III, J.H.	$49.99/$58.00 | HC

DC COMICS READING ORDER

	ISBN	DIAMOND CODE	TITLE	AUTHOR	ARTIST	US$/$CAN	FORMAT
23.	9781401271619	MAY170339	LEGENDS OF THE DARK KNIGHT: JIM APARO VOL. 3	VARIOUS	APARO, JIM	$49.99/$65.99	HC
24.	9781401285128		LEGENDS OF THE DARK KNIGHT: NORM BREYFOGLE VOL. 2	VARIOUS	BREYFOGLE, NORM	$49.99/$65.99	HC

BATMAN: FROM PAGE TO SCREEN

	ISBN	DIAMOND CODE	TITLE	AUTHOR	ARTIST	US$/$CAN	FORMAT
1.	9781401252779	SEP140283	BATMAN: THE JIRO KUWATA BATMANGA VOL. 1	KUWATA, JIRO	KUWATA, JIRO	$14.99/$17.99	TP
2.	9781401255527	APR150260	BATMAN: THE JIRO KUWATA BATMANGA VOL. 2	KUWATA, JIRO	KUWATA, JIRO	$12.99/$15.99	TP
3.	9781401257569	OCT150250	BATMAN: THE JIRO KUWATA BATMANGA VOL. 3	KUWATA, JIRO	KUWATA, JIRO	$14.99/$17.99	TP
4.	9781401249311	JUL140252	BATMAN '66 VOL. 1	PARKER, JEFF	CASE, JONATHAN	$14.99/$17.99	TP
5.	9781401254612	JAN150377	BATMAN '66 VOL. 2	PARKER, JEFF	CASE, JONATHAN	$14.99/$17.99	TP
6.	9781401257507	SEP150287	BATMAN '66 VOL. 3	PARKER, JEFF	CASE, JONATHAN	$14.99/$17.99	TP
7.	9781401261047	FEB160229	BATMAN '66 VOL. 4	PARKER, JEFF	CASE, JONATHAN	$14.99/$17.99	TP
8.	9781401264833	SEP160337	BATMAN '66 VOL. 5	PARKER, JEFF	CASE, JONATHAN	$14.99/$19.99	TP
9.	9781401257996	AUG150260	BATMAN '66 MEETS THE GREEN HORNET	SMITH, KEVIN; GARMAN, RALPH	TEMPLETON, TY	$14.99/$17.99	TP
10.	9781401268640	JAN170384	BATMAN '66 MEETS THE MAN FROM U.N.C.L.E.	PARKER, JEFF	HAHN, DAVID	$19.99/$25.99	TP
11.	9781401273842	JUN170394	BATMAN '66 MEETS STEED & MRS. PEEL	EDINGTON, IAN	VARIOUS	$16.99/$22.99	TP
12.	9781401278038	DEC170384	BATMAN '66 MEETS WONDER WOMAN '77	PARKER, JEFF; ANDREYKO, MARC	VARIOUS	$16.99/$22.99	TP
13.	9781401283285	FEB180295	BATMAN '66 OMNIBUS	PARKER, JEFF	ALLRED, MIKE	$125.00/$163.00	HC
14.	9781401244958	OCT130248	BATMAN: THE TV STORIES	VARIOUS	VARIOUS	$14.99 /$17.99	TP
15.	9781401252298	AUG140337	BATMAN ADVENTURES VOL. 1	PUCKETT, KELLEY	TEMPLETON, TY	$19.99/$23.99	TP
16.	9781401254636	FEB150269	BATMAN ADVENTURES VOL. 2	PUCKETT, KELLEY	PAROBECK, MIKE	$19.99/$23.99	TP
17.	9781401258726	JUL150309	BATMAN ADVENTURES VOL. 3	DINI, PAUL	PUCKETT, KELLEY	$16.99/$19.99	TP
18.	9781401260613	JUL150309	BATMAN ADVENTURES VOL. 4	PUCKETT, KELLEY	PAROBECK, MIKE	$19.99/$23.99	TP
19.	9781401267834	SEP160338	BATMAN & ROBIN ADVENTURES VOL. 1	DINI, PAUL	VARIOUS	$24.99/$33.99	TP
20.	9781401274054	SEP170409	BATMAN & ROBIN ADVENTURES VOL. 2	DINI, PAUL	TEMPLETON, TY	$19.99/$25.99	TP
21.	9781401281380	APR180263	BATMAN & ROBIN ADVENTURES VOL. 3	PUCKETT, KELLEY	HAMPTON, BO	$24.99/$33.99	TP
22.	9781401255121	NOV140306	BATMAN ADVENTURES: MAD LOVE DELUXE EDITION	DINI, PAUL	TIMM, BRUCE	$24.99/$29.99	HC
23.	9781401288990		BATMAN AND HARLEY QUINN	TEMPLETON, TY	BURCHETT, RICK	$16.99/$22.99	TP
24.	9781401276935	JUN170398	BATMAN: HIS GREATEST ADVENTURES	VARIOUS	VARIOUS	$9.99/$13.50	TP
25.	9781401280710	APR180264	BATMAN/TEENAGE MUTANT NINJA TURTLES DELUXE EDITION	TYNION IV, JAMES	WILLIAMS, FREDDIE, II	$39.99/$53.99	HC
26.	9781401280314	MAY180573	BATMAN/TEENAGE MUTANT NINJA TURTLES II	TYNION IV, JAMES	WILLIAMS, FREDDIE, II	$24.99/$33.99	HC
27.	9781401250607	AUG140338	BATMAN BEYOND 2.0: REWIRED	HIGGINS, KYLE; SIEGEL, ALEC	SILAS, THONY	$16.99/$19.99	TP
28.	9781401254643	DEC140388	BATMAN BEYOND 2.0 VOL. 2: JUSTICE LORDS BEYOND	HIGGINS, KYLE; SIEGEL, ALEC	GAGE, CHRISTOS; SILAS, THONY	$16.99/$19.99	TP
29.	9781401258016	JUN150298	BATMAN BEYOND 2.0 VOL. 3: MARK OF THE PHANTASM	HIGGINS, KYLE	SILAS, THONY; HESTER, PHIL	$16.99/$19.99	TP
30.	9781401261917	DEC150317	BATMAN BEYOND VOL. 1: BRAVE NEW WORLDS	JURGENS, DAN	CHANG, BERNARD	$14.99/$17.99	TP
31.	9781401264703	JUN160330	BATMAN BEYOND VOL. 2: CITY OF YESTERDAY	JURGENS, DAN	CHANG, BERNARD	$14.99/$19.99	TP
32.	9781401270391	NOV160326	BATMAN BEYOND VOL. 3: WIRED FOR DEATH	JURGENS, DAN	CHANG, BERNARD	$14.99/$14.99	TP
33.	9781401271039	MAR170403	BATMAN BEYOND VOL. 1: ESCAPING THE GRAVE (REBIRTH)	JURGENS, DAN	SOOK, RYAN; CHANG, BERNARD	$16.99/$22.99	TP
34.	9781401275228	OCT170358	BATMAN BEYOND VOL. 2: RISE OF THE DEMON (REBIRTH)	JURGENS, DAN	CHANG, BERNARD	$16.99/$22.99	TP
35.	9781401280369	MAY180568	BATMAN BEYOND VOL. 3: THE LONG PAYBACK	JURGENS, DAN	CHANG, BERNARD	$16.99/$22.99	TP
36.	9781401285630		BATMAN BEYOND VOL. 4	JURGENS, DAN	HESTER, PHIL	$16.99/$22.99	TP
37.	9781401234935	JUN120243	BATMAN: ARKHAM CITY	DINI, PAUL	D'ANDA, CARLOS	$16.99 /$19.99	TP
38.	9781401240189	MAY130229	BATMAN: ARKHAM UNHINGED VOL. 1	DINI, PAUL; FRIDOLFS, DEREK	VARIOUS	$14.99 /$17.99	TP
39.	9781401242831	OCT130249	BATMAN: ARKHAM UNHINGED VOL. 2	FRIDOLFS, DEREK	VARIOUS	$14.99 /$17.99	TP
40.	9781401246808	MAY140377	BATMAN: ARKHAM UNHINGED VOL. 3	FRIDOLFS, DEREK	ALEXANDER, JASON SHAWN	$16.99 /$19.99	TP
41.	9781401250423	NOV140307	BATMAN: ARKHAM UNHINGED VOL. 4	TRAVISS, KAREN	DUCE, CHRISTIAN	$14.99/$17.99	TP
42.	9781401254650	APR150288	BATMAN: ARKHAM ORIGINS	BEECHEN, ADAM	WAGNER, DOUG; DUCE, CHRISTIAN	$14.99/$17.99	TP
43.	9781401264444	JUN160334	BATMAN: ARKHAM KNIGHT GENESIS	TOMASI, PETER J.	BOGDANOVIC, VIKTOR	$14.99/$19.99	TP
44.	9781401266011	OCT150245	BATMAN: ARKHAM KNIGHT VOL. 1	TOMASI, PETER J.	BOGDANOVIC, VIKTOR	$14.99/$19.99	TP
45.	9781401263409	APR160383	BATMAN: ARKHAM KNIGHT VOL. 2	TOMASI, PETER J.	BOGDANOVIC, VIKTOR	$14.99/$17.99	TP
46.	9781401265052	AUG160320	BATMAN: ARKHAM KNIGHT VOL. 3	TOMASI, PETER J.	BOGDANOVIC, VIKTOR	$19.99/$25.99	TP
47.	9781401284329	MAR180337	BATMAN: THE ARKHAM SAGA OMNIBUS	DINI, PAUL; FRIDOLFS, DEREK; TOMASI, PETER J.	VARIOUS	$150.00/$195.00	HC
48.	9781401284237		BATMAN: SINS OF THE FATHER	GAGE, CHRISTOS	IENCO, RAFFAELE	$16.99/$22.99	TP

BATMAN STANDALONE GRAPHIC NOVELS

	ISBN	DIAMOND CODE	TITLE	AUTHOR	ARTIST	US$/$CAN	FORMAT
1.	9781401220082	MAR090174	ALL-STAR BATMAN & ROBIN, THE BOY WONDER VOL. 1	MILLER, FRANK	LEE, JIM	$19.99 /$23.99	TP
2.	9781401247638	JAN140348	ABSOLUTE ALL-STAR BATMAN AND ROBIN, THE BOY WONDER	MILLER, FRANK	LEE, JIM	$99.99/$112.00	HC
3.	9781401265069	AUG160319	THE DARK KNIGHT RETURNS: THE LAST CRUSADE	MILLER, FRANK; AZZARELLO, BRIAN	ROMITA JR., JOHN	$17.99/$23.99	HC
4.	9781401263119	NOV150279	BATMAN: THE DARK KNIGHT RETURNS	MILLER, FRANK	MILLER, FRANK; JANSON, KLAUS	$14.99 /$17.99	TP
5.	9781401255145	DEC140389	BATMAN NOIR: DARK KNIGHT RETURNS	MILLER, FRANK	MILLER, FRANK; JANSON, KLAUS	$34.99/$41.99	HC
6.	9781401270131	JUN160337	THE DARK KNIGHT RETURNS SLIPCASE SET	MILLER, FRANK	KUBERT, ANDY; JANSON, KLAUS	$49.99/$65.99	BOXED SET
7.	9781401285319	STL089379	BATMAN: THE DARK KNIGHT RETURNS (DC MODERN CLASSICS EDITION)	MILLER, FRANK	VARLEY, LYNN	$49.99/$65.99	HC
8.	9781563899294	FEB058404	BATMAN: THE DARK KNIGHT STRIKES AGAIN	MILLER, FRANK	MILLER, FRANK	$19.99 /$23.99	HC
9.	9781401278045	DEC170388	BATMAN NOIR: THE DARK KNIGHT STRIKES AGAIN	MILLER, FRANK	MILLER, FRANK	$39.99/$53.99	HC
10.	9781401256913	MAY150234	BATMAN: THE DARK KNIGHT SAGA DELUXE EDITION	MILLER, FRANK	MILLER, FRANK; JANSON, KLAUS	$49.99/$58.00	HC

DC COMICS READING ORDER

ISBN | DIAMOND CODE	TITLE	AUTHOR | ARTIST	US$/$CAN | FORMAT
11. 9781401284312 JUN180575	BATMAN: THE DARK KNIGHT: MASTER RACE	MILLER, FRANK; AZZARELLO, BRIAN | KUBERT, ANDY; JANSON, KLAUS	$24.99/$33.99 | TP
12. 9781401267384 JUN170391	BATMAN: THE ART OF THE DARK KNIGHT: THE MASTER RACE	MILLER, FRANK | KUBERT, ANDY; JANSON, KLAUS	$24.99/$33.99 | HC
13. 9781401224196 JUN100204	BATMAN: CACOPHONY	SMITH, KEVIN | FLANAGAN, WALT	$14.99/$17.99 | TP
14. 9781401228767 JUN110270	BATMAN: THE WIDENING GYRE	SMITH, KEVIN | FLANAGAN, WALT	$17.99/$20.99 | TP
15. 9781401280635	BATMAN: CREATURE OF THE NIGHT	BUSIEK, KURT | LEON, JOHN PAUL	$24.99/$33.99 | HC
16. 9781401251277 NOV140310	BATMAN: DARK NIGHT, DARK CITY	MILLIGAN, PETER | DWYER, KIERON; APARO, JIM	$16.99/$19.99 | TP
17. 9781401283322	BATMAN: THE DARK PRINCE CHARMING	MARINI, ENRICO | MARINI, ENRICO	$34.99/$45.99 | HC
18. 9781401247225 FEB140258	BATMAN/DEATHBLOW: AFTER THE FIRE	AZZARELLO, BRIAN | BERMEJO, LEE	$14.99/$17.99 | TP
19. 9781401258061 SEP150288	BATMAN: THE DOOM THAT CAME TO GOTHAM	MIGNOLA, MIKE | NIXEY, TROY	$16.99/$19.99 | TP
20. 9781401232092 JUL158202	BATMAN: EARTH ONE	JOHNS, GEOFF | FRANK, GARY	$14.99/$15.99 | TP
21. 9781401262518 MAR160257	BATMAN: EARTH ONE VOL. 2	JOHNS, GEOFF | FRANK, GARY	$14.99/$17.99 | TP
22. 9781401260743 JAN160319	ELSEWORLDS: BATMAN VOL. 1	VARIOUS | VARIOUS	$34.99/$41.99 | TP
23. 9781401269821 JUL160407	ELSEWORLDS: BATMAN VOL. 2	MOENCH, DOUG | VARIOUS	$24.99/$33.99 | TP
24. 9781401265960 NOV170367	ELSEWORLDS: BATMAN VOL. 3	VARIOUS | VARIOUS	$34.99/$45.99 | TP
25. 9781401270780 MAR170419	DC COMICS/DARK HORSE: BATMAN VS. PREDATOR	GIBBONS, DAVE | KUBERT, ANDY	$34.99/$45.99 | TP
26. 9781401285555	BATMAN: EUROPA	AZZARELLO, BRIAN | LEE, JIM	$16.99/$22.99 | TP
27. 9781401278632 FEB180299	BATMAN: GHOSTS	KIETH, SAM | KIETH, SAM	$19.99/$25.99 | TP
28. 9781401211530 DEC120332	BATMAN: GOTHAM BY GASLIGHT	AUGUSTYN, BRIAN | MIGNOLA, MIKE	$12.99/$15.99 | TP
29. 9781401288914	BATMAN NOIR: GOTHAM BY GASLIGHT	AUGUSTYN, BRIAN | MIGNOLA, MIKE	$29.99/$39.99 | HC
30. 9781401236786 SEP130278	THE BATMAN/JUDGE DREDD COLLECTION	GRANT, ALAN | WAGNER, JOHN	$19.99/$23.99 | TP
31. 9781401284695	BATMAN & THE JUSTICE LEAGUE VOL. 1	TESHIROGI, SHIORI | TESHIROGI, SHIORI	$12.99/$17.50 | TP
32. 9781401290597	BATMAN & THE JUSTICE LEAGUE VOL. 2	TESHIROGI, SHIORI | TESHIROGI, SHIORI	$12.99/$17.50 | TP
33. 9781401244941 NOV130255	BATMAN: LI'L GOTHAM VOL. 1	NGUYEN, DUSTIN; FRIDOLFS, DEREK | NGUYEN, DEREK	$12.99/$15.99 | TP
34. 9781401247232 APR140285	BATMAN: LI'L GOTHAM VOL. 2	NGUYEN, DUSTIN; FRIDOLFS, DEREK | NGUYEN, DEREK	$12.99/$15.99 | TP
35. 9781401273941 MAR180336	BATMAN: A LOT OF LI'L GOTHAM	NGUYEN, DUSTIN | FRIDOLFS, DEREK	$24.99/$33.99 | TP
36. 9781401236847 JUL130240	BATMAN: ODYSSEY	ADAMS, NEAL | ADAMS, NEAL	$19.99/$23.99 | TP
37. 9781401232139 JUL110245	BATMAN: NOEL	BERMEJO, LEE | BERMEJO, LEE	$22.99/$26.99 | HC
38. 9781401285616 AUG170332	BATMAN/THE SHADOW: THE MURDER GENIUSES	ORLANDO, STEVE; SNYDER, SCOTT | ROSSMO, RILEY	$16.99/$22.99 | TP
39. 9781401275419 DEC170391	BATMAN: TALES OF THE THE MAN-BAT	DIXON, CHUCK | VARIOUS	$19.99/$25.99 | TP
40. 9781401280741 APR180265	BATMAN: THRILLKILLER (NEW EDITION)	BRERETON, DAN | CHAYKIN, HOWARD	$16.99/$22.99 | TP
41. 9781401279592 JUL180733	BATMAN: WHITE KNIGHT	MURPHY, SEAN | MURPHY, SEAN	$19.99/$25.99 | TP
42. 9781401211929 JAN130309	BATMAN: YEAR ONE HUNDRED	POPE, PAUL | POPE, PAUL	$19.99/$23.99 | TP
43. 9781401258078 JUN150299	BATMAN: YEAR 100 & OTHER TALES DELUXE EDITION	POPE, PAUL | POPE, PAUL	$29.99/$35.00 | HC

SUPERMAN BACKLIST AND SUGGESTED READING ORDER

ISBN | DIAMOND CODE	TITLE	AUTHOR | ARTIST	US$/$CAN | FORMAT
1. 9781401278892 NOV170373	SUPERMAN: THE MANY WORLDS OF KRYPTON	BYRNE, JOHN | BYRNE, JOHN	$19.99/$25.99 | TP
2. 9781401274467 AUG170342	SUPERMAN: AMERICAN ALIEN	LANDIS, MAX | MANAPUL, FRANCIS; JOCK; DRAGOTTA, NICK	$19.99/$25.99 | TP
3. 9781401261092 DEC150348	SUPERMAN: THE GOLDEN AGE VOL. 1	SIEGEL, JERRY | SHUSTER, JOE	$19.99/$23.99 | TP
4. 9781401265304 AUG160338	SUPERMAN: THE GOLDEN AGE VOL. 2	SIEGEL, JERRY | SHUSTER, JOE	$19.99/$25.99 | TP
5. 9781401270896 MAR170432	SUPERMAN: THE GOLDEN AGE VOL. 3	SIEGEL, JERRY | SHUSTER, JOE	$19.99/$25.99 | HC
6. 9781401278670 FEB180314	SUPERMAN: THE GOLDEN AGE VOL. 4	VARIOUS | VARIOUS	$24.99/$33.99 | TP
7. 9781401287979	SUPERMAN: THE GOLDEN AGE VOL. 5	VARIOUS | VARIOUS	$24.99/$33.99 | TP
8. 9781401241896 FEB130227	SUPERMAN: THE GOLDEN AGE OMNIBUS VOL. 1	SIEGEL, JERRY | SHUSTER, JOE	$17.99/$20.99 | HC
9. 9781401263249 MAR160271	SUPERMAN: THE GOLDEN AGE OMNIBUS VOL. 2	VARIOUS | VARIOUS	$75.00/$85.00 | HC
10. 9781401270117 JUL160413	SUPERMAN: THE GOLDEN AGE OMNIBUS VOL. 3	VARIOUS | VARIOUS	$75.00/$99.00 | HC
11. 9781401272579 DEC160389	SUPERMAN: THE GOLDEN AGE OMNIBUS VOL. 4	VARIOUS | VARIOUS	$75.00/$99.00 | HC
12. 9781401274764 AUG170343	SUPERMAN: THE GOLDEN AGE OMNIBUS VOL. 5	VARIOUS | VARIOUS	$125.00/$163.00 | HC
13. 9781401288853	SUPERMAN'S PAL, JIMMY OLSEN BY JACK KIRBY	KIRBY, JACK | KIRBY, JACK	$29.99/$39.99 | TP
14. 9781401269685 OCT160311	SUPERMAN/BATMAN: SAGA OF THE SUPER SONS (NEW EDITION)	HANEY, BOB | DILLIN, DICK	$16.99/$22.99 | TP
15. 9781401243067 JUL130247	SUPERMAN: DARK KNIGHT OVER METROPOLIS	VARIOUS | VARIOUS	$14.99/$17.99 | TP
16. 9781401227319 APR100219	SUPERMAN: WHATEVER HAPPENED TO THE MAN OF TOMORROW?	MOORE, ALAN | SWAN, CURT	$14.99/$17.99 | TP
17. 9781401281090 APR180280	SUPERMAN FOR ALL SEASONS (NEW EDITION)	LOEB, JEPH | SALE, TIM	$19.99/$25.99 | TP
18. 9781401275259	SUPERMAN: KRYPTONITE DELUXE EDITION	COOKE, DARWYN | SALE, TIM	$29.99/$39.99 | HC
19. 9781401263232 MAR160279	SUPERMAN: PANIC IN THE SKY (NEW EDITION)	JURGENS, DAN | JURGENS, DAN | ORDWAY, JERRY	$19.99/$23.99 | TP
20. 9781401260972 DEC150344	SUPERMAN & JUSTICE LEAGUE AMERICA VOL. 1	JURGENS, DAN | JURGENS, DAN	$17.99/$21.99 | TP
21. 9781401263843 MAY160325	SUPERMAN & JUSTICE LEAGUE AMERICA VOL. 2	JURGENS, DAN | JURGENS, DAN	$19.99/$23.99 | TP
22. 9781401266653 JAN168880	SUPERMAN: THE DEATH OF SUPERMAN (NEW EDITION)	DAN JURGENS | JURGENS, DAN; ORDWAY, JERRY; SIMONSON, LOUISE; BOGDANOVE, JON; GRUMMETT, TOM	$17.99/$21.99 | TP
23. 9781401266646 JAN168881	SUPERMAN: FUNERAL FOR A FRIEND	DAN JURGENS | JURGENS, DAN	$19.99/$23.99 | TP
24. 9781401266639 JAN168884	SUPERMAN: REIGN OF THE SUPERMEN	DAN JURGENS | JURGENS, DAN	$24.99/$29.99 | TP
25. 9781401266622 JAN168882	SUPERMAN: THE RETURN OF SUPERMAN	DAN JURGENS | JURGENS, DAN	$29.99/$35.00 | TP
26. 9781401266660 JAN168883	SUPERMAN: DOOMSDAY	DAN JURGENS | JURGENS, DAN	$19.99/$23.99 | TP
27. 9781401280536 MAR180355	SUPERMAN: ZERO HOUR	JURGENS, DAN | BOGDANOVE, JON	$29.99/$39.99 | TP
28. 9781401278236 OCT170379	SUPERMAN: EXILE AND OTHER STORIES OMNIBUS	ORDWAY, JERRY | VARIOUS	$125.00/$163.00 | HC
29. 9781401280918 APR180281	SUPERMAN BLUE VOL. 1	KESEL, KARL | VARIOUS	$24.99/$33.99 | TP

DC COMICS READING ORDER

	ISBN | DIAMOND CODE	TITLE	AUTHOR | ARTIST	US$/$CAN | FORMAT
30.	9781401277659 NOV170374	SUPERMAN: PRESIDENT LUTHOR (NEW EDITION)	LOEB, JEPH | VARIOUS	$29.99/$39.99 | TP
31.	9781401262136 JAN160324	EMPEROR JOKER	VARIOUS | VARIOUS	$19.99/$23.99 | TP
32.	9781401237806 NOV120270	SUPERMAN: FOR TOMORROW	AZZARELLO, BRIAN | LEE, JIM	$24.99/$28.99 | TP
33.	9781401290221 MAR188894	SUPERMAN: SECRET ORIGIN (NEW EDITION)	JOHNS, GEOFF | FRANK, GARY	$19.99/$25.99 | TP
34.	9781401237790 OCT120270	SUPERMAN: LAST SON OF KRYPTON	JOHNS, GEOFF; DONNER, RICHARD | KUBERT, ADAM; FRANK, GARY	$19.99/$23.99 | TP
35.	9781401290238 MAR188895	SUPERMAN: BRAINIAC (NEW EDITION)	JOHNS, GEOFF | FRANK, GARY	$14.99/$19.99 | TP
36.	9781401235475 FEB130215	SUPERMAN: ACTION COMICS VOL. 1: SUPERMAN AND THE MEN OF STEEL	MORRISON, GRANT | MORALES, RAGS	$16.99/$19.99 | TP
37.	9781401242541 SEP130275	SUPERMAN: ACTION COMICS VOL. 2: BULLETPROOF	MORRISON, GRANT | MORALES, RAGS	$16.99/$19.99 | TP
38.	9781401246068 APR140268	SUPERMAN - ACTION COMICS VOL. 3: AT THE END OF DAYS	MORRISON, GRANT | MORALES, RAGS; WALKER, BRAD	$16.99/$19.99 | TP
39.	9781401250775 SEP140312	SUPERMAN - ACTION COMICS VOL. 4: HYBRID	DIGGLE, ANDY | DANIEL, TONY S.	$16.99/$19.99 | TP
40.	9781401254889 MAR150272	SUPERMAN - ACTION COMICS VOL. 5: WHAT LIES BENEATH	PAK, GREG | KUDER, AARON	$14.99/$17.99 | TP
41.	9781401258658 SEP150306	SUPERMAN - ACTION COMICS VOL. 6: SUPERDOOM	PAK, GREG | KUDER, AARON	$16.99/$19.99 | TP
42.	9781401262624 APR160404	SUPERMAN - ACTION COMICS VOL. 7: UNDER THE SKIN	PAK, GREG | KUDER, AARON	$16.99/$19.99 | TP
43.	9781401269203 SEP160355	SUPERMAN-ACTION COMICS VOL. 8: TRUTH	PAK, GREG | KUDER, AARON	$16.99/$22.99 | TP
44.	9781401269197 AUG160337	SUPERMAN-ACTION COMICS VOL. 9: LAST RITES	TOMASI, PETER J. | VARIOUS	$24.99/$33.99 | TP
45.	9781401236861 MAR130274	SUPERMAN VOL. 1: WHAT PRICE TOMORROW?	PÉREZ, GEORGE | MERINO, JESUS; SCOTT, NICOLA	$14.99/$17.99 | TP
46.	9781401240288 OCT130246	SUPERMAN VOL. 2: SECRETS & LIES	JURGENS, DAN | GIFFEN, KEITH; JURGENS, DAN	$16.99/$19.99 | TP
47.	9781401246228 MAY140370	SUPERMAN VOL. 3: FURY AT WORLD'S END	LOBDELL, SCOTT | ROCAFORT, KENNETH	$14.99/$17.99 | TP
48.	9781401246129 MAR140259	SUPERMAN: H'EL ON EARTH	LOBDELL, SCOTT | VARIOUS	$19.99/$23.99 | TP
49.	9781401250942 NOV140301	SUPERMAN VOL. 4: PSI-WAR	LOBDELL, SCOTT | ROCAFORT, KENNETH; KUDER, AARON	$16.99/$19.99 | TP
50.	9781401250959 OCT140360	SUPERMAN VOL. 5: UNDER FIRE	LOBDELL, SCOTT | LASHLEY, KEN; BOOTH, BRETT	$24.99/$28.99 | TP
51.	9781401255442 MAY150247	SUPERMAN: KRYPTON RETURNS	LOBDELL, SCOTT | ROCAFORT, KENNETH	$16.99/$19.99 | TP
52.	9781401257699 SEP150305	SUPERMAN: DOOMED	SOULE, CHARLES; PAK, GREG | KUDER, AARON	$29.99/$35.00 | TP
53.	9781401258689 JAN160314	SUPERMAN: THE MEN OF TOMORROW	JOHNS, GEOFF | ROMITA, JOHN JR; JANSON, KLAUS	$16.99/$19.99 | TP
54.	9781401265106 JUN160356	SUPERMAN VOL. 1: BEFORE TRUTH	YANG, GENE LUEN | ROMITA JR., JOHN	$16.99/$22.99 | TP
55.	9781401268305 DEC160390	SUPERMAN VOL. 2: RETURN TO GLORY	YANG, GENE LUEN | PORTER, HOWARD	$16.99/$22.99 | TP
56.	9781401271251 APR170438	SUPERMAN: SAVAGE DAWN	TOMASI, PETER J.;YANG, GENE LUEN; PAK, GREG | VARIOUS	$24.99/$33.99 | TP
57.	9781401250935 DEC150346	SUPERMAN UNCHAINED	SNYDER, SCOTT | LEE, JIM; NGUYEN, DUSTIN	$24.99/$29.99 | TP
58.	9781401262716 JUL160401	CONVERGENCE	KING, JEFF; LOBDELL, SCOTT | PAGULAYAN, CARLO	$19.99/$23.99 | TP
59.	9781401258351 JUL150298	CONVERGENCE: FLASHPOINT BOOK ONE	RUCKA, GREG | WEEKS, LEE; HAMNER, CULLY	$19.99/$23.99 | TP
60.	9781401262495 MAY160323	SUPERMAN: LOIS AND CLARK	JURGENS, DAN | WEEKS, LEE	$17.99/$21.99 | TP
61.	9781401269142 FEB170317	SUPERMAN: THE FINAL DAYS OF SUPERMAN	TOMASI, PETER J. | VARIOUS	$19.99/$25.99 | TP
62.	9781401267766 OCT160297	SUPERMAN VOL. 1: SON OF SUPERMAN (REBIRTH)	TOMASI, PETER J. | GLEASON, PATRICK; MAHNKE, DOUG	$16.99/$19.99 | TP
63.	9781401268602 JAN170383	SUPERMAN VOL. 2: TRIALS OF THE SUPER SONS (REBIRTH)	TOMASI, PETER J. | GLEASON, PATRICK; MAHNKE, DOUG	$16.99/$19.99 | TP
64.	9781401271541 MAY170327	SUPERMAN VOL. 3: MULTIPLICITY (REBIRTH)	TOMASI, PETER J. | GLEASON, PATRICK	$16.99/$22.99 | TP
65.	9781401278625 FEB180289	SUPERMAN REBORN (REBIRTH)	TOMASI, PETER J.; JURGENS, DAN | GLEASON, PATRICK; MAHNKE, DOUG	$16.99/$22.99 | TP
66.	9781401274689 AUG170325	SUPERMAN VOL. 4: BLACK DAWN (REBIRTH)	TOMASI, PETER J. | GLEASON, PATRICK; MAHNKE, DOUG	$16.99/$22.99 | TP
67.	9781401277291 JAN180391	SUPERMAN VOL. 5: HOPES AND FEARS (REBIRTH)	TOMASI, PETER J. | GLEASON, PATRICK	$16.99/$22.99 | TP
68.	9781401281236 MAY180592	SUPERMAN VOL. 6: IMPERIUS LEX (REBIRTH)	TOMASI, PETER J. | GLEASON, PATRICK	$16.99/$22.99 | TP
69.	9781401285241	SUPERMAN VOL. 7	TOMASI, PETER J. | GLEASON, PATRICK	$16.99/$22.99 | TP
70.	9781401271558 JUN170388	SUPERMAN: THE REBIRTH DELUXE EDITION BOOK 1	TOMASI, PETER J. | GLEASON, PATRICK; MAHNKE, DOUG	$34.99/$45.99 | HC
71.	9781401278663 FEB180290	SUPERMAN: THE REBIRTH DELUXE EDITION BOOK 2	TOMASI, PETER J. | GLEASON, PATRICK	$34.99/$45.99 | HC
72.	9781401284510	SUPERMAN: THE REBIRTH DELUXE EDITION BOOK 3	TOMASI, PETER J. | GLEASON, PATRICK	$34.99/$45.99 | HC
73.	9781401289355	SUPERMAN: THE REBIRTH DELUXE EDITION BOOK 4	TOMASI, PETER J. | GLEASON, PATRICK	$34.99/$45.99 | HC
74.	9781401268046 NOV160319	SUPERMAN: ACTION COMICS VOL. 1: PATH OF DOOM (REBIRTH)	JURGENS, DAN | KIRKHAM, TYLER; ZIRCHER, PATRICK	$16.99/$19.99 | TP
75.	9781401269111 JAN170382	SUPERMAN: ACTION COMICS VOL. 2: WELCOME TO THE PLANET (REBIRTH)	JURGENS, DAN | KIRKHAM, TYLER; ZIRCHER, PATRICK	$16.99/$19.99 | TP
76.	9781401273576 MAR170407	SUPERMAN: ACTION COMICS VOL. 3: MEN OF STEEL (REBIRTH)	JURGENS, DAN | KIRKHAM, TYLER; ZIRCHER, PATRICK	$16.99/$22.99 | TP
77.	9781401287863 NOV170353	SUPERMAN - ACTION COMICS: THE OZ EFFECT	JURGENS, DAN | BOGDANOVIC, VIKTOR; SOOK, RYAN	$19.99/$25.99 | TP
78.	9781401274405 AUG170317	SUPERMAN: ACTION COMICS VOL. 4: THE NEW WORLD (REBIRTH)	JURGENS, DAN | ZIRCHER, PATRICK	$19.99/$25.99 | TP
79.	9781401275280 MAY180591	SUPERMAN: ACTION COMICS VOL. 5: BOOSTER SHOT	JURGENS, DAN | JURGENS, DAN	$19.99/$25.99 | TP
80.	9781401273569 MAR170408	SUPERMAN: ACTION COMICS: THE REBIRTH DELUXE EDITION BOOK 1	JURGENS, DAN | KIRKHAM, TYLER; ZIRCHER, PATRICK	$34.99/$45.99 | HC
81.	9781401277604 NOV170354	SUPERMAN: ACTION COMICS: THE REBIRTH DELUXE EDITION BOOK 2	JURGENS, DAN | ZIRCHER, PATRICK; KIRKHAM, TYLER	$34.99/$45.99 | HC
82.	9781401280437	SUPERMAN: ACTION COMICS: THE REBIRTH DELUXE EDITION BOOK 3	JURGENS, DAN; WILLIAMS, ROB | MARCH, GUILLEM	$34.99/$45.99 | HC
83.	9781401285975 JUN180558	ACTION COMICS #1000: THE DELUXE EDITION	BENDIS, BRIAN MICHAEL; JOHNS, GEOFF; SNYDER, SCOTT; KING, TOM | LEE, JIM; CASSADAY, JOHN; SWAN, CURT	$19.99/$25.99 | HC
84.	9781401283483 JUL180765	THE MAN OF STEEL	BENDIS, BRIAN MICHAEL | REIS, IVAN; FABOK, JASON; HUGHES, ADAM; SOOK, RYAN	$24.99/$33.99 | HC
85.	9781401288198 JUN188697	SUPERMAN VOL. 1	BENDIS, BRIAN MICHAEL | REIS, IVAN	$16.99/$22.99 | TP
86.	9781401288723 JUN188698	SUPERMAN: ACTION COMICS VOL. 1	BENDIS, BRIAN MICHAEL | GLEASON, PATRICK	$16.99/$22.99 | TP

SUPERMAN/BATMAN

	ISBN | DIAMOND CODE	TITLE	AUTHOR | ARTIST	US$/$CAN | FORMAT
1.	9781401268336 DEC160382	BATMAN & SUPERMAN IN WORLD'S FINEST: THE SILVER AGE VOL. 1	VARIOUS | VARIOUS	$19.99/$25.99 | TP
2.	9781401201876 APR050327	BATMAN/SUPERMAN/WONDER WOMAN: TRINITY	WAGNER, MATT | WAGNER, MATT	$17.99/$20.99 | TP

DC COMICS READING ORDER

	ISBN | DIAMOND CODE	TITLE	AUTHOR | ARTIST	US$/$CAN | FORMAT
3.	9781401248185 JAN140354	SUPERMAN/BATMAN VOL. 1	LOEB, JEPH | MCGUINESS, ED; TURNER, MICHAEL	$19.99/$23.99 | TP
4.	9781401250799 SEP140323	SUPERMAN/BATMAN VOL. 2	LOEB, JEPH | MCGUINESS, ED; PACHECO, CARLOS	$19.99/$23.99 | TP
5.	9781401240967 FEB130216	ABSOLUTE SUPERMAN/BATMAN VOL. 1	LOEB, JEPH | MCGUINESS, ED; TURNER, MICHAEL	$99.99/$112.00 | HC
6.	9781401248178 OCT130253	ABSOLUTE SUPERMAN/BATMAN VOL. 2	LOEB, JEPH | MCGUINESS, ED; PACHECO, CARLOS	$99.99/$112.00 | HC
7.	9781401263850 MAY160324	SUPERMAN/BATMAN VOL. 4	BURNETT, ALAN; GREEN, MICHAEL | VARIOUS	$24.99/$29.99 | TP
8.	9781401265281 NOV160339	SUPERMAN/BATMAN VOL. 5	JOHNSON, MIKE; GREEN, MICHAEL | VARIOUS	$19.99/$25.99 | TP
9.	9781401275037 SEP170428	SUPERMAN/BATMAN VOL. 6	CASEY, JOE; LEVITZ, PAUL; KOLINS, SCOTT	$29.99/$39.99 | TP
10.	9781401288013	SUPERMAN/BATMAN VOL. 7	FIALKOV, JOSHUA HALE | VARIOUS	$29.99/$39.99 | TP
11.	9781401249342 AUG140333	BATMAN/SUPERMAN VOL. 1: CROSS WORLD	PAK, GREG | LEE, JAE; OLIVER, BEN	$14.99/$17.99 | TP
12.	9781401254230 FEB150252	BATMAN/SUPERMAN VOL. 2: GAME OVER	PAK, GREG | LEE, JAE; BOOTH, BRETT	$16.99/$19.99 | TP
13.	9781401257545 SEP150290	BATMAN/SUPERMAN VOL. 3: SECOND CHANCE	PAK, GREG | LEE, JAE	$14.99/$17.99 | TP
14.	9781401263683 AUG150267	BATMAN/SUPERMAN VOL. 4: SIEGE	PAK, GREG | SYAF, ARDIAN	$16.99/$19.99 | TP
15.	9781401268183 JAN170388	BATMAN/SUPERMAN VOL. 5: TRUTH HURTS	PAK, GREG | SYAF, ARDIAN	$16.99/$22.99 | TP
16.	9781401271565 MAY170334	BATMAN/SUPERMAN VOL. 6: UNIVERSE'S FINEST	TOMASI, PETER J. | VARIOUS	$19.99/$25.99 | TP
17.	9781401285371	SUPERMAN/SHAZAM!: FIRST THUNDER DELUXE EDITION	WINICK, JUDD | MIDDLETON, JOSHUA	$24.99/$33.99 | HC
18.	9781401253462 DEC140383	SUPERMAN/WONDER WOMAN VOL. 1: POWER COUPLE	SOULE, CHARLES | DANIEL, TONY S.; SIQUEIRA, PAULO	$16.99/$19.99 | TP
19.	9781401257675 AUG150280	SUPERMAN/WONDER WOMAN VOL. 2: WAR AND PEACE	SOULE, CHARLES | DANIEL, TONY S.; BENES, ED	$16.99/$19.99 | TP
20.	9781401263218 MAR160276	SUPERMAN/WONDER WOMAN VOL. 3: CASUALTIES OF WAR	TOMASI, PETER J. | MAHNKE, DOUG	$16.99/$19.99 | TP
21.	9781401265441 SEP160356	SUPERMAN/WONDER WOMAN VOL. 4: DARK TRUTH	TOMASI, PETER J. | MAHNKE, DOUG	$16.99/$22.99 | TP
22.	9781401268787 FEB170318	SUPERMAN/WONDER WOMAN VOL. 5: TRUTH HURTS	TOMASI, PETER J. | MAHNKE, DOUG	$16.99/$22.99 | TP
23.	9781401274665 SEP170407	TRINITY VOL. 1: BETTER TOGETHER (REBIRTH)	MANAPUL, FRANCIS | MANAPUL, FRANCIS; MANN, CLAY	$16.99/$22.99 | TP
24.	9781401280505 MAR180357	TRINITY VOL. 2: DEAD SPACE (REBIRTH)	MANAPUL, FRANCIS | MANAPUL, FRANCIS; MANN, CLAY	$14.99/$19.99 | TP
25.	9781401280512 APR180283	TRINITY VOL. 3: DARK DESTINY	WILLIAMS, ROB | MANN, CLAY	$16.99/$22.99 | TP
26.	9781401285500	TRINITY VOL. 4	ROBINSON, JAMES | ZIRCHER, PATRICK	$24.99/$33.99 | TP

SUPERMAN COMPILATIONS

1.	9781401247041 JUL130224	SUPERMAN: A CELEBRATION OF 75 YEARS	VARIOUS | VARIOUS	$39.99 /$47.99 | HC
2.	9781401278878 DEC170241	ACTION COMICS: 80 YEARS OF SUPERMAN DELUXE EDITION	VARIOUS | VARIOUS	$29.99/$39.99 | HC
3.	9781401256982 SEP150285	BATMAN VS. SUPERMAN: THE GREATEST BATTLES	VARIOUS | VARIOUS	$9.99/$11.99 | TP
4.	9781401278748 FEB180313	SUPERMAN BY MARK MILLAR	MILLAR, MARK | VARIOUS	$29.99/$39.99 | TP

SUPERMAN: FROM PAGE TO SCREEN

1.	9781401258672 AUG150279	SUPERMAN ADVENTURES VOL. 1	MCCLOUD, SCOTT | BURCHETT, RICK	$19.99/$23.99 | TP
2.	9781401260941 FEB160238	SUPERMAN ADVENTURES VOL. 2	MCCLOUD, SCOTT | VARIOUS	$19.99/$23.99 | TP
3.	9781401272425 FEB170319	SUPERMAN ADVENTURES VOL. 3	MILLAR, MARK | VARIOUS	$19.99/$23.99 | TP
4.	9781401275112 SEP170427	SUPERMAN ADVENTURES VOL. 4	MILLAR, MARK | VARIOUS	$19.99/$25.99 | TP
5.	9781401261597 FEB160237	SMALLVILLE SEASON 11 VOL. 8: CHAOS	MILLER, BRYAN Q. | VARIOUS	$16.99/$19.99 | TP
6.	9781401276065 SEP170423	SMALLVILLE SEASON 11 VOL. 9: CONTINUITY	MILLER, BRYAN Q. | VARIOUS	$16.99/$23.99 | TP

SUPERMAN GRAPHIC NOVELS

1.	9781401290832 AUG180593	ALL-STAR SUPERMAN (DC BLACK LABEL EDITION)	MORRISON, GRANT | QUITELY, FRANK	$29.99/$39.99 | TP
2.	9781401202521 JUL050214	SUPERMAN: BIRTHRIGHT	WAID, MARK | YU, LEINIL FRANCIS	$19.99/$23.99 | TP
3.	9781401274894 OCT170380	SUPERMAN: THE COMING OF THE SUPERMEN	ADAMS, NEAL | ADAMS, NEAL	$16.99/$22.99 | TP
4.	9781401224691 FEB130226	SUPERMAN: EARTH ONE	STRACZYNSKI, J. MICHAEL | DAVIS, SHANE	$12.99/$15.99 | TP
5.	9781401235598 DEC130312	SUPERMAN: EARTH ONE VOL. 2	STRACZYNSKI, J. MICHAEL | DAVIS, SHANE	$14.99/$17.99 | TP
6.	9781401259099 AUG150278	SUPERMAN: EARTH ONE VOL. 3	STRACZYNSKI, J. MICHAEL | SYAF, ARDIAN	$14.99/$17.99 | TP
7.	9781401271183 MAR180341	ELSEWORLDS: SUPERMAN VOL. 1	VARIOUS | VARIOUS	$34.99/$45.99 | TP
8.	9781401288938	ELSEWORLDS: SUPERMAN VOL. 2	VARIOUS | VARIOUS	$34.99/$45.99 | TP
9.	9781401268596	SUPERMAN & BATMAN: GENERATIONS (ELSEWORLDS)	BYRNE, JOHN | BYRNE, JOHN	$29.99/$39.99 | TP
10.	9781401247119 JAN140353	SUPERMAN: RED SON (NEW EDITION)	MILLAR, MARK | JOHNSON, DAVE; PLUNKETT, KILLIAN	$17.99/$20.99 | TP
11.	9781401228415 APR100224	SUPERMAN VS. MUHAMMAD ALI DELUXE EDITION	O'NEIL, DENNIS | ADAMS, NEIL	$19.99/$23.99 | HC
12.	9781401276119 JUN170359	SUPERMAN AND THE MISERABLE, ROTTEN, NO FUN, REALLY BAD DAY	CROATTO, DAVE | RICHMOND, TOM	$14.99/$19.99 | HC

WONDER WOMAN BACKLIST AND SUGGESTED READING ORDER

1.	9781401274474 AUG170340	THE ODYSSEY OF THE AMAZONS	GREVIOUX, KEVIN | BENJAMIN, RYAN	$16.99/$22.99 | TP
2.	9781401274443 AUG170345	WONDER WOMAN: THE GOLDEN AGE VOL. 1	MARSTON, WILLIAM MOULTON | VARIOUS	$24.99/$33.99 | TP
3.	9781401285364 JUL170466	WONDER WOMAN: THE GOLDEN AGE VOL. 2	MARSTON, WILLIAM MOULTON | VARIOUS	$29.99/$39.99 | TP
4.	9781401264963 MAY160331	WONDER WOMAN: THE GOLDEN AGE OMNIBUS VOL. 1	VARIOUS | VARIOUS	$75.00/$85.00 | HC
5.	9781401271466 FEB170322	WONDER WOMAN: THE GOLDEN AGE OMNIBUS VOL. 2	MARSTON, WILLIAM MOULTON | VARIOUS	$75.00/$99.00 | HC
6.	9781401280826 APR180285	WONDER WOMAN: THE GOLDEN AGE OMNIBUS VOL. 3	VARIOUS | VARIOUS	$125.00/$163.00 | HC
7.	9781401285296 MAY180594	WONDER WOMAN, DIANA PRINCE OMNIBUS (50TH ANNIVERSARY)	VARIOUS | VARIOUS	$125.00/$163.00 | HC
8.	9781401263751 MAY160328	WONDER WOMAN BY GEORGE PEREZ VOL. 1	PEREZ, GEORGE | PEREZ, GEORGE	$24.99/$29.99 | TP
9.	9781401269067 MAR170433	WONDER WOMAN BY GEORGE PEREZ VOL. 2	PEREZ, GEORGE | PEREZ, GEORGE	$24.99/$33.99 | TP

DC COMICS READING ORDER

	ISBN	DIAMOND CODE	TITLE	AUTHOR	ARTIST	US$/$CAN	FORMAT
10.	9781401278328	JAN180410	WONDER WOMAN BY GEORGE PEREZ VOL. 3	PEREZ, GEORGE	PEREZ, GEORGE	$29.99/$39.99	TP
11.	9781401255473	APR150306	WONDER WOMAN BY GEORGE PEREZ OMNIBUS VOL. 1	PEREZ, GEORGE	PEREZ, GEORGE	$75.00/$85.00	HC
12.	9781401263447		WONDER WOMAN BY GEORGE PEREZ OMNIBUS VOL. 2	PEREZ, GEORGE	PEREZ, GEORGE	$49.99/$58.00	HC
13.	9781401280390	DEC170399	WONDER WOMAN BY GEORGE PEREZ OMNIBUS VOL. 3	PEREZ, GEORGE	PEREZ, GEORGE	$99.99/$130.99	HC
14.	9781401261078	DEC150347	WONDER WOMAN: WAR OF THE GODS	PEREZ, GEORGE	PEREZ, GEORGE	$16.99/$24.99	TP
15.	9781401270841	FEB170321	WONDER WOMAN BY JOHN BYRNE VOL. 1	BYRNE, JOHN	BYRNE, JOHN	$24.99/$33.99	TP
16.	9781401280727	APR180286	WONDER WOMAN BY JOHN BYRNE VOL. 2	BYRNE, JOHN	BYRNE, JOHN	$39.99/$53.99	HC
17.	9781401268343	DEC160391	WONDER WOMAN & THE JUSTICE LEAGUE AMERICA VOL. 1	VADO, DAN	VARIOUS	$29.99/$39.99	TP
18.	9781401274009	JUL170488	WONDER WOMAN & THE JUSTICE LEAGUE AMERICA VOL. 2	VARIOUS	VARIOUS	$24.99/$33.99	TP
19.	9781401285883		WONDER WOMAN BY WALT SIMONSON & JERRY ORDWAY	SIMONSON, WALT	ORDWAY, JERRY	$19.99/$25.99	TP
20.	9781401277956	DEC170400	WONDER WOMAN: FORGOTTEN LEGENDS	BUSIEK, KURT	ROBBINS, TRINA	$16.99/$22.99	TP
21.	9781401261061	FEB160243	WONDER WOMAN BY MIKE DEODATO	MESSNER-LOEBS, WILLIAM	DEODATO, MIKE	$19.99/$23.99	TP
22.	9781401288570		WONDER WOMAN BY PHIL JIMENEZ OMNIBUS	JIMENEZ, PHIL	JIMENEZ, PHIL	$75.00/$99.00	HC
23.	9781401263324	APR160406	WONDER WOMAN BY GREG RUCKA VOL. 1	RUCKA, GREG	VARIOUS	$29.99/$35.00	TP
24.	9781401271176	APR170440	WONDER WOMAN BY GREG RUCKA VOL. 2	RUCKA, GREG	VARIOUS	$29.99/$39.99	TP
25.	9781401272333	JAN170403	WONDER WOMAN: WHO IS WONDER WOMAN? (NEW PRINTING)	HEINBERG, ALLAN	DODSON, TERRY	$14.99/$19.99	TP
26.	9781401234102	DEC110279	FLASHPOINT: WORLD OF FLASHPOINT FEATURING WONDER WOMAN	VARIOUS	VARIOUS	$17.99/$20.99	TP
27.	9781401235628	OCT120256	WONDER WOMAN VOL. 1: BLOOD	AZZARELLO, BRIAN	CHIANG, CLIFF	$14.99/$17.99	TP
28.	9781401238100	JUN130271	WONDER WOMAN VOL. 2: GUTS	AZZARELLO, BRIAN	CHIANG, CLIFF	$14.99/$17.99	TP
29.	9781401246075	DEC130308	WONDER WOMAN VOL. 3: IRON	AZZARELLO, BRIAN	CHIANG, CLIFF; AKINS, TONY	$16.99/$19.99	TP
30.	9781401249540	JUL140247	WONDER WOMAN VOL. 4: WAR	AZZARELLO, BRIAN	CHIANG, CLIFF; AKINS, TONY	$14.99/$17.99	TP
31.	9781401253493	JAN150375	WONDER WOMAN VOL. 5: FLESH	AZZARELLO, BRIAN	CHIANG, CLIFF; SUDZUKA, GORAN	$16.99/$19.99	TP
32.	9781401257750	JUN150295	WONDER WOMAN VOL. 6: BONES	AZZARELLO, BRIAN	CHIANG, CLIFF; SUDZUKA, GORAN	$14.99/$17.99	TP
33.	9781401268480	AUG160321	ABSOLUTE WONDER WOMAN BY BRIAN AZZARELLO & CLIFF CHIANG VOL. 1	AZZARELLO, BRIAN	CHIANG, CLIFF	$100.00/$131.00	HC
34.	9781401277499	JUL170487	ABSOLUTE WONDER WOMAN BY BRIAN AZZARELLO & CLIFF CHIANG VOL. 2	AZZARELLO, BRIAN	CHIANG, CLIFF	$125.00/$163.00	HC
35.	9781401261634	FEB160244	WONDER WOMAN VOL. 7: WAR-TORN	FINCH, MEREDITH	FINCH, DAVID	$16.99/$19.99	TP
36.	9781401265830	JUN160363	WONDER WOMAN VOL. 8: A TWIST OF FAITH	FINCH, MEREDITH	FINCH, DAVID	$16.99/$22.99	TP
37.	9781401268053	NOV160341	WONDER WOMAN VOL. 9: RESURRECTION	FINCH, MEREDITH	FINCH, DAVID	$16.99/$22.99	TP
38.	9781401267780	NOV160320	WONDER WOMAN VOL. 1: THE LIES (REBIRTH)	RUCKA, GREG	SHARPE, LIAM	$16.99/$19.99	TP
39.	9781401268800	FEB170298	WONDER WOMAN VOL. 2: YEAR ONE (REBIRTH)	RUCKA, GREG	SCOTT, NICOLA	$16.99/$19.99	TP
40.	9781401271411	MAY170328	WONDER WOMAN VOL. 3: THE TRUTH (REBIRTH)	RUCKA, GREG	SHARP, LIAM	$16.99/$22.99	TP
41.	9781401274603	AUG170329	WONDER WOMAN VOL. 4: GODWATCH (REBIRTH)	RUCKA, GREG	SHARP, LIAM	$16.99/$22.99	TP
42.	9781401277345	FEB180292	WONDER WOMAN VOL. 5: HEART OF THE AMAZON (REBIRTH)	FONTANA, SHEA	ANDOLFO, MIRKA	$16.99/$22.99	TP
43.	9781401284244	JUN180592	WONDER WOMAN VOL. 6: CHILDREN OF THE GODS (REBIRTH)	ROBINSON, JAMES	SEGOVIA, STEPHEN	$16.99/$22.99	TP
44.	9781401285340		WONDER WOMAN VOL. 7: AMAZONS ATTACKED	ROBINSON, JAMES	SEGOVIA, STEPHEN	$16.99/$22.99	TP
45.	9781401289010		WONDER WOMAN VOL. 8: DARK GODS	ROBINSON, JAMES	MERINO, JESUS	$16.99/$22.99	TP
46.	9781401276782	APR180287	WONDER WOMAN: THE REBIRTH DELUXE EDITION BOOK 1 (REBIRTH)	RUCKA, GREG	SHARP, LIAM	$34.99/$45.99	HC
47.	9781401280932	APR180287	WONDER WOMAN: THE REBIRTH DELUXE EDITION BOOK 2	RUCKA, GREG	SHARP, LIAM	$34.99/$45.99	HC
48.	9781401285722		WONDER WOMAN: THE REBIRTH DELUXE EDITION BOOK 3	FONTANA, SHEA	LUPACCHINO, EMANUELA	$34.99/$45.99	HC
49.	9781401290733		WONDER WOMAN & THE JUSTICE LEAGUE: THE WITCHING HOUR	TYNION IV, JAMES	MARTINEZ, ALVARO	$16.99/$22.99	TP
50.	9781401283438		THE BRAVE AND THE BOLD: BATMAN AND WONDER WOMAN	SHARP, LIAM	SHARP, LIAM	$24.99/$33.99	HC

WONDER WOMAN COMPILATION GRAPHIC NOVELS

	ISBN	DIAMOND CODE	TITLE	AUTHOR	ARTIST	US$/$CAN	FORMAT
1.	9781401268978	NOV160343	WONDER WOMAN: HER GREATEST BATTLES	VARIOUS	VARIOUS	$9.99/$13.50	HC
2.	9781401265120	MAY160330	WONDER WOMAN: A CELEBRATION OF 75 YEARS	VARIOUS	VARIOUS	$39.99/$53.99	HC
3.	9781401265366	MAY160329	WONDER WOMAN 75TH ANNIVERSARY BOX SET	VARIOUS	VARIOUS	$49.99/$65.99	BOXED SET

WONDER WOMAN GRAPHIC NOVELS

	ISBN	DIAMOND CODE	TITLE	AUTHOR	ARTIST	US$/$CAN	FORMAT
1.	9781401268633	JAN170402	WONDER WOMAN: EARTH ONE VOL. 1	MORRISON, GRANT	PAQUETTE, YANICK	$14.99/$19.99	TP
2.	9781401281175	JUL180591	WONDER WOMAN: EARTH ONE VOL. 2	MORRISON, GRANT	PAQUETTE, YANICK	$24.99/$33.99	HC
3.	9781401253448	DEC140392	SENSATION COMICS FEATURING WONDER WOMAN VOL. 1	SIMONE, GAIL	VAN SCIVER, ETHAN	$14.99/$17.99	TP
4.	9781401258627	JUL150320	SENSATION COMICS FEATURING WONDER WOMAN VOL. 2	TYNION IV, JAMES	STEVENSON, NOELLE	$14.99/$17.99	TP
5.	9781401261573	FEB160236	SENSATION COMICS FEATURING WONDER WOMAN VOL. 3	VARIOUS	VARIOUS	$14.99/$17.99	TP
6.	9781401274504	AUG170346	WONDER WOMAN: THE TRUE AMAZON	THOMPSON, JILL	THOMPSON, JILL	$16.99/$22.99	HC
7.	9781401263287	MAR160277	WONDER WOMAN '77 VOL. 1	VARIOUS	VARIOUS	$16.99/$19.99	TP
8.	9781401267889	NOV160342	WONDER WOMAN '77 VOL. 2	VARIOUS	VARIOUS	$16.99/$22.99	TP
9.	9781401280215	MAR180358	WONDER WOMAN/CONAN	SIMONE, GAIL	LOPRESTI, AARON	$24.99/$33.99	HC

JUSTICE LEAGUE OF AMERICA BACKLIST AND SUGGESTED READING ORDER

	ISBN	DIAMOND CODE	TITLE	AUTHOR	ARTIST	US$/$CAN	FORMAT
1.	9781401278687		JLA: YEAR ONE (NEW EDITION)	WAID, MARK	KITSON, BARRY	$29.99/$39.99	TP
2.	9781401261115	NOV150283	JUSTICE LEAGUE OF AMERICA: THE SILVER AGE VOL. 1	VARIOUS	VARIOUS	$19.99/$23.99	TP
3.	9781401265151	SEP160348	JUSTICE LEAGUE OF AMERICA: THE SILVER AGE VOL. 2	VARIOUS	VARIOUS	$19.99/$25.99	TP
4.	9781401268626	JAN170393	JUSTICE LEAGUE OF AMERICA: THE SILVER AGE VOL. 3	VARIOUS	VARIOUS	$19.99/$25.99	TP
5.	9781401280611	APR180273	JUSTICE LEAGUE OF AMERICA: THE SILVER AGE VOL. 4	FOX, GARDNER	VARIOUS	$24.99/$33.99	TP

	ISBN | DIAMOND CODE	TITLE	AUTHOR | ARTIST	US$/$CAN | FORMAT
6.	9781401248420 NOV130241	JUSTICE LEAGUE OF AMERICA: THE SILVER AGE OMNIBUS VOL. 1	VARIOUS | VARIOUS	$99.99/$112.00 | HC
7.	9781401266608 FEB160235	JUSTICE LEAGUE OF AMERICA: THE SILVER AGE OMNIBUS VOL. 2	VARIOUS | VARIOUS	$99.99/$112.00 | HC
8.	9781401289201	JUSTICE LEAGUE OF AMERICA: THE BRONZE AGE VOL. 1	VARIOUS | VARIOUS	$29.99/$39.99 | TP
9.	9781401268060 OCT160309	JUSTICE LEAGUE OF AMERICA: THE BRONZE AGE OMNIBUS VOL. 1	O'NEIL, DENNIS | VARIOUS	$100.00/$122.00 | HC
10.	9781401277857 SEP170417	JUSTICE LEAGUE OF AMERICA: THE BRONZE AGE OMNIBUS VOL. 2	O'NEIL, DENNIS | VARIOUS	$125.00/$163.00 | HC
11.	9781401289485	JUSTICE LEAGUE OF AMERICA: THE BRONZE AGE OMNIBUS VOL. 3	VARIOUS | VARIOUS	$125.00/$163.00 | HC
12.	9781563897504 AUG058162	CRISIS ON INFINITE EARTHS	WOLFMAN, MARV | PÉREZ, GEORGE	$29.99 /$35.00 | TP
13.	9781401258412 JUN150303	CRISIS ON INFINITE EARTHS 30TH ANNIVERSARY DELUXE EDITION	WOLFMAN, MARV | PEREZ, GEORGE	$49.99/$58.00 | HC
14.	9781401274597 MAY180572	CRISIS ON INFINITE EARTHS COMPANION DELUXE EDITION VOL. 1	WOLFMAN, MARV | VARIOUS	$75.00/$99.00 | HC
15.	9781401289218	CRISIS ON INFINITE EARTHS COMPANION DELUXE EDITION VOL. 2	WOLFMAN, MARV | VARIOUS	$75.00/$99.00 | HC
16.	9781401276850 JUL170483	JUSTICE LEAGUE: THE DETROIT ERA OMNIBUS	CONWAY, GERRY | VARIOUS	$125.00/$163.00 | HC
17.	9781401273866 APR170428	JUSTICE LEAGUE INTERNATIONAL OMNIBUS VOL. 1	GIFFEN, KEITH; DEMATTEIS, J.M. | MAGUIRE, KEVIN	$99.99/$130.99 | HC
18.	9781401278519 FEB180317	ZERO HOUR: A CRISIS IN TIME	JURGENS, DAN | JURGENS, DAN	$24.99/$33.99 | HC
19.	9781401277963 DEC170396	JUSTICE LEAGUE TASK FORCE VOL. 1: PURIFICATION PLAGUE	MICHELINIE, DAVID | VELLUTO, SAL	$29.99/$39.99 | TP
20.	9781401274320 JUL170480	JLA: A MIDSUMMER'S NIGHTMARE DELUXE EDITION	WAID, MARK | VARIOUS	$24.99/$33.99 | HC
21.	9781401288655	JLA: NEW WORLD ORDER (DC ESSENTIAL EDITION)	MORRISON, GRANT | PORTER, HOWARD	$29.99/$39.99 | TP
22.	9781401233143 JUN110276	JLA VOL. 1	MORRISON, GRANT | PORTER, HOWARD	$19.99 /$23.99 | TP
23.	9781401235185 APR120256	JLA VOL. 2	MORRISON, GRANT | PORTER, HOWARD	$24.99 /$28.99 | TP
24.	9781401238322 OCT120267	JLA VOL. 3	MORRISON, GRANT | PORTER, HOWARD	$24.99 /$28.99 | TP
25.	9781401243852 NOV130242	JLA VOL. 4	MORRISON, GRANT; WAID, MARK | PORTER, HOWARD; PAJARILLO, MARK	$24.99 /$28.99 | TP
26.	9781401247508 MAR140266	JLA VOL. 5	WAID, MARK | HITCH, BRYAN	$24.99 /$28.99 | TP
27.	9781401251369 OCT140369	JLA VOL. 6	KELLY, JOE | MAHNKE, DOUG	$24.99 /$28.99 | TP
28.	9781401255282 FEB150260	JLA VOL. 7	KELLY, JOE | MAHNKE, DOUG	$24.99 /$28.99 | TP
29.	9781401263423 FEB160234	JLA VOL. 8	KELLY, JOE | MAHNKE, DOUG	$24.99 /$29.99 | TP
30.	9781401265670 SEP160345	JLA VOL. 9	KELLY, JOE | VARIOUS	$19.99 /$25.99 | TP
31.	9781401204587 AUG118125	IDENTITY CRISIS	MELTZER, BRAD | MORALES, RAGS	$17.99 /$20.99 | TP
32.	9781401210601 FEB118149	INFINITE CRISIS	JOHNS, GEOFF | JIMENEZ, PHIL	$17.99 /$20.99 | TP
33.	9781401263256 JUL160394	ABSOLUTE INFINITE CRISIS	JOHNS, GEOFF | JIMENEZ, PHIL; ORDWAY, JERRY; PEREZ, GEORGE	$99.99/$130.99 | HC
34.	9781401263256 MAR160270	52 BOOK 1	MORRISON, GRANT; JOHNS, GEOFF; RUCKA, GREG; WAID, MARK | GIFFEN, KEITH	$29.99/$35.00 | TP
35.	9781401265649 SEP160340	52 BOOK 2	MORRISON, GRANT; JOHNS, GEOFF; WAID, MARK; RUCKA, GREG | GIFFEN, KEITH	$29.99/$39.99 | TP
36.	9781401235567 JUL120217	52 OMNIBUS	JOHNS, GEOFF; MORRISON, GRANT; WAID, MARK; RUCKA, GREG | GIFFEN, KEITH	$150.00 /$176.00 | HC
37.	9781401215804 JUN080244	JUSTICE LEAGUE OF AMERICA: THE TORNADO'S PATH, VOL. 1	MELTZER, BRAD | BENES, ED	$17.99 /$21.99 | TP
38.	9781401245177 JAN140352	FINAL CRISIS	MORRISON, GRANT | JONES, J.G.; MAHNKE, DOUG; PACHECO, CARLOS	$19.99 /$23.99 | TP
39.	9781401290955	FINAL CRISIS (DC ESSENTIAL EDITION)	MORRISON, GRANT | JONES, J.G.; MAHNKE, DOUG	$24.99 /$33.99 | TP
40.	9781401285036 MAR180342	FINAL CRISIS 10TH ANNIVERSARY OMNIBUS	MORRISON, GRANT; JOHNS, GEOFF | PEREZ, GEORGE; MAHNKE, DOUG	$150.00/$195.00 | HC
41.	9781401229535 APR110192	BLACKEST NIGHT	JOHNS, GEOFF | REIS, IVAN	$19.99 /$23.99 | TP
42.	9781401233389 OCT138324	FLASHPOINT	JOHNS, GEOFF | KUBERT, ANDY	$16.99 /$17.99 | TP
43.	9781401286262 APR180259	ABSOLUTE FLASHPOINT	JOHNS, GEOFF | KUBERT, ANDY	$75.00/$99.99 | HC
44.	9781401277673 NOV170368	FLASHPOINT UNWRAPPED	JOHNS, GEOFF | KUBERT, ANDY	$29.99/$39.99 | HC
45.	9781401287917	ELSEWORLDS: JUSTICE LEAGUE VOL. 3	VARIOUS | VARIOUS	$34.99/$45.99 | TP
46.	9781401237882 OCT120252	JUSTICE LEAGUE VOL. 1: ORIGIN	JOHNS, GEOFF | LEE, JIM	$16.99 /$19.99 | TP
47.	9781401274375 MAY170343	ABSOLUTE JUSTICE LEAGUE: ORIGIN	JOHNS, GEOFF | LEE, JIM	$99.99/$130.99 | HC
48.	9781401268503 JAN170394	JUSTICE LEAGUE UNWRAPPED BY JIM LEE	LEE, JIM | LEE, JIM	$34.99/$45.99 | TP
49.	9781401237653 JUN130261	JUSTICE LEAGUE VOL. 2: THE VILLAIN'S JOURNEY	JOHNS, GEOFF | LEE, JIM	$16.99 /$19.99 | TP
50.	9781401246983 JAN140339	JUSTICE LEAGUE VOL. 3: THRONE OF ATLANTIS	JOHNS, GEOFF | REIS, IVAN; DANIEL, TONY S.	$16.99/$19.99 | TP
51.	9781401250089 JUN140272	JUSTICE LEAGUE VOL. 4: THE GRID	JOHNS, GEOFF | REIS, IVAN	$16.99/$19.99 | TP
52.	9781401249441 AUG140331	JUSTICE LEAGUE: TRINITY WAR	JOHNS, GEOFF; LEMIRE, JEFF | REIS, IVAN; MAHNKE, DOUG	$19.99/$23.99 | TP
53.	9781401253387 FEB150254	FOREVER EVIL	JOHNS, GEOFF | FINCH, DAVID	$19.99/$23.99 | TP
54.	9781401254193 DEC140382	JUSTICE LEAGUE VOL. 5: FOREVER HEROES	JOHNS, GEOFF | REIS, IVAN; MAHNKE, DOUG	$14.99/$17.99 | TP
55.	9781401249397 JUN140268	FOREVER EVIL: A.R.G.U.S.	GATES, STERLING | TAN, PHILIP	$14.99/$17.99 | TP
56.	9781401249403 JUN140267	FOREVER EVIL: ARKHAM WAR	TOMASI, PETER | EATON, SCOTT	$16.99/$19.99 | TP
57.	9781401250065 JUN140269	FOREVER EVIL: BLIGHT	FAWKES, RAY; DEMATTEIS, J.M. | JANIN, MIKEL	$24.99/$28.99 | TP
58.	9781401249410 JUN140270	FOREVER EVIL: ROGUES REBELLION	BUCCELLATO, BRIAN | HEPBURN, SCOTT; ZIRCHER, PATRICK	$16.99/$19.99 | TP
59.	9781401258528 DEC150328	JUSTICE LEAGUE VOL. 6: INJUSTICE LEAGUE	JOHNS, GEOFF | MAHNKE, DOUG; FABOK, JASON	$19.99/$23.99 | TP
60.	9781401264871 JUL160401	CONVERGENCE	KING, JEFF | PAGULAYAN, CARLO	$24.99/$29.99 | TP
61.	9781401258085 JUL150295	CONVERGENCE: CRISIS BOOK ONE	WOLFMAN, MARV; PARKER, JEFF | TRUMAN, TIM	$19.99/$23.99 | TP
62.	9781401258344 JUL150297	CONVERGENCE: CRISIS BOOK TWO	WEIN, LEN | JONES, KELLEY	$19.99/$23.99 | TP
63.	9781401258351 JUL150298	CONVERGENCE: FLASHPOINT BOOK ONE	RUCKA, GREG | WEEKS, LEE; HAMNER, CULLY	$19.99/$23.99 | TP
64.	9781401258368 JUL150300	CONVERGENCE: FLASHPOINT BOOK TWO	KWITNEY, ALISA | YEOWELL, STEVE; WINSLADE, PHIL	$19.99/$23.99 | TP
65.	9781401258375 JUL150299	CONVERGENCE: INFINITE EARTHS BOOK ONE	LEVITZ, PAUL | ORDWAY, JERRY; CALDWELL, BEN	$19.99/$23.99 | TP
66.	9781401258382 JUL150301	CONVERGENCE: INFINITE EARTHS BOOK TWO	JURGENS, DAN; PARKER, JEFF | SHANER, EVAN	$19.99/$23.99 | TP
67.	9781401258399 JUL150294	CONVERGENCE: ZERO HOUR BOOK ONE	MARZ, RON | MORALES, RAGS	$19.99/$23.99 | TP
68.	9781401258405 JUL150294	CONVERGENCE: ZERO HOUR BOOK TWO	GIFFEN, KEITH; BEDARD, TONY | RICHARDS, CLIFF	$19.99/$23.99 | TP
69.	9781401264529 JUN160346	JUSTICE LEAGUE VOL. 7: DARKSEID WAR PART 1	JOHNS, GEOFF | FABOK, JASON	$16.99/$22.99 | TP

DC COMICS READING ORDER

	ISBN	DIAMOND CODE	TITLE	AUTHOR	ARTIST	US$/$CAN	FORMAT
70.	9781401265397	SEP160347	JUSTICE LEAGUE VOL. 8: DARKSEID WAR PART 2	JOHNS, GEOFF	FABOK, JASON; MANPUL, FRANCIS	$16.99/$22.99	TP
71.	9781401265243	AUG160331	JUSTICE LEAGUE: DARKSEID WAR - GODS AND MEN	MANAPUL, FRANCIS	MANAPUL, FRANCIS; KOLINS, SCOTT	$16.99/$22.99	TP
72.	9781401284558	JUL180763	JUSTICE LEAGUE: THE DARKSEID WAR (DC ESSENTIAL EDITION)	JOHNS, GEOFF	FABOK, JASON; MANPUL, FRANCIS	$29.99/$39.99	TP
73.	9781401276126	APR170429	JUSTICE LEAGUE BY GEOFF JOHNS BOX SET VOL. 1	JOHNS, GEOFF	LEE, JIM; REIS, IVAN	$49.99/$65.99	BOXED
74.	9781401270728	AUG160316	DC UNIVERSE: REBIRTH DELUXE EDITION	JOHNS, GEOFF	FRANK, GARY; REIS, IVAN; VAN SCIVER, ETHAN; JIMENEZ, PHIL	$17.99/$23.99	HC
75.	9781401267421	JUL160392	DC REBIRTH OMNIBUS	JOHNS, GEOFF; RUCKA, GREG; KING, TOM; TOMASI, PETER J.	VARIOUS	$75.00/$99.00	HC
76.	9781401276454	APR170411	DC REBIRTH OMNIBUS EXPANDED EDITION	VARIOUS	VARIOUS	$99.99/$130.99	HC
77.	9781401267797	OCT160295	JUSTICE LEAGUE VOL. 1: THE EXTINCTION MACHINE (REBIRTH)	HITCH, BRYAN	DANIEL, TONY S.	$16.99/$19.99	TP
78.	9781401268701	JAN170380	JUSTICE LEAGUE VOL. 2: OUTBREAK (REBIRTH)	HITCH, BRYAN	EDWARDS, NEIL	$16.99/$19.99	TP
79.	9781401271121	APR170415	JUSTICE LEAGUE VOL. 3: TIMELESS (REBIRTH)	HITCH, BRYAN	DANIEL, TONY S.	$16.99/$22.99	TP
80.	9781401273972	AUG170324	JUSTICE LEAGUE VOL. 4: ENDLESS (REBIRTH)	HITCH, BRYAN	VARIOUS	$16.99/$22.99	TP
81.	9781401277253	NOV170352	JUSTICE LEAGUE VOL. 5: LEGACY (REBIRTH)	HITCH, BRYAN	PASARIN, FERNANDO	$16.99/$22.99	TP
82.	9781401280765	MAR180349	JUSTICE LEAGUE VOL. 6: THE PEOPLE VS. THE JUSTICE LEAGUE	PRIEST, CHRISTOPHER	WOODS, PETE	$14.99/$19.99	TP
83.	9781401284251	JUN180582	JUSTICE LEAGUE VOL. 7: JUSTICE LOST	PRIEST, CHRISTOPHER	WOODS, PETE	$14.99/$19.99	TP
84.	9781401274788	SEP170405	JUSTICE LEAGUE VS. SUICIDE SQUAD	WILLIAMSON, JOSHUA	FABOK, JASON	$24.99/$33.99	TP
85.	9781401278281	JAN180386	JUSTICE LEAGUE: THE REBIRTH DELUXE EDITION BOOK 2	HITCH, BRYAN	PASARIN, FERNANDO; HENRIQUES, DANIEL	$34.99/$45.99	HC
86.	9781401284367		JUSTICE LEAGUE: THE REBIRTH DELUXE EDITION BOOK 3	HITCH, BRYAN	PASARIN, FERNANDO	$34.99/$45.99	HC
87.	9781401288761		JUSTICE LEAGUE: THE REBIRTH DELUXE EDITION BOOK 4	PRIEST, CHRISTOPHER	WOODS, PETE	$34.99/$45.99	HC
88.	9781401287627	JUN188675	DARK DAYS: THE ROAD TO METAL	SNYDER, SCOTT	LEE, JIM; KUBERT, ANDY; ROMITA JR., JOHN	$19.99/$25.99	TP
89.	9781401288587	JUN188676	DARK NIGHTS: METAL	SNYDER, SCOTT	CAPULLO, GREG	$19.99/$25.99	TP
90.	9781401289072	JUN188677	DARK NIGHTS: METAL: DARK KNIGHTS RISING	MORRISON, GRANT; SNYDER, SCOTT; TOMASI, PETER J.	MANAPUL, FRANCIS	$24.99/$33.99	TP
91.	9781401282981	JAN180381	DARK NIGHTS: METAL: THE RESISTANCE	WILLIAMSON, JOSHUA; LEMIRE, JEFF	VAN SCIVER, ETHAN; SHARP, LIAM.	$24.99/$33.99	TP
92.	9781401283346	JUN180583	JUSTICE LEAGUE: NO JUSTICE	SNYDER, SCOTT; WILLIAMSON, JOSHUA; TYNION IV, JAMES	MANAPUL, FRANCIS	$16.99/$22.99	TP
93.	9781401284992	AUG180630	JUSTICE LEAGUE VOL. 1	SNYDER, SCOTT; TYNION IV, JAMES	CHEUNG, JIM; JIMENEZ, JORGE	$16.99/$22.99	TP
94.	9781401288495		JUSTICE LEAGUE VOL. 2	SNYDER, SCOTT; TYNION IV, JAMES	CHEUNG, JIM; JIMENEZ, JORGE	$16.99/$22.99	TP

JUSTICE LEAGUE

	ISBN	DIAMOND CODE	TITLE	AUTHOR	ARTIST	US$/$CAN	FORMAT
1.	9781401246891	APR140266	JUSTICE LEAGUE OF AMERICA VOL. 1: WORLD'S MOST DANGEROUS	JOHNS, GEOFF	FINCH, DAVID; MAHNKE, DOUG	$16.99/$19.99	TP
2.	9781401278007	DEC170395	JUSTICE LEAGUE OF AMERICA: POWER AND GLORY	HITCH, BRYAN	HITCH, BRYAN	$19.99/$25.99	TP
3.	9781401257651	SEP150300	JUSTICE LEAGUE UNITED VOL. 1: JUSTICE LEAGUE CANADA	LEMIRE, JEFF	MCKONE, MIKE	$16.99/$19.99	TP
4.	9781401270353	JUL160418	JUSTICE LEAGUE UNITED VOL. 2: THE INFINITUS SAGA	LEMIRE, JEFF	EDWARDS, NEIL	$14.99/$17.99	TP
5.	9781401237042	JUL120211	JUSTICE LEAGUE DARK VOL. 1: IN THE DARK	MILLIGAN, PETER	JANIN, MIKEL	$14.99/$19.99	TP
6.	9781401240240	APR130217	JUSTICE LEAGUE DARK VOL. 2: THE BOOKS OF MAGIC	LEMIRE, JEFF	JANIN, MIKEL	$16.99/$19.99	TP
7.	9781401242459	OCT130241	JUSTICE LEAGUE DARK VOL. 3: THE DEATH OF MAGIC	LEMIRE, JEFF	JANIN, MIKEL	$16.99/$19.99	TP
8.	9781401247256	MAY140365	JUSTICE LEAGUE DARK VOL. 4: THE REBIRTH OF EVIL	LEMIRE, JEFF	JANIN, MIKEL	$16.99/$19.99	TP
9.	9781401250072	NOV140299	JUSTICE LEAGUE DARK VOL. 5: PARADISE LOST	DEMATTEIS, J.M.	JANIN, MIKEL	$14.99/$19.99	TP
10.	9781401254810	MAY150242	JUSTICE LEAGUE DARK VOL. 6: LOST IN FOREVER	DEMATTEIS, J.M.	GUINALDO, ANDRES	$16.99/$19.99	TP
11.	9781401288112	JUN188686	JUSTICE LEAGUE DARK VOL. 1	TYNION IV, JAMES	MARTINEZ, ALVARO	$16.99/$22.99	TP
12.	9781401289492	JUN188687	JUSTICE LEAGUE ODYSSEY VOL. 1	WILLIAMSON, JOSHUA	SEJIC, STJEPAN	$16.99/$22.99	TP
13.	9781401250461	JUL140244	JUSTICE LEAGUE 3000 VOL. 1: YESTERDAY LIVES	GIFFEN, KEITH; DEMATTEIS, J.M.	PORTER, HOWARD	$16.99/$19.99	TP
14.	9781401254148	JAN150372	JUSTICE LEAGUE 3000 VOL. 2: THE CAMELOT WAR	GIFFEN, KEITH; DEMATTEIS, J.M.	PORTER, HOWARD	$14.99/$19.99	TP
15.	9781401261481	DEC150334	JUSTICE LEAGUE 3001 VOL. 1: DÉJÀ VU ALL OVER AGAIN	GIFFEN, KEITH; DEMATTEIS, J.M.	PORTER, HOWARD	$16.99/$19.99	TP
16.	9781401264727	JUN160345	JUSTICE LEAGUE 3001 VOL. 2: THINGS FALL APART	GIFFEN, KEITH	BATISTA, CHRIS; KOLINS, SCOTT; DORAN, COLLEEN	$14.99/$17.99	TP
17.	9781401273521	MAR170413	JUSTICE LEAGUE OF AMERICA: THE ROAD TO REBIRTH (REBIRTH)	ORLANDO, STEVE	REIS, IVAN	$14.99/$19.99	TP
18.	9781401273538	MAY170326	JUSTICE LEAGUE OF AMERICA VOL. 1: THE EXTREMISTS (REBIRTH)	ORLANDO, STEVE	REIS, IVAN	$16.99/$22.99	TP
19.	9781401274498	AUG170322	JUSTICE LEAGUE OF AMERICA VOL. 2: CURSE OF THE KINGBUTCHER (REBIRTH)	ORLANDO, STEVE	REIS, IVAN	$14.99/$19.99	TP
20.	9781401277840	DEC170380	JUSTICE LEAGUE OF AMERICA VOL. 3: PANIC IN THE MICROVERSE (REBIRTH)	ORLANDO, STEVE	REIS, IVAN	$16.99/$22.99	TP
21.	9781401280581	APR180272	JUSTICE LEAGUE OF AMERICA VOL. 4: SURGICAL STRIKE	ORLANDO, STEVE	REIS, IVAN	$14.99/$19.99	TP
22.	9781401284497	JUN180581	JUSTICE LEAGUE OF AMERICA VOL. 5: DEADLY FABLE	ORLANDO, STEVE	PETRUS, HUGO	$19.99/$25.99	TP
23.	9781401276928	AUG170323	JUSTICE LEAGUE OF AMERICA: THE REBIRTH DELUXE EDITION BOOK 1	ORLANDO, STEVE	REIS, IVAN	$34.99/$45.99	HC

JUSTICE LEAGUE: FROM PAGE TO SCREEN

	ISBN	DIAMOND CODE	TITLE	AUTHOR	ARTIST	US$/$CAN	FORMAT
1.	9781401267865	NOV160331	JUSTICE LEAGUE: GODS AND MONSTERS	DEMATTEIS, J.M.	SILAS, THONY	$16.99/$22.99	TP
2.	9781401248437	MAR140265	INJUSTICE: GODS AMONG US VOL. 1	TAYLOR, TOM	RAAPACK, JHEREMY	$16.99/$19.99	TP
3.	9781401250454	OCT140368	INJUSTICE: GODS AMONG US VOL. 2	TAYLOR, TOM	MILLER, MIKE S.; DERENICK, TOM	$16.99/$19.99	TP
4.	9781401260811	DEC150338	INJUSTICE: GODS AMONG US YEAR ONE: THE COMPLETE EDITION	TAYLOR, TOM	VARIOUS	$24.99/$29.99	TP
5.	9781401284343	JUN180580	INJUSTICE: GODS AMONG US: YEAR ONE: THE DELUXE EDITION	TAYLOR, TOM	MILLER, MIKE S.; REDONDO, BRUNO	$49.99/$65.99	HC
6.	9781401253400	JAN150372	INJUSTICE: GODS AMONG US: YEAR TWO VOL. 1	TAYLOR, TOM	REDONDO, BRUNO	$14.99/$19.99	TP
7.	9781401258504	JUL150315	INJUSTICE: GODS AMONG US: YEAR TWO VOL. 2	TAYLOR, TOM	REDONDO, BRUNO	$16.99/$19.99	TP
8.	9781401265601	OCT160308	INJUSTICE: GODS AMONG US YEAR TWO: THE COMPLETE EDITION	TAYLOR, TOM	REDONDO, BRUNO	$24.99/$33.99	TP
9.	9781401263140	AUG150266	INJUSTICE: GODS AMONG US: YEAR THREE VOL. 1	TAYLOR, TOM	REDONDO, BRUNO	$14.99/$19.99	TP
10.	9781401261290	JAN160330	INJUSTICE: GODS AMONG US: YEAR THREE VOL. 2	BUCCELLATO, BRIAN	REDONDO, BRUNO	$16.99/$19.99	TP
11.	9781401275242	OCT170370	INJUSTICE: GODS AMONG US YEAR THREE - THE COMPLETE COLLECTION	TAYLOR, TOM	REDONDO, BRUNO	$24.99/$33.99	TP

	ISBN	DIAMOND CODE	TITLE	AUTHOR	ARTIST	US$/$CAN	FORMAT
12.	9781401262679	APR160397	INJUSTICE: GODS AMONG US: YEAR FOUR VOL. 1	BUCCELLATO, BRIAN | REDONDO, BRUNO	$14.99/$17.99 | TP
13.	9781401267377	MAY160315	INJUSTICE: GODS AMONG US: YEAR FOUR VOL. 2	BUCCELLATO, BRIAN | REDONDO, BRUNO	$14.99/$19.99 | TP
14.	9781401285807		INJUSTICE: GODS AMONG US YEAR FOUR - THE COMPLETE COLLECTION	BUCCELLATO, BRIAN | REDONDO, BRUNO	$29.99/$39.99 | TP
15.	9781401268831	AUG160330	INJUSTICE: GODS AMONG US: YEAR FIVE VOL. 1	BUCCELLATO, BRIAN | REDONDO, BRUNO	$16.99/$22.99 | TP
16.	9781401272470	MAR170426	INJUSTICE: GODS AMONG US: YEAR FIVE VOL. 2	BUCCELLATO, BRIAN | REDONDO, BRUNO	$16.99/$22.99 | TP
17.	9781401274269	JUL170479	INJUSTICE: GODS AMONG US: YEAR FIVE VOL. 3	BUCCELLATO, BRIAN | REDONDO, BRUNO	$16.99/$22.99 | TP
18.	9781401273873	SEP170415	INJUSTICE: GROUND ZERO VOL. 1	SEBELA, CHRIS | VARIOUS	$16.99/$22.99 | TP
19.	9781401277871	FEB180303	INJUSTICE: GROUND ZERO VOL. 2	SEBELA, CHRIS | VARIOUS	$16.99/$22.99 | TP
20.	9781401278403	JAN180404	INJUSTICE 2 VOL. 1	TAYLOR, TOM | REDONDO, BRUNO	$16.99/$22.99 | TP
21.	9781401281342	MAY180583	INJUSTICE 2 VOL. 2	TAYLOR, TOM | REDONDO, BRUNO	$16.99/$22.99 | TP
22.	9781401285326	MAY180584	INJUSTICE 2 VOL. 3	TAYLOR, TOM | REDONDO, BRUNO; MILLER, MIKE S.	$16.99/$22.99 | TP
23.	9781401289157		INJUSTICE 2 VOL. 4	TAYLOR, TOM | REDONDO, BRUNO	$16.99/$22.99 | TP
24.	9781401289164		INJUSTICE 2 VOL. 5	TAYLOR, TOM | REDONDO, BRUNO	$24.99/$33.99 | HC
25.	9781401288372		INJUSTICE VS. MASTERS OF THE UNIVERSE	SEELEY, TIM | WILLIAMS III, FREDDIE	$24.99/$33.99 | HC

JUSTICE LEAGUE GRAPHIC NOVELS

	ISBN	DIAMOND CODE	TITLE	AUTHOR	ARTIST	US$/$CAN	FORMAT
1.	9781401263782	MAR160267	DC: THE NEW FRONTIER	COOKE, DARWYN | COOKE, DARWYN	$34.99/$41.99 | TP
2.	9781401270094	AUG160325	DC COMICS/DARK HORSE COMICS: JUSTICE LEAGUE VOL. 1	VARIOUS | VARIOUS	$24.99/$33.99 | TP
3.	9781401263775	APR160395	ELSEWORLDS: JUSTICE LEAGUE VOL. 1	VARIOUS | VARIOUS	$34.99/$41.99 | TP
4.	9781401268558	APR170423	ELSEWORLDS: JUSTICE LEAGUE VOL. 2	VARIOUS | VARIOUS	$34.99/$45.99 | TP
5.	9781401269050	JUL170481	JUSTICE LEAGUE OF AMERICA: THE NAIL: THE COMPLETE DELUXE EDITION	DAVIS, ALAN | DAVIS, ALAN	$39.99/$53.99 | HC
6.	9781401235260	MAR120254	JUSTICE	ROSS, ALEX | ROSS, ALEX	$29.99/$35.00 | TP
7.	9781401273705	MAR170415	ABSOLUTE JUSTICE LEAGUE: THE WORLD'S GREATEST SUPERHEROES BY ALEX ROSS & PAUL DINI (NEW EDITION)	DINI, PAUL | ROSS, ALEX	$75.00/$99.00 | HC
8.	9781401285548		JUSTICE LEAGUE: THE WORLD'S GREATEST SUPERHEROES BY ALEX ROSS & PAUL DINI	DINI, PAUL | ROSS, ALEX	$29.99/$39.99 | TP
9.	9781401273514	JUL170482	JUSTICE LEAGUE: THEIR GREATEST TRIUMPHS	JOHNS, GEOFF | LEE, JIM	$9.99/$13.50 | TP
10.	9781401220341	SEP138294	KINGDOM COME	WAID, MARK | ROSS, ALEX	$19.99/$19.99 | TP
11.	9781401290962		KINGDOM COME (DC BLACK LABEL EDITION)	WAID, MARK | ROSS, ALEX	$19.99 /$25.99 | TP
12.	9781401260828	JAN160321	KINGDOM COME 20TH ANNIVERSARY DELUXE EDITION	WAID, MARK | ROSS, ALEX	$39.99/$48.99 | HC
13.	9781401284626	FEB180293	ABSOLUTE KINGDOM COME (NEW EDITION)	WAID, MARK | ROSS, ALEX	$99.99/$130.99 | HC
14.	9781401285159	SEP170418	JUSTICE LEAGUE/POWER RANGERS	TAYLOR, TOM | BYRNE, STEPHEN	$16.99/$22.99 | TP

GREEN LANTERN BACKLIST AND SUGGESTED READING ORDER

	ISBN	DIAMOND CODE	TITLE	AUTHOR	ARTIST	US$/$CAN	FORMAT
1.	9781401263485	JUL160410	GREEN LANTERN: THE SILVER AGE VOL. 1	VARIOUS | VARIOUS	$19.99/$23.99 | TP
2.	9781401271077	AUG170336	GREEN LANTERN: THE SILVER AGE VOL. 2	BROOME, JOHN | KANE, GIL	$29.99/$39.99 | TP
3.	9781401278472	JAN180402	GREEN LANTERN: THE SILVER AGE VOL. 3	VARIOUS | VARIOUS	$29.99/$39.99 | TP
4.	9781401268572	OCT160303	GREEN LANTERN: THE SILVER AGE OMNIBUS VOL. 1	VARIOUS | VARIOUS	$100.00/$131.00 | HC
5.	9781401278021	SEP170414	GREEN LANTERN: THE SILVER AGE OMNIBUS VOL. 2	VARIOUS | VARIOUS	$125.00/$163.00 | HC
6.	9781401280420	MAR180345	GREEN LANTERN/GREEN ARROW: HARD TRAVELIN' HEROES DELUXE EDITION	O'NEIL, DENNY | ADAMS, NEAL	$49.99/$65.99 | HC
7.	9781401265755	OCT160306	GREEN LANTERN: HAL JORDAN BOOK ONE	MARZ, RON | VARIOUS	$19.99/$25.99 | TP
8.	9781401276874	JUL170476	GREEN LANTERN: KYLE RAYNER VOL. 1	MARZ, RON | BANKS, DARRYL	$29.99/$39.99 | TP
9.	9781401278502	FEB180302	GREEN LANTERN: KYLE RAYNER VOL. 2	MARZ, RON | BANKS, DARRYL	$29.99/$39.99 | TP
10.	9781401285715		GREEN LANTERN: KYLE RAYNER VOL. 3	MARZ, RON | BANKS, DARRYL	$24.99/$33.99 | TP
11.	9781401227555	FEB100185	GREEN LANTERN: REBIRTH	JOHNS, GEOFF | VAN SCIVER, ETHAN	$14.99/$17.99 | TP
12.	9781401288280		GREEN LANTERN BY GEOFF JOHNS BOOK ONE	JOHNS, GEOFF | REIS, IVAN; VAN SCIVER, ETHAN	$24.99/$33.99 | TP
13.	9781401233013	JUN110275	GREEN LANTERN: THE SINESTRO CORPS WAR	JOHNS, GEOFF | REIS, IVAN	$29.99/$35.00 | TP
14.	9781401230869	JAN110337	GREEN LANTERN: SECRET ORIGIN	JOHNS, GEOFF | REIS, IVAN	$14.99/$17.99 | TP
15.	9781401224202	AUG100204	GREEN LANTERN: AGENT ORANGE	JOHNS, GEOFF | TAN, PHILIP	$14.99/$17.99 | TP
16.	9781401229535	APR110192	BLACKEST NIGHT	JOHNS, GEOFF | REIS, IVAN	$19.99 /$23.99 | TP
17.	9781401229528	APR110193	BLACKEST NIGHT: GREEN LANTERN	JOHNS, GEOFF | MAHNKE, DOUG	$19.99 /$23.99 | TP
18.	9781401290917		GREEN LANTERN: BLACKEST NIGHT: THE COMPLETE COLLECTION (DC ESSENTIAL EDITION)	JOHNS, GEOFF | REIS, IVAN; MAHNKE, DOUG	$29.99/$39.99 | TP
19.	9781401232764	SEP110177	BRIGHTEST DAY VOL. 1	JOHNS, GEOFF | REIS, IVAN	$19.99 /$23.99 | TP
20.	9781401232177	JUN120244	BRIGHTEST DAY VOL. 3	JOHNS, GEOFF | REIS, IVAN	$16.99 /$19.99 | TP
21.	9781401231415	FEB120254	GREEN LANTERN: BRIGHTEST DAY	JOHNS, GEOFF | MAHNKE, DOUG	$19.99 /$23.99 | TP
22.	9781401245979	APR140272	BRIGHTEST DAY OMNIBUS	JOHNS, GEOFF; TOMASI, PETER J. | VARIOUS	$75.00/$85.00 | TP
23.	9781401234065	DEC110280	FLASHPOINT: THE WORLD OF FLASHPOINT FEATURING GREEN LANTERN	VARIOUS | VARIOUS	$17.99/$20.99 | TP
24.	9781401234553	OCT120257	GREEN LANTERN VOL. 1: SINESTRO	JOHNS, GEOFF | MAHNKE, DOUG	$14.99/$17.99 | TP
25.	9781401237677	JUL130229	GREEN LANTERN VOL. 2: THE REVENGE OF BLACK HAND	JOHNS, GEOFF | MAHNKE, DOUG; VAN SCIVER, ETHAN	$16.99/$19.99 | TP
26.	9781401246846	JAN140338	GREEN LANTERN VOL. 3: THE END	JOHNS, GEOFF | MAHNKE, DOUG	$19.99/$23.99 | TP
27.	9781401246136	DEC130302	GREEN LANTERN: RISE OF THE THIRD ARMY	JOHNS, GEOFF; TOMASI, PETER J. | VARIOUS	$24.99/$28.99 | TP
28.	9781401246938	MAY140373	GREEN LANTERN: WRATH OF THE FIRST LANTERN	JOHNS, GEOFF; TOMASI, PETER J. | VARIOUS	$19.99/$23.99 | TP
29.	9781401251345	SEP140319	GREEN LANTERN BY GEOFF JOHNS OMNIBUS VOL. 1	JOHNS, GEOFF | REIS, IVAN; VAN SCIVER, ETHAN	$125.00/$144.00 | HC
30.	9781401255268	MAR150274	GREEN LANTERN BY GEOFF JOHNS OMNIBUS VOL. 2	JOHNS, GEOFF | REIS, IVAN; MAHNKE, DOUG	$99.99/$112.00 | HC
31.	9781401258207	NOV150285	GREEN LANTERN BY GEOFF JOHNS OMNIBUS VOL. 3	JOHNS, GEOFF | MAHNKE, DOUG	$99.99/$112.00 | HC

ISBN | DIAMOND CODE		TITLE	AUTHOR | ARTIST	US$/SCAN | FORMAT
32.	9781401249427 JUL140243	GREEN LANTERN VOL. 4: DARK DAYS	VENDITTI, ROBERT | TAN, BILLY	$16.99/$19.99 | TP
33.	9781401249434 SEP140306	GREEN LANTERN: LIGHTS OUT	VENDITTI, ROBERT; JORDAN, JUSTIN; JENSEN, VAN; CHARLES SOULE | TAN, BILLY	$16.99/$19.99 | TP
34.	9781401254162 FEB150255	GREEN LANTERN VOL. 5: TEST OF WILLS	VENDITTI, ROBERT | TAN, BILLY	$17.99/$20.99 | TP
35.	9781401258467 JAN160317	GREEN LANTERN VOL. 6: THE LIFE EQUATION	VENDITTI, ROBERT | TAN, BILLY; PORTELA, FRANCIS	$16.99/$19.99 | TP
36.	9781401261276 FEB160233	GREEN LANTERN/NEW GODS: GODHEAD	VENDITTI, ROBERT; JENSEN, VAN | TAN, BILLY	$24.99/$29.99 | TP
37.	9781401265229 JUN160341	GREEN LANTERN VOL. 7: RENEGADE	VENDITTI, ROBERT | TAN, BILLY	$16.99/$22.99 | TP
38.	9781401272494 NOV160335	GREEN LANTERN VOL. 8: REFLECTIONS	VENDITTI, ROBERT | TAN, BILLY	$24.99/$33.99 | TP
39.	9781401268008 NOV160318	HAL JORDAN & THE GREEN LANTERN CORPS VOL. 1: SINESTRO'S LAW (REBIRTH)	VENDITTI, ROBERT | SANDOVAL, RAFA; VAN SCIVER, ETHAN	$16.99/$19.99 | TP
40.	9781401269135 FEB170295	HAL JORDAN & THE GREEN LANTERN CORPS VOL. 2: BOTTLED LIGHT (REBIRTH)	VENDITTI, ROBERT | SANDOVAL, RAFA; VAN SCIVER, ETHAN	$16.99/$19.99 | TP
41.	9781401271640 MAY170325	HAL JORDAN AND THE GREEN LANTERN CORPS VOL. 3: QUEST FOR HOPE (REBIRTH)	VENDITTI, ROBERT | SANDOVAL, RAFAEL	$19.99/$25.99 | TP
42.	9781401275198 OCT170359	HAL JORDAN AND THE GREEN LANTERN CORPS VOL. 4: FRACTURE (REBIRTH)	VENDITTI, ROBERT | VAN SCIVER, ETHAN	$19.99/$25.99 | TP
43.	9781401280376 MAR180347	HAL JORDAN AND THE GREEN LANTERN CORPS VOL. 5: TWILIGHT OF THE GUARDIANS	VENDITTI, ROB | SANDOVAL, RAFA	$16.99/$22.99 | TP
44.	9781401284442 JUN180577	HAL JORDAN AND THE GREEN LANTERN CORPS VOL. 6	VENDITTI, ROBERT | SANDOVAL, RAFA	$14.99/$19.99 | TP
45.	9781401285647	HAL JORDAN AND THE GREEN LANTERN CORPS VOL. 7	VENDITTI, ROBERT | SANDOVAL, RAFA	$14.99/$19.99 | TP
46.	9781401288976	HAL JORDAN AND THE GREEN LANTERN CORPS VOL. 8	VENDITTI, ROBERT | SANDOVAL, RAFA	$16.99/$22.99 | TP
47.	9781401267759 OCT160294	GREEN LANTERNS VOL. 1: RAGE PLANET (REBIRTH)	HUMPHRIES, SAM | ROCHA, ROBSON	$16.99/$19.99 | TP
48.	9781401268497 JAN170379	GREEN LANTERNS VOL. 2: PHANTOM LANTERNS (REBIRTH)	HUMPHRIES, SAM | ROCHA, ROBSON	$16.99/$19.99 | TP
49.	9781401273712 JUN170382	GREEN LANTERNS VOL. 3: POLARITY (REBIRTH)	HUMPHRIES, SAM | PANSICA, EDUARDO; ROCHA, ROBSON	$16.99/$22.99 | TP
50.	9781401275051 SEP170404	GREEN LANTERNS VOL. 4: THE FIRST RINGS (REBIRTH)	HUMPHRIES, SAM | CLIQUET, RONAN	$14.99/$19.99 | TP
51.	9781401278793 DEC170378	GREEN LANTERNS VOL. 5: OUT OF TIME (REBIRTH)	HUMPHRIES, SAM | CLIQUET, RONAN; PANSICA, EDUARDO	$16.99/$22.99 | TP
52.	9781401280666 MAR180346	GREEN LANTERNS VOL. 6: A WORLD OF OUR OWN	SEELEY, TIM | FERREIRA, JULIO	$16.99/$22.99 | TP
53.	9781401284541	GREEN LANTERNS VOL. 7: SUPERHUMAN TRAFFICKING	SEELEY, TIM | MARION, V. KEN	$16.99/$22.99 | TP
54.	9781401285906	GREEN LANTERNS VOL. 8	SEELEY, TIM | BARBERI, CARLO	$16.99/$22.99 | TP
55.	9781401258191 MAY150241	GREEN LANTERN: A CELEBRATION OF 75 YEARS	JOHNS, GEOFF | KANE, GIL	$39.99/$48.99 | HC

LANTERN CORPS

1.	9781401277505 NOV170369	GREEN LANTERN CORPS: BEWARE THEIR POWER VOL. 1	VARIOUS | VARIOUS	$39.99/$53.99 | HC
2.	9781401265502 AUG160329	GREEN LANTERN CORPS: EDGE OF OBLIVION VOL. 1	TAYLOR, TOM | VAN SCIVER, ETHAN	$14.99/$19.99 | TP
3.	9781401288624 DEC170239	GREEN LANTERN: EARTH ONE VOL. 1	HARDMAN, GABRIEL; BECHKO, CORINNA | HARDMAN, GABRIEL	$16.99/$22.99 | TP
4.	9781401234911 MAR120243	RED LANTERNS VOL. 1: BLOOD AND RAGE	MILLIGAN, PETER | BENES, ED	$14.99 /$17.99 | TP
5.	9781401238476 DEC120329	RED LANTERNS VOL. 2: THE DEATH OF THE RED LANTERNS	MILLIGAN, PETER | SEPULVEDA, MIGUEL; BENES, ED	$16.99 /$19.99 | TP
6.	9781401244149 AUG130296	RED LANTERNS VOL. 3: THE SECOND PROPHECY	MILLIGAN, PETER | SEPULVEDA, MIGUEL	$19.99 /$23.99 | TP
7.	9781401247423 FEB140256	RED LANTERNS VOL. 4: BLOOD BROTHERS	SOULE, CHARLES | VITTI, ALESSANDRO	$16.99/$19.99 | TP
8.	9781401250904 SEP140311	RED LANTERNS VOL. 5: ATROCITIES	SOULE, CHARLES; BEDARD, TONY | VITTI, ALESSANDRO	$19.99/$23.99 | TP
9.	9781401254841 APR150297	RED LANTERNS VOL. 6: FORGED IN BLOOD	SOULE, CHARLES | CALIFORE, J.	$14.99/$17.99 | TP
10.	9781401250508 OCT140359	SINESTRO VOL. 1: THE DEMON WITHIN	BUNN, CULLEN | EAGLESHAM, DALE	$14.99/$17.99 | TP
11.	9781401254865 APR150300	SINESTRO VOL. 2: SACRIFICE	BUNN, CULLEN | EAGLESHAM, DALE	$14.99/$17.99 | TP
12.	9781401261580 NOV150286	SINESTRO VOL. 3: RISING	BUNN, CULLEN | WALKER, BRAD	$16.99/$19.99 | TP
13.	9781401264659 AUG160339	SINESTRO VOL. 4: THE FALL OF SINESTRO	BUNN, CULLEN | WALKER, BRAD; EDWARDS, NEIL	$14.99/$19.99 | TP

THE FLASH BACKLIST AND SUGGESTED READING ORDER

1.	9781401261108 MAR160261	THE FLASH: THE SILVER AGE VOL. 1	KANIGHER, ROBERT | VARIOUS	$19.99/$23.99 | TP
2.	9781401270889 JUN170401	THE FLASH: THE SILVER AGE VOL. 2	BROOME, JOHN | INFANTINO, CARMINE	$29.99/$39.99 | TP
3.	9781401278267 JAN180399	THE FLASH: THE SILVER AGE VOL. 3	VARIOUS | VARIOUS	$29.99/$39.99 | TP
4.	9781401288235	THE FLASH: THE SILVER AGE VOL. 4	VARIOUS | VARIOUS	$24.99/$33.99 | TP
5.	9781401290757 JAN180398	THE FLASH: THE SILVER AGE OMNIBUS VOL. 1	KANIGHER, ROBERT | BROOME, JOHN; INFANTINO, CARMINE	$99.99/$130.99 | HC
6.	9781401265380 AUG160326	THE FLASH: THE SILVER AGE OMNIBUS VOL. 2	BROOME, JOHN | VARIOUS	$99.99/$130.99 | HC
7.	9781401281045 JAN180398	THE FLASH: THE SILVER AGE OMNIBUS VOL. 3	VARIOUS | VARIOUS	$99.99/$130.99 | HC
8.	9781401267353 JUN160339	THE FLASH BY MARK WAID BOOK ONE	WAID, MARK | VARIOUS	$24.99/$33.99 | TP
9.	9781401268442 JAN170392	THE FLASH BY MARK WAID BOOK TWO	WAID, MARK | VARIOUS	$24.99/$33.99 | TP
10.	9781401273927 JUL170473	THE FLASH BY MARK WAID BOOK THREE	WAID, MARK | WIERIGO, MIKE	$34.99/$45.99 | TP
11.	9781401278212 JAN180397	THE FLASH BY MARK WAID BOOK FOUR	WAID, MARK | LAROCCA, SALVADOR	$34.99/$45.99 | TP
12.	9781401284602	THE FLASH BY MARK WAID BOOK FIVE	WAID, MARK | VARIOUS	$34.99/$45.99 | TP
13.	9781401261023 JAN160327	THE FLASH BY GRANT MORRISON & MARK MILLAR	MORRISON, GRANT; MILLAR, MARK | VARIOUS	$24.99/$29.99 | TP
14.	9781401258733 AUG150268	THE FLASH BY GEOFF JOHNS BOOK ONE	JOHNS, GEOFF | KOLINS, SCOTT	$24.99/$29.99 | TP
15.	9781401261016 FEB160225	THE FLASH BY GEOFF JOHNS BOOK TWO	JOHNS, GEOFF | KOLINS, SCOTT	$29.99/$35.00 | TP
16.	9781401264987 JUL160403	THE FLASH BY GEOFF JOHNS BOOK THREE	JOHNS, GEOFF | WINSLADE, PHIL	$24.99/$33.99 | TP
17.	9781401273651 AUG170334	THE FLASH BY GEOFF JOHNS BOOK FOUR	JOHNS, GEOFF | PORTER, HOWARD	$29.99/$39.99 | TP
18.	9781401281076 APR180269	THE FLASH BY GEOFF JOHNS BOOK FIVE	JOHNS, GEOFF | KOLINS, SCOTT	$24.99/$33.99 | TP
19.	9781401230012 JAN110329	THE FLASH: REBIRTH	JOHNS, GEOFF | VAN SCIVER, ETHAN	$14.99 /$17.99 | TP
20.	9781401231958 OCT110249	THE FLASH: THE DASTARDLY DEATH OF THE ROGUES	JOHNS, GEOFF | MANAPUL, FRANCIS	$14.99 /$17.99 | TP
21.	9781401234485 JUN120245	THE FLASH: ROAD TO FLASHPOINT	JOHNS, GEOFF | MANAPUL, FRANCIS	$14.99 /$17.99 | TP
22.	9781401233389 OCT138324	FLASHPOINT	JOHNS, GEOFF | KUBERT, ANDY	$16.99 /$19.99 | TP

	ISBN | DIAMOND CODE		TITLE	AUTHOR | ARTIST	US$/SCAN | FORMAT
23.	9781401277673	NOV170368	FLASHPOINT UNWRAPPED	JOHNS, GEOFF | KUBERT, ANDY	$29.99/$39.99 | HC
24.	9781401286262	APR180259	ABSOLUTE FLASHPOINT	JOHNS, GEOFF | KUBERT, ANDY	$75.00/$99.99 | HC
25.	9781401234058	DEC110277	FLASHPOINT: WORLD OF FLASHPOINT FEATURING BATMAN	VARIOUS | VARIOUS	$17.99 /$20.99 | TP
26.	9781401234065	DEC110280	FLASHPOINT: WORLD OF FLASHPOINT FEATURING GREEN LANTERN	VARIOUS | VARIOUS	$17.99 /$20.99 | TP
27.	9781401234102	DEC110279	FLASHPOINT: WORLD OF FLASHPOINT FEATURING WONDER WOMAN	VARIOUS | VARIOUS	$17.99 /$20.99 | TP
28.	9781401234089	DEC110281	FLASHPOINT: WORLD OF FLASHPOINT FEATURING THE FLASH	VARIOUS | VARIOUS	$17.99 /$20.99 | TP
29.	9781401234348	DEC110278	FLASHPOINT: WORLD OF FLASHPOINT FEATURING SUPERMAN	VARIOUS | VARIOUS	$17.99 /$20.99 | TP
30.	9781401235543	MAY130224	THE FLASH VOL. 1: MOVE FORWARD	MANAPUL, FRANCIS; BUCCELLATO, BRIAN | MANAPUL, FRANCIS	$16.99 /$19.99 | TP
31.	9781401242732	NOV130229	THE FLASH VOL. 2: ROGUES REVOLUTION	MANAPUL, FRANCIS; BUCCELLATO, BRIAN | MANAPUL, FRANCIS	$16.99 /$19.99 | TP
32.	9781401284763	JUL180755	THE FLASH: STARTING LINE (DC ESSENTIAL EDITION)	BUCCELLATO, BRIAN | MANAPUL, FRANCIS	$24.99/$33.99 | TP
33.	9781401247126	MAY140367	THE FLASH VOL. 3: GORILLA WARFARE	MANAPUL, FRANCIS; BUCCELLATO, BRIAN | MANAPUL, FRANCIS	$16.99/$19.99 | TP
34.	9781401249496	OCT140357	THE FLASH VOL. 4: REVERSE	MANAPUL, FRANCIS; BUCCELLATO, BRIAN | MANAPUL, FRANCIS	$16.99/$19.99 | TP
35.	9781401265045	MAR170422	THE FLASH BY FRANCIS MANAPUL UNWRAPPED	MANAPUL, FRANCIS; BUCCELLATO, BRIAN | MANAPUL, FRANCIS	$34.99/$45.99 | HC
36.	9781401261030	JUN160338	THE FLASH BY FRANCIS MANAPUL AND BRIAN BUCCELLATO OMNIBUS	MANAPUL, FRANCIS; BUCCELLATO, BRIAN | MANAPUL, FRANCIS	$99.99/$130.99 | HC
37.	9781401257729	JUN150293	THE FLASH VOL. 5: HISTORY LESSONS	BUCCELLATO, BRIAN | ZIRCHER, PATRICK	$14.99/$17.99 | TP
38.	9781401258740	OCT150257	THE FLASH VOL. 6: OUT OF TIME	VENDITTI, ROBERT; JENSEN, VAN | BOOTH, BRETT	$16.99/$19.99 | TP
39.	9781401263652	MAY160313	THE FLASH VOL. 7: SAVAGE WORLD	VENDITTI, ROBERT; JENSEN, VAN | BOOTH, BRETT	$16.99/$19.99 | TP
40.	9781401269265	AUG160324	THE FLASH VOL. 8: ZOOM	VENDITTI, ROBERT; JENSEN, VAN | BOOTH, BRETT	$17.99/$23.99 | TP
41.	9781401274122	MAR170421	THE FLASH VOL. 9: FULL STOP	VENDITTI, ROBERT | PELLETIER, PAUL	$16.99/$22.99 | TP
42.	9781401270728	AUG160316	DC UNIVERSE: REBIRTH DELUXE EDITION	JOHNS, GEOFF | FRANK, GARY; REIS, IVAN; VAN SCIVER, ETHAN; JIMENEZ, PHIL	$17.99/$23.99 | HC
43.	9781401267841	OCT160292	THE FLASH VOL. 1: LIGHTNING STRIKES TWICE (REBIRTH)	WILLIAMSON, JOSH | DI GIANMENICO, CARMINE; GOOGE, NEIL	$17.99/$23.99 | TP
44.	9781401268930	FEB170294	THE FLASH VOL. 2: SPEED OF DARKNESS (REBIRTH)	WILLIAMSON, JOSHUA | WATANABE, FELIPE	$16.99/$19.99 | TP
45.	9781401271572	AUG170320	THE FLASH VOL. 3: ROGUES RELOADED (REBIRTH)	WILLIAMSON, JOSHUA | DI GIANMENICO, CARMINE	$16.99/$22.99 | TP
46.	9781401274627	DEC170377	THE FLASH VOL. 4: RUNNING SCARED (REBIRTH)	WILLIAMSON, JOSHUA | GIANDOMENICO, CARMINE DI	$14.99/$19.99 | TP
47.	9781401277277	MAR180343	THE FLASH VOL. 5: NEGATIVE (REBIRTH)	WILLIAMSON, JOSHUA | GOOGE, NEIL; DUCE, CHRISTIAN	$14.99/$19.99 | TP
48.	9781401280789	MAR180343	THE FLASH VOL. 6: COLD DAY IN HELL	WILLIAMSON, JOSHUA | PORTER, HOWARD	$16.99/$22.99 | TP
49.	9781401284527	JUN180576	THE FLASH VOL. 7: PERFECT STORM	WILLIAMSON, JOSHUA | DI GIANDOMENICO, CARMINE; D'ANDA, CARLOS	$16.99/$22.99 | TP
50.	9781401283506		THE FLASH VOL. 8: FLASH WAR	WILLIAMSON, JOSHUA | PORTER, HOWARD; KOLINS, SCOTT	$16.99/$22.99 | TP
51.	9781401288556		THE FLASH VOL. 9	WILLIAMSON, JOSHUA | .	$16.99/$22.99 | TP
52.	9781401271589	APR170414	THE FLASH: THE REBIRTH DELUXE EDITION BOOK 1	WILLIAMSON, JOSHUA | DI GIANMENICO, CARMINE; GOOGE, NEIL	$34.99/$45.99 | HC
53.	9781401278427	JAN180385	THE FLASH: THE REBIRTH DELUXE EDITION BOOK 2	WILLIAMSON, JOSHUA | DI GIANDOMENICO, CARMINE	$34.99/$45.99 | HC
54.	9781401281403	MAY180578	THE FLASH: THE REBIRTH DELUXE EDITION BOOK 3	WILLIAMSON, JOSHUA | DI GIANDOMENICO, CARMINE	$34.99/$45.99 | HC
55.	9781401289393		THE FLASH: THE REBIRTH DELUXE EDITION BOOK 4	WILLIAMSON, JOSHUA | PORTER, HOWARD; DI GIANDOMENICO	$34.99/$45.99 | HC
56.	9781401251789	SEP140317	THE FLASH: A CELEBRATION OF 75 YEARS	FOX, GARDNER; JOHNS, GEOFF | INFANTINO, CARMINE	$39.99/$47.99 | HC
57.	9781401281595	MAY180577	THE FLASH ROGUES: CAPTAIN COLD	VARIOUS | VARIOUS	$16.99/$22.99 | TP
58.	9781401289256		THE FLASH ROGUES: REVERSE FLASH	VARIOUS | VARIOUS	$16.99/$22.99 | TP
59.	9781401257712	JUN150297	THE FLASH SEASON ZERO	KREISBERG, ANDREW | HESTER, PHIL; TO, MARCUS	$19.99/$23.99 | TP

AQUAMAN BACKLIST AND SUGGESTED READING ORDER

	ISBN | DIAMOND CODE		TITLE	AUTHOR | ARTIST	US$/SCAN | FORMAT
1.	9781401274399	AUG170330	AQUAMAN: THE ATLANTIS CHRONICLES DELUXE EDITION	DAVID, PETER | MAROTO, ESTEBAN	$49.99/$65.99 | HC
2.	9781401277932	DEC170382	AQUAMAN: THE LEGEND OF AQUAMAN	GIFFEN, KEITH | SWAN, CURT	$19.99/$25.99 | TP
3.	9781401285227		AQUAMAN: THE SEARCH FOR MERA DELUXE EDITION	SKEATES, STEVE | APARO, JIM	$34.99/$45.99 | HC
4.	9781401289560		AQUAMAN & THE JUSTICE LEAGUE OF AMERICA VOL. 1	CONWAY, GERRY | VARIOUS	$29.99/$39.99 | TP
5.	9781401277468	NOV170357	AQUAMAN BY PETER DAVID BOOK ONE	DAVID, PETER | VARIOUS	$29.99/$39.99 | TP
6.	9781401281434	MAY180564	AQUAMAN BY PETER DAVID BOOK TWO	DAVID, PETER | VARIOUS	$29.99/$39.99 | TP
7.	9781401255107	APR150284	AQUAMAN: SUB-DIEGO	PFEIFER, WILL | GLEASON, PATRICK	$16.99/$19.99 | TP
8.	9781401263829	APR160388	AQUAMAN: TO SERVE AND PROTECT	ARCUDI, JOHN | GLEASON, PATRICK	$16.99/$19.99 | TP
9.	9781401271299	APR170417	AQUAMAN: KINGDOM LOST	ARCUDI, JOHN | GLEASON, PATRICK	$16.99/$22.99 | TP
10.	9781401275143	OCT170363	AQUAMAN: THE WATERBEARER (NEW EDITION)	VEITCH, RICK | GUICHET, YVEL	$19.99/$25.99 | TP
11.	9781401280482	MAR180333	AQUAMAN: TEMPEST	JIMENEZ, PHIL | JIMENEZ, PHIL	$16.99/$22.99 | TP
12.	9781401237103	FEB130206	AQUAMAN VOL. 1: THE TRENCH	JOHNS, GEOFF | REIS, IVAN	$14.99 /$17.99 | TP
13.	9781401242954	AUG130295	AQUAMAN VOL. 2: THE OTHERS	JOHNS, GEOFF | REIS, IVAN	$14.99 /$17.99 | TP
14.	9781401246952	FEB140252	AQUAMAN VOL. 3: THRONE OF ATLANTIS	JOHNS, GEOFF | PELLETIER, PAUL	$16.99/$19.99 | TP
15.	9781401283582	AUG180587	AQUAMAN: WAR FOR THE THRONE	JOHNS, GEOFF | REIS, IVAN	$12.99/$17.50 | TP
16.	9781401249953	AUG140327	AQUAMAN VOL. 4: DEATH OF A KING	JOHNS, GEOFF | PELLETIER, PAUL	$16.99/$19.99 | TP
17.	9781401285463		AQUAMAN BY GEOFF JOHNS OMNIBUS	JOHNS, GEOFF | REIS, IVAN	$75.00/$99.00 | HC
18.	9781401254407	APR150283	AQUAMAN VOL. 5: SEA OF STORMS	PARKER, JEFF | PELLETIER, PAUL	$16.99/$19.99 | TP
19.	9781401260965	DEC150329	AQUAMAN VOL. 6: MAELSTROM	PARKER, JEFF | PELLETIER, PAUL	$16.99/$19.99 | TP
20.	9781401264741	JUL160395	AQUAMAN VOL. 7: EXILED	BUNN, CULLEN | MCCARTHY, TREVOR	$16.99/$19.99 | TP
21.	9781401268749	DEC160378	AQUAMAN VOL. 8: OUT OF DARKNESS	ABNETT, DAN | CIFUENTES, VINCENTE	$16.99/$22.99 | TP
22.	9781401267827	OCT160290	AQUAMAN VOL. 1: THE DROWNING (REBIRTH)	ABNETT, DAN | WALKER, BRAD; BRIONES, PHILLIPE	$16.99/$22.99 | TP
23.	9781401272272	APR160388	AQUAMAN VOL. 2: BLACK MANTA RISING (REBIRTH)	ABNETT, DAN | WALKER, BRAD; BRIONES, PHILLIPE	$16.99/$22.99 | TP
24.	9781401271497	MAY170320	AQUAMAN VOL. 3: CROWN OF ATLANTIS (REBIRTH)	ABNETT, DAN | WALKER, BRAD; BRIONES, PHILLIPE	$19.99/$25.99 | TP

DC COMICS READING ORDER

	ISBN	DIAMOND CODE	TITLE	AUTHOR	ARTIST	US$/SCAN	FORMAT
25.	9781401275426	OCT170357	AQUAMAN VOL. 4: UNDERWORLD (REBIRTH)	ABNETT, DAN	SEJIC, STJEPAN	$16.99/$22.99	TP
26.	9781401285043		AQUAMAN: UNDERWORLD DELUXE EDITION	ABNETT, DAN	SEJIC, STJEPAN	$29.99/$39.99	HC
27.	9781401280697	APR180258	AQUAMAN VOL. 5: THE CROWN COMES DOWN	ABNETT, DAN	FEDERICI, RICCARDO	$14.99/$19.99	TP
28.	9781401285432		AQUAMAN VOL. 6: KINGSLAYER	ABNETT, DAN	COLAK, MIRKO	$16.99/$22.99	TP
29.	9781401290726		AQUAMAN/SUICIDE SQUAD: SINK ATLANTIS	ABNETT, DAN	WILLIAMS, ROB	$14.99/$19.99	TP
30.	9781401264468	JUN160329	AQUAMAN: A CELEBRATION OF 75 YEARS	VARIOUS	VARIOUS	$39.99/$53.99	HC

GREEN ARROW BACKLIST AND SUGGESTED READING ORDER

	ISBN	DIAMOND CODE	TITLE	AUTHOR	ARTIST	US$/SCAN	FORMAT
1.	9781401277208	JUN170402	GREEN ARROW: THE GOLDEN AGE OMNIBUS VOL. 1	WEISINGER, MORT	VARIOUS	$125.00/$163.00	HC
2.	9781401217433	JAN090227	GREEN ARROW: YEAR ONE	DIGGLE, ANDY	JOCK	$14.99/$17.99	TP
3.	9781401280420	MAR180345	GREEN LANTERN/GREEN ARROW: HARD TRAVELIN' HEROES DELUXE EDITION	O'NEIL, DENNY	ADAMS, NEAL	$49.99/$65.99	HC
4.	9781401238629	JUN120250	GREEN ARROW: THE LONGBOW HUNTERS	GRELL, MIKE	GRELL, MIKE	$14.99/$17.99	TP
5.	9781401243265	AUG130304	GREEN ARROW VOL. 1: HUNTERS MOON	GRELL, MIKE; GIORDANO, DICK	HANNIGAN, ED	$14.99/$17.99	TP
6.	9781401251338	JUL140250	GREEN ARROW VOL. 2: HERE THERE BE DRAGONS	GRELL, MIKE	HANNIGAN, ED	$14.99/$17.99	TP
7.	9781401255237	MAR150279	GREEN ARROW VOL. 3: THE TRIAL OF OLIVER QUEEN	GRELL, MIKE	JURGENS, DAN; HANNIGAN, ED	$16.99/$19.99	TP
8.	9781401258221	SEP150297	GREEN ARROW VOL. 4: BLOOD OF THE DRAGON	GRELL, MIKE	JURGENS, DAN	$17.99/$19.99	TP
9.	9781401260798	FEB160231	GREEN ARROW VOL. 5: BLACK ARROW	GRELL, MIKE	VARIOUS	$19.99/$23.99	TP
10.	9781401264574	JUN160340	GREEN ARROW VOL. 6: LAST ACTION HERO	GRELL, MIKE	VARIOUS	$19.99/$25.99	TP
11.	9781401265748	OCT160302	GREEN ARROW VOL. 7: HOMECOMING	GRELL, MIKE	VARIOUS	$19.99/$25.99	TP
12.	9781401269036	FEB170311	GREEN ARROW VOL. 8: THE HUNT FOR THE RED DRAGON	GRELL, MIKE	VARIOUS	$19.99/$25.99	TP
13.	9781401275310	OCT170372	GREEN ARROW VOL. 9: OLD TRICKS	GRELL, MIKE	VARIOUS	$24.99/$33.99	TP
14.	9781401265267	APR160396	GREEN ARROW BY KEVIN SMITH	SMITH, KEVIN	PARKS, ANDRE	$24.99/$29.99	TP
15.	9781401255480	SEP140315	ABSOLUTE GREEN ARROW BY KEVIN SMITH	SMITH, KEVIN	HESTER, PHIL	$99.99/$112.00	HC
16.	9781401275402	OCT170371	GREEN ARROW: ARCHER'S QUEST (NEW EDITION)	MELTZER, BRAD	HESTER, PHIL	$16.99/$22.99	TP
17.	9781401234867	FEB120249	GREEN ARROW VOL. 1: THE MIDAS TOUCH	KRUL, J.T.	PÉREZ, GEORGE	$14.99/$17.99	TP
18.	9781401238421	OCT120254	GREEN ARROW VOL. 2: TRIPLE THREAT	NOCENTI, ANN	TOLIBAO, HARVEY	$14.99/$17.99	TP
19.	9781401244057	JUN130266	GREEN ARROW VOL. 3: HARROW	NOCENTI, ANN	WILLIAMS II, FREDDIE	$14.99/$17.99	TP
20.	9781401246907	DEC130306	GREEN ARROW VOL. 4: THE KILL MACHINE	LEMIRE, JEFF	SORRENTINO, ANDREA	$16.99/$19.99	TP
21.	9781401250447	JUL140242	GREEN ARROW VOL. 5: THE OUTSIDERS WAR	LEMIRE, JEFF	SORRENTINO, ANDREA	$16.99/$19.99	TP
22.	9781401254742	JAN150370	GREEN ARROW VOL. 6: BROKEN	LEMIRE, JEFF	SORRENTINO, ANDREA	$14.99/$17.99	TP
23.	9781401285623		GREEN ARROW: WAR OF THE CLANS (DC ESSENTIAL EDITION)	LEMIRE, JEFF	SORRENTINO, ANDREA	$29.99/$39.99	TP
24.	9781401257620	AUG150270	GREEN ARROW VOL. 7: KINGDOM	KREISBERG, ANDREW; SOKOLOWSKI, BEN	SAMPERE, DANIEL	$14.99/$17.99	TP
25.	9781401262556	APR160392	GREEN ARROW VOL. 8: THE NIGHTBIRDS	PERCY, BENJAMIN	ZIRCHER, PATRICK	$16.99/$19.99	TP
26.	9781401270025	JUL160409	GREEN ARROW VOL. 9: OUTBREAK	PERCY, BENJAMIN	KUDRANSKI, SZYMON	$17.99/$23.99	TP
27.	9781401267810	OCT160293	GREEN ARROW VOL. 1: THE DEATH AND LIFE OF OLIVER QUEEN (REBIRTH)	PERCY, BENJAMIN	SCHMIDT, OTTO; FERRYERA, JUAN	$16.99/$19.99	TP
28.	9781401270407	JAN170378	GREEN ARROW VOL. 2: ISLAND OF SCARS (REBIRTH)	PERCY, BENJAMIN	SCHMIDT, OTTO; FERRYERA, JUAN	$16.99/$16.99	TP
29.	9781401271336	MAY170324	GREEN ARROW VOL. 3: EMERALD OUTLAW (REBIRTH)	PERCY, BENJAMIN	SCHMIDT, OTTO; FERREYRA, JUAN	$16.99/$22.99	TP
30.	9781401274542	SEP170403	GREEN ARROW VOL. 4: THE RISE OF STAR CITY (REBIRTH)	PERCY, BENJAMIN	CARLINI, ELEONORA; ANDOLFO, MIRKA	$19.99/$25.99	TP
31.	9781401278533	FEB180285	GREEN ARROW VOL. 5: HARD TRAVELIN' HERO (REBIRTH)	PERCY, BENJAMIN	SCHMIDT, OTTO; FERREYRA, JUAN	$16.99/$22.99	TP
32.	9781401281717	MAY180579	GREEN ARROW VOL. 6: TRIAL OF TWO CITIES	PERCY, BENJAMIN	FERRERYA, JUAN	$16.99/$22.99	TP
33.	9781401284701		GREEN ARROW: THE REBIRTH DELUXE EDITION BOOK 1	PERCY, BENJAMIN	SCHMIDT, OTTO	$34.99/$45.99	HC
34.	9781401263867	FEB160232	GREEN ARROW: A CELEBRATION OF 75 YEARS	VARIOUS	VARIOUS	$39.99/$48.99	HC

GREEN ARROW: FROM PAGE TO SCREEN

	ISBN	DIAMOND CODE	TITLE	AUTHOR	ARTIST	US$/SCAN	FORMAT
1.	9781401242992	JUN130265	ARROW VOL. 1	GUGGENHEIM, MARC; KREISBERG, ANDREW	GRELL, MIKE	$16.99/$19.99	TP
2.	9781401246037	JAN140347	ARROW VOL. 2	VARIOUS	VARIOUS	$16.99/$19.99	TP
3.	9781401257484	JUN150296	ARROW SEASON 2.5	GUGGENHEIM, MARC	BENNETT, JOE	$19.99/$23.99	TP
4.	9781401263294	MAY160301	ARROW: THE DARK ARCHER	BARROWMAN, JOHN; BARROWMAN, CAROLE	SAMPERE, DANIEL	$16.99/$22.99	TP

HARLEY QUINN AND THE SUICIDE SQUAD

	ISBN	DIAMOND CODE	TITLE	AUTHOR	ARTIST	US$/SCAN	FORMAT
1.	9781401216573	SEP080168	HARLEY QUINN: PRELUDES & KNOCK-KNOCK JOKES	KESEL, KARLF DODSON, TERRY		$19.99/$23.99	TP
2.	9781401240417	MAR130276	HARLEY QUINN: NIGHT AND DAY	KESEL, KARL	DODSON, TERRY; WOODS, PETE	$16.99/$19.99	TP
3.	9781401276423	MAY170342	HARLEY QUINN BY KARL KESEL AND TERRY DODSON: THE DELUXE EDITION BOOK ONE	KESEL, KARL	DODSON, TERRY	$29.99/$39.99	HC
4.	9781401285098		HARLEY QUINN BY KARL KESEL AND TERRY DODSON: THE DELUXE EDITION BOOK TWO	KESEL, KARL	DODSON, TERRY	$29.99/$39.99	HC
5.	9781401245955	DEC130313	HARLY QUINN: WELCOME TO METROPOLIS	KESEL, KARL	DODSON, TERRY; BADEAUX, BRANDON	$19.99/$23.99	TP
6.	9781401250683	JUN140280	HARLEY QUINN: VENGEANCE UNLIMITED	LIEBERMAN, A.J.	HUDDLESTON, MIKE; NIXEY, TROY	$19.99/$23.99	TP
7.	9781401278397	OCT170369	HARLEY QUINN & THE GOTHAM CITY SIRENS OMNIBUS	DINI, PAUL	MARCH, GUILLEM	$75.00/$99.00	HC
8.	9781401254155	JAN150369	HARLEY QUINN VOL. 1: HOT IN THE CITY	CONNER, AMANDA; PALMIOTTI, JIMMY	HARDIN, CHAD	$16.99/$19.99	TP
9.	9781401257637	SEP150302	HARLEY QUINN VOL. 2: POWER OUTAGE	CONNER, AMANDA; PALMIOTTI, JIMMY	HARDIN, CHAD	$16.99/$19.99	TP
10.	9781401262525	MAR160265	HARLEY QUINN VOL. 3: KISS KISS BANG STAB	CONNER, AMANDA; PALMIOTTI, JIMMY	HARDIN, CHAD	$16.99/$19.99	TP
11.	9781401259747	DEC150324	HARLEY QUINN AND POWER GIRL	CONNER, AMANDA; PALMIOTTI, JIMMY	ROUX, STEPHANE	$14.99/$17.99	TP
12.	9781401269296	JUN160344	HARLEY QUINN VOL. 4: A CALL TO ARMS	CONNER, AMANDA; PALMIOTTI, JIMMY	HARDIN, CHAD	$16.99/$22.99	TP
13.	9781401271992	OCT160305	HARLEY QUINN VOL. 5: THE JOKER'S LAST LAUGH	CONNER, AMANDA; PALMIOTTI, JIMMY	HARDIN, CHAD	$16.99/$22.99	TP

	ISBN | DIAMOND CODE	TITLE	AUTHOR | ARTIST	US$/$CAN | FORMAT
14.	9781401272593 FEB170313	HARLEY QUINN VOL. 6: BLACK, WHITE AND RED ALL OVER	CONNER, AMANDA; PALMIOTTI, JIMMY | HARDIN, CHAD	$16.99/$22.99 | TP
15.	9781401267858 NOV160332	HARLEY QUINN AND HER GANG OF HARLEYS	PALMIOTTI, JIMMY; TIERI, FRANK | TIERI, FRANK	$16.99/$22.99 | TP
16.	9781401273606 MAY170341	HARLEY'S LITTLE BLACK BOOK	CONNER, AMANDA; PALMIOTTI, JIMMY | ADAMS, NEAL; TUCCI, BILLY	$24.99/$33.99 | TP
17.	9781401268312 DEC160373	HARLEY QUINN VOL. 1: DIE LAUGHING (REBIRTH)	CONNER, AMANDA; PALMIOTTI, JIMMY | HARDIN, CHAD; TIMMS, JOHN	$16.99/$22.99 | TP
18.	9781401270957 MAR170404	HARLEY QUINN VOL. 2: JOKER LOVES HARLEY (REBIRTH)	CONNER, AMANDA; PALMIOTTI, JIMMY | HARDIN, CHAD	$16.99/$22.99 | TP
19.	9781401273699 JUN170383	HARLEY QUINN VOL. 3: RED MEAT (REBIRTH)	CONNER, AMANDA; PALMIOTTI, JIMMY | TIMMS, JOHN	$16.99/$22.99 | TP
20.	9781401275266 OCT170360	HARLEY QUINN VOL. 4: SURPRISE, SURPRISE (REBIRTH)	CONNER, AMANDA; PALMIOTTI, JIMMY | TIMMS, JOHN	$16.99/$22.99 | TP
21.	9781401278823 FEB180286	HARLEY QUINN VOL. 5: VOTE HARLEY (REBIRTH)	CONNER, AMANDA; PALMIOTTI, JIMMY | TIMMS, JOHN	$16.99/$22.99 | TP
22.	9781401281526 MAY180581	HARLEY QUINN VOL. 6: ANGRY BIRD	TIERI, FRANK | MIRANDA, INAKI	$16.99/$22.99 | TP
23.	9781401283490	HARLEY LOVES JOKER	DINI, PAUL; PALMIOTTI, JIMMY | TEMPLETON, TY	$24.99/$33.99 | HC
24.	9781401273682 JUN170384	HARLEY QUINN: THE REBIRTH DELUXE EDITION BOOK 1	CONNER, AMANDA; PALMIOTTI, JIMMY | HARDIN, CHAD; TIMMS, JOHN	$34.99/$45.99 | HC
25.	9781401280659 APR180270	HARLEY QUINN: THE REBIRTH DELUXE EDITION BOOK 2	CONNER, AMANDA; PALMIOTTI, JIMMY | HARDIN, CHAD; TIMMS, JOHN	$34.99/$45.99 | HC
26.	9781401285531	HARLEY QUINN: THE REBIRTH DELUXE EDITION BOOK 3	CONNER, AMANDA; PALMIOTTI, JIMMY | HARDIN, CHAD; TIMMS, JOHN	$34.99/$45.99 | HC
27.	9781401276430 APR170426	HARLEY QUINN BY AMANDA CONNER & JIMMY PALMIOTTI OMNIBUS VOL. 1	CONNER, AMANDA; PALMIOTTI, JIMMY | HARDIN, CHAD	$99.99/$130.99 | HC
28.	9781401284565 MAR180348	HARLEY QUINN BY AMANDA CONNER & JIMMY PALMIOTTI OMNIBUS VOL. 2	CONNER, AMANDA; PALMIOTTI, JIMMY | HARDIN, CHAD	$99.99/$130.99 | HC
29.	9781401285074	HARLEY QUINN VOL. 1: HARLEY VS. APOKOLIPS	HUMPHRIES, SAM | ANDOLFO, MIRKA	$16.99/$22.99 | TP
30.	9781401288099	HARLEY QUINN VOL. 2	HUMPHRIES, SAM | TIMMS, JOHN	$16.99/$22.99 | TP
31.	9781401274238 JUL170477	HARLEY QUINN: A ROGUE'S GALLERY - THE DELUXE COVER ART COLLECTION	VARIOUS | VARIOUS	$24.99/$33.99 | HC
32.	9781401275990 JUN170403	HARLEY QUINN: A CELEBRATION OF 25 YEARS	DINI, PAUL; TIMM, BRUCE; CONNER, AMANDA; DODSON, TERRY	$39.99/$53.99 | HC
33.	9781401260804 OCT150255	HARLEY AND IVY: THE DELUXE EDITION	DINI, PAUL; WINICK, JUDD | TIMM, BRUCE; CHIODO, JOE	$24.99/$29.99 | HC
34.	9781401279578 DEC170385	BATMAN AND HARLEY QUINN	TEMPLETON, TY | VARIOUS	$16.99/$22.99 | TP
35.	9781401255176 APR170289	BATMAN: HARLEY QUINN	DINI, PAUL | GOOGE, NEIL	$19.99/$23.99 | TP
36.	9781401270087 MAR168712	HARLEY QUINN'S GREATEST HITS	VARIOUS | VARIOUS	$9.99/$11.99 | HC
37.	9781401280338 MAY180580	HARLEY & IVY MEET BETTY & VERONICA	DINI, PAUL; ANDREYKO, MARC | BRAGA, LAURA	$24.99/$33.99 | HC
38.	9781401275167 OCT170374	SUICIDE SQUAD: THE SILVER AGE	KANIGHER, ROBERT | VARIOUS	$29.99/$39.99 | TP
39.	9781401258313 JUN150292	SUICIDE SQUAD VOL. 1: TRIAL BY FIRE	OSTRANDER, JOHN | MCDONNELL, LUKE	$19.99/$23.99 | TP
40.	9781401258337 SEP150307	SUICIDE SQUAD VOL. 2: THE NIGHTSHADE ODYSSEY	OSTRANDER, JOHN | MCDONNELL, LUKE	$19.99/$23.99 | TP
41.	9781401260910 JAN160335	SUICIDE SQUAD VOL. 3 ROGUES	OSTRANDER, JOHN | VARIOUS	$19.99/$23.99 | TP
42.	9781401262617 APR160402	SUICIDE SQUAD VOL. 4: THE JANUS DIRECTIVE	OSTRANDER, JOHN | SNYDER, JOHN K	$19.99/$23.99 | TP
43.	9781401265427 SEP160353	SUICIDE SQUAD VOL. 5: APOKOLIPS NOW	OSTRANDER, JOHN | SNYDER, JOHN K	$19.99/$25.99 | TP
44.	9781401269043 FEB170315	SUICIDE SQUAD VOL. 6: THE PHOENIX GAMBIT	OSTRANDER, JOHN | VARIOUS	$19.99/$25.99 | TP
45.	9781401274573 SEP170426	SUICIDE SQUAD VOL. 7: THE DRAGON'S HOARD	OSTRANDER, JOHN | ISHERWOOD, GEOF	$19.99/$25.99 | TP
46.	9781401289539	SUICIDE SQUAD VOL. 8: LEGERDEMAIN	OSTRANDER, JOHN | ISHERWOOD, GEOF	$19.99/$25.99 | TP
47.	9781401235444 APR120250	SUICIDE SQUAD VOL. 1: KICKED IN THE TEETH	GLASS, ADAM | DALLOCCHIO, FREDERICO	$14.99/$17.99 | TP
48.	9781401238445 NOV120264	SUICIDE SQUAD VOL. 2: BASILISK RISING	GLASS, ADAM | DAGNINO, FERNANDO	$16.99/$19.99 | TP
49.	9781401243166 JUL130239	SUICIDE SQUAD VOL. 3: DEATH IS FOR SUCKERS	GLASS, ADAM | VARIOUS	$14.99/$17.99 | TP
50.	9781401247010 JAN140341	SUICIDE SQUAD VOL. 4: DISCIPLINE AND PUNISH	KOT, ALES | ZIRCHER, PATRICK	$14.99/$17.99 | TP
51.	9781401250126 JUL140245	SUICIDE SQUAD VOL. 5: WALLED IN	KINDT, MATT | ZIRCHER, PATRICK	$16.99/$19.99 | TP
52.	9781401252380 APR150302	NEW SUICIDE SQUAD VOL. 1: PURE INSANITY	RYAN, SEAN | ROBERTS, JEREMY	$16.99/$19.99 | TP
53.	9781401261528 NOV150280	NEW SUICIDE SQUAD VOL. 2: MONSTERS	RYAN, SEAN | BRIONES, PHILIPPE	$16.99/$19.99 | TP
54.	9781401262648 APR160401	NEW SUICIDE SQUAD VOL. 3: FREEDOM	RYAN, SEAN | BRIONES, PHILIPPE	$16.99/$19.99 | TP
55.	9781401270001 AUG160335	NEW SUICIDE SQUAD VOL. 4: KILL ANYTHING	SEELEY, TIM | FERREYRA, JUAN	$16.99/$22.99 | TP
56.	9781401263805 MAY160326	SUICIDE SQUAD MOST WANTED: DEADSHOT	BUCCELLATO, BRIAN | BOGDANOVIC, VIKTOR	$16.99/$19.99 | TP
57.	9781401268657 JAN170398	SUICIDE SQUAD MOST WANTED: EL DIABLO	VARIOUS | RICHARDS, CLIFF	$16.99/$22.99 | TP
58.	9781401264642 JUN160358	SUICIDE SQUAD MOST WANTED: KATANA	BARR, MIKE | NEVES, DIOGENES	$16.99/$22.99 | TP
59.	9781401269814 DEC160375	SUICIDE SQUAD VOL. 1: THE BLACK VAULT (REBIRTH)	WILLIAMS, ROB | LEE, JIM; TAN, PHILIP	$16.99/$19.99 | TP
60.	9781401270971 MAR170409	SUICIDE SQUAD VOL. 2: GOING SANE (REBIRTH)	WILLIAMS, ROB | TAN, PHILLIP	$16.99/$22.99 | TP
61.	9781401274788 SEP170405	JUSTICE LEAGUE VS. SUICIDE SQUAD	WILLIAMSON, JOSHUA | FABOK, JASON	$24.99/$33.99 | TP
62.	9781401274221 JUN170386	SUICIDE SQUAD VOL. 3: BURNING DOWN THE HOUSE (REBIRTH)	WILLIAMS, ROB | ROMITA JR., JOHN	$16.99/$22.99 | TP
63.	9781401275396 SEP170406	SUICIDE SQUAD VOL. 4: EARTHLINGS ON FIRE (REBIRTH)	WILLIAMS, ROB | DANIEL, TONY S.	$14.99/$19.99 | TP
64.	9781401278809 JAN180389	SUICIDE SQUAD VOL. 5: KILL YOUR DARLINGS (REBIRTH)	WILLIAMS, ROB | VARIOUS	$14.99/$19.99 | TP
65.	9781401280987 APR180278	SUICIDE SQUAD VOL. 6: THE SECRET HISTORY OF TASK FORCE X	WILLIAMS, ROB | BAGENDA, BARNABY	$16.99/$22.99 | TP
66.	9781401284749	SUICIDE SQUAD VOL. 7: DRAIN THE SWAMP	WILLIAMS, ROB | VARIOUS	$16.99/$22.99 | TP
67.	9781401288877	SUICIDE SQUAD VOL. 8	WILLIAMS, ROB | FERREIRA, EDUARDO	$16.99/$22.99 | TP
68.	9781401274214 JUL170463	SUICIDE SQUAD: THE REBIRTH DELUXE EDITION BOOK 1	WILLIAMS, ROB | LEE, JIM	$34.99/$45.99 | HC
69.	9781401278915 FEB180288	SUICIDE SQUAD: THE REBIRTH DELUXE EDITION BOOK 2	WILLIAMS, ROB | ROMITA JR., JOHN; DANIEL, TONY S.	$34.99/$45.99 | HC
70.	9781401285166	SUICIDE SQUAD: THE REBIRTH DELUXE EDITION BOOK 3	WILLIAMS, ROB | BAGENDA, BARNABY	$34.99/$45.99 | HC
71.	9781401287788	SUICIDE SQUAD: HELL TO PAY	PARKER, JEFF | STAGGS, CAT	$16.99/$22.99 | TP

TEEN TITANS BACKLIST AND SUGGESTED READING ORDER

	ISBN | DIAMOND CODE	TITLE	AUTHOR | ARTIST	US$/$CAN | FORMAT
1.	9781401267247 SEP160349	TEEN TITANS: YEAR ONE (NEW EDITION)	WOLFRAM, AMY | KERSCHL, KARL	$16.99/$22.99 | TP
2.	9781401275082 SEP170431	TEEN TITANS: THE SILVER AGE VOL. 1	HANEY, BOB | VARIOUS	$29.99/$39.99 | TP
3.	9781401285173	TEEN TITANS: THE SILVER AGE VOL. 2	VARIOUS | VARIOUS	$34.99/$45.99 | TP

DC COMICS READING ORDER

	ISBN | DIAMOND CODE	TITLE	AUTHOR | ARTIST	US$/SCAN | FORMAT
4.	9781401267568 JUN160360	TEEN TITANS: THE SILVER AGE OMNIBUS VOL. 1	HANEY, BOB | VARIOUS	$99.99/$130.99 | HC
5.	9781401251437 JUN140283	THE NEW TEEN TITANS VOL. 1	WOLFMAN, MARV | PEREZ, GEORGE	$19.99/$23.99 | TP
6.	9781401255329 JAN150380	THE NEW TEEN TITANS VOL. 2	WOLFMAN, MARV | PEREZ, GEORGE; TANGHAL, ROMEO	$19.99/$23.99 | TP
7.	9781401258542 JUN150304	THE NEW TEEN TITANS VOL. 3	WOLFMAN, MARV | PEREZ, GEORGE	$19.99/$23.99 | TP
8.	9781401260859 OCT150259	THE NEW TEEN TITANS VOL. 4	WOLFMAN, MARV | PEREZ, GEORGE	$19.99/$23.99 | TP
9.	9781401263584 APR160399	THE NEW TEEN TITANS VOL. 5	WOLFMAN, MARV | PEREZ, GEORGE	$19.99/$23.99 | TP
10.	9781401265762 NOV160338	THE NEW TEEN TITANS VOL. 6	WOLFMAN, MARV | PEREZ, GEORGE	$19.99/$25.99 | TP
11.	9781401271626 MAY170348	THE NEW TEEN TITANS VOL. 7	WOLFMAN, MARV | PEREZ, GEORGE	$19.99/$25.99 | TP
12.	9781401274962 SEP170421	THE NEW TEEN TITANS VOL. 8	WOLFMAN, MARV | PEREZ, GEORGE	$19.99/$25.99 | TP
13.	9781401281250 MAY180588	THE NEW TEEN TITANS VOL. 9	WOLFMAN, MARV | PEREZ, GEORGE	$19.99/$25.99 | TP
14.	9781401288242	THE NEW TEEN TITANS VOL. 10	WOLFMAN, MARV | PEREZ, GEORGE	$19.99/$25.99 | TP
15.	9781401278649 FEB180315	TITANS: TOTAL CHAOS	WOLFMAN, MARV | PEREZ, GEORGE	$29.99/$39.99 | TP
16.	9781401275778 SEP170420	THE NEW TEEN TITANS: THE JUDAS CONTRACT DELUXE EDITION	WOLFMAN, MARV | PEREZ, GEORGE	$29.99/$39.99 | HC
17.	9781401271282 MAR170425	THE NEW TEEN TITANS OMNIBUS VOL. 1 (NEW EDITION)	WOLFMAN, MARV | PEREZ, GEORGE	$75.00/$99.00 | HC
18.	9781401277628 AUG170339	THE NEW TEEN TITANS OMNIBUS VOL. 2 (NEW EDITION)	WOLFMAN, MARV | PEREZ, GEORGE	$75.00/$99.00 | HC
19.	9781401281106 FEB180307	THE NEW TEEN TITANS OMNIBUS VOL. 3 (NEW EDITION)	WOLFMAN, MARV | PEREZ, GEORGE	$99.99/$130.99 | HC
20.	9781401289300	THE NEW TEEN TITANS OMNIBUS VOL. 4	WOLFMAN, MARV | PEREZ, GEORGE	$99.99/$130.99 | HC
21.	9781401270759 JAN170401	TEEN TITANS: THE BRONZE AGE OMNIBUS	SCHWARTZ, JULIUS; HANEY, BOB | HECK, DON	$125.00/$163.00 | HC
22.	9781401284282 JUN180590	TITANS BOOK 1: TOGETHER FOREVER	WINICK, JUDD | CHURCHILL, IAN	$24.99/$33.99 | TP
23.	9781401265984 DEC160383	TEEN TITANS BY GEOFF JOHNS BOOK ONE	JOHNS, GEOFF | MCKONE, MIKE	$24.99/$33.99 | TP
24.	9781401277529 NOV170375	TEEN TITANS BY GEOFF JOHNS BOOK TWO	JOHNS, GEOFF | MCKONE, MIKE	$29.99/$39.99 | TP
25.	9781401289522	TEEN TITANS BY GEOFF JOHNS BOOK THREE	JOHNS, GEOFF | DANIEL, TONY S.	$29.99/$39.99 | TP
26.	9781401236939 SEP120242	TEEN TITANS BY GEOFF JOHNS OMNIBUS	JOHNS, GEOFF | VARIOUS	$150.00 /$176.00 | TP
27.	9781401236984 JUN120239	TEEN TITANS VOL. 1: IT'S OUR RIGHT TO FIGHT	LOBDELL, SCOTT | BOOTH, BRETT	$14.99/$17.99 | TP
28.	9781401241032 MAR130272	TEEN TITANS VOL. 2: THE CULLING	LOBDELL, SCOTT | BOOTH, BRETT	$16.99/$19.99 | TP
29.	9781401243210 SEP130274	TEEN TITANS VOL. 3: DEATH OF THE FAMILY	LOBDELL, SCOTT | BOOTH, BRETT	$14.99/$17.99 | TP
30.	9781401246242 APR140262	TEEN TITANS VOL. 4: LIGHT AND DARK	LOBDELL, SCOTT | BARROWS, EDDY	$14.99/$17.99 | TP
31.	9781401250539 NOV140302	TEEN TITANS VOL. 5: THE TRIAL OF KID FLASH	LOBDELL, SCOTT | KIRKHAM, TYLER	$17.99/$20.99 | TP
32.	9781401252373 MAY150249	TEEN TITANS VOL. 1: BLINDED BY THE LIGHT	PFEIFER, WILL | ROCAFORT, KENNETH	$16.99/$19.99 | TP
33.	9781401261627 DEC150336	TEEN TITANS VOL. 2: ROGUE TARGETS	PFEIFER, WILL | ROCAFORT, KENNETH	$16.99/$19.99 | TP
34.	9781401265205 MAY160321	TEEN TITANS VOL. 3: THE SUM OF IT'S PARTS	PFEIFER, WILL | CHURCHILL, IAN	$16.99/$19.99 | TP
35.	9781401269777 NOV160340	TEEN TITANS VOL. 4: WHEN TITANS FALLS	PFEIFER, WILL | CHURCHILL, IAN	$16.99/$22.99 | TP
36.	9781401265557 JUN160361	TITANS HUNT	ABNETT, DAN | SIQUEIRA, PAULO	$19.99/$25.99 | TP
37.	9781401268176 DEC160376	TITANS VOL. 1: THE RETURN OF WALLY WEST (REBIRTH)	ABNETT, DAN | BOOTH, BRETT	$16.99/$19.99 | TP
38.	9781401273774 JUN170389	TITANS VOL. 2: MADE IN MANHATTAN (REBIRTH)	ABNETT, DAN | BOOTH, BRETT	$16.99/$22.99 | TP
39.	9781401277598 NOV170356	TITANS VOL. 3: A JUDAS AMONG US (REBIRTH)	ABNETT, DAN | BOOTH, BRETT	$16.99/$22.99 | TP
40.	9781401284480 JUN180591	TITANS VOL. 4: TITANS APART	ABNETT, DAN | PELLETIER, PAUL	$16.99/$22.99 | TP
41.	9781401287740	TITANS VOL. 5	ABNETT, DAN | PETERSON, BRANDON	$16.99/$22.99 | TP
42.	9781401270773 MAR170410	TEEN TITANS VOL. 1: DAMIAN KNOWS BEST (REBIRTH)	PERCY, BENJAMIN | MEYERS, JONBOY; PHAM, KHOI	$16.99/$22.99 | TP
43.	9781401275044 NOV170355	TEEN TITANS VOL. 2: THE RISE OF AQUALAD (REBIRTH)	PERCY, BENJAMIN | PHAM, KHOI	$14.99/$19.99 | TP
44.	9781401284596	TEEN TITANS VOL. 3	PERCY, BENJAMIN | BORGES, ALISON	$16.99/$22.99 | TP
45.	9781401288785	TEEN TITANS VOL. 4	GLASS, ADAM | CHANG, BERNARD	$16.99/$22.99 | TP
46.	9781401280970 APR180282	TITANS: THE LAZARUS CONTRACT	PRIEST, CHRISTOPHER; ABNETT, DAN; PERCY, BENJAMIN | BOOTH, BRETT	$16.99/$22.99 | TP

TEEN TITANS: FROM PAGE TO SCREEN

	ISBN | DIAMOND CODE	TITLE	AUTHOR | ARTIST	US$/SCAN | FORMAT
1.	9781401253677 JUL140263	TEEN TITANS GO!: TITANS TOGETHER	TORRES, J. | NORTON, MIKE	$12.99/$15.99 | TP
2.	9781401261962 SEP150298	TEEN TITANS GO!: TRUTH, JUSTICE, PIZZA	VARIOUS | VARIOUS	$12.99/$15.99 | TP
3.	9781401268992 FEB170320	TEEN TITANS GO!: READY FOR ACTION	VARIOUS | STUCKER, LARRY	$12.99/$17.50 | TP
4.	9781401264680 JUL160417	TEEN TITANS GO!: BRING IT ON	TORRES, J. | STUCKER, LARRY	$12.99/$17.50 | TP
5.	9781401252427 DEC140400	TEEN TITANS GO! VOL. 1: PARTY, PARTY	FISCH, SHOLLY | HERNANDEZ, LEA	$12.99/$17.50 | TP
6.	9781401267308 APR160400	TEEN TITANS GO! VOL. 2: WELCOME TO THE PIZZA DOME	FISCH, SHOLLY | VARIOUS	$12.99/$15.99 | TP
7.	9781401267650 OCT160313	TEEN TITANS GO! VOL. 3: MUMBO JUMBLE	FISCH, SHOLLY | VARIOUS	$12.99/$17.50 | TP
8.	9781401273743 SEP170430	TEEN TITANS GO! VOL. 4: SMELLS LIKE TEEN TITANS SPIRIT	VARIOUS | VARIOUS	$12.99/$17.50 | TP
9.	9781401278731	TEEN TITANS GO! VOL. 5	FISCH, SHOLLY | VARIOUS	$12.99/$17.50 | TP
10.	9781401282400 MAR180356	TEEN TITANS GO!: THEIR GREATEST HIJINKS	VARIOUS | VARIOUS	$9.99/$13.50 | TP
11.	9781401283599 MAR180356	TEEN TITANS GO! BOX SET	FISCH, SHOLLY | VARIOUS	$34.99/$45.99 | BOXED SET

TEEN TITANS GRAPHIC NOVELS

	ISBN | DIAMOND CODE	TITLE	AUTHOR | ARTIST	US$/SCAN | FORMAT
1.	9781401259082 JUL150302	TEEN TITANS: EARTH ONE VOL. 1	LEMIRE, JEFF | DODSON, RACHAEL; DODSON, TERRY	$14.99/$17.99 | TP
2.	9781401271534 MAY170346	TEEN TITANS: EARTH ONE VOL. 2	LEMIRE, JEFF | MACDONALD, ANDY	$16.99/$22.99 | TP

DC COMICS READING ORDER

	ISBN | DIAMOND CODE	TITLE	AUTHOR | ARTIST	US$/$CAN | FORMAT
		ROBIN		
3.	9781401277642 AUG170341	ROBIN: YEAR ONE DELUXE EDITION	DIXON, CHUCK | BEATTY, SCOTT	$34.99/$45.99 | HC
4.	9781401258573 AUG150276	ROBIN VOL. 1: REBORN	DIXON, CHUCK | LYLE, ROM	$19.99/$23.99 | TP
5.	9781401260897 DEC150339	ROBIN VOL. 2 TRIUMPHANT	DIXON, CHUCK | GRUMMETT, TOM	$19.99/$24.99 | TP
6.	9781401263621 AUG160341	ROBIN VOL. 3: SOLO	DIXON, CHUCK | GRUMMETT, TOM	$24.99/$33.99 | TP
7.	9781401265878 APR170435	ROBIN VOL. 4: TURNING POINT	DIXON, CHUCK | GRUMMETT, TOM	$24.99/$33.99 | TP
8.	9781401275129 SEP170422	ROBIN VOL. 5: WAR OF THE DRAGONS	DIXON, CHUCK | GRUMMETT, TOM	$24.99/$33.99 | TP
9.	9781401264796 JUN160348	ROBIN: SON OF BATMAN VOL. 1: THE YEAR OF BLOOD	GLEASON, PATRICK | GLEASON, PATRICK	$16.99/$22.99 | TP
10.	9781401267896 NOV160337	ROBIN: SON OF BATMAN VOL. 2: DAWN OF DEMONS	GLEASON, PATRICK | BACHS, RAMÓN F.	$16.99/$22.99 | TP
11.	9781401259822 DEC150326	WE ARE ROBIN VOL. 1: THE VIGILANTE BUSINESS	BERMEJO, LEE | HAYNES, ROB; RANDOLPH, KHARY	$14.99/$17.99 | TP
12.	9781401264901 JUL160419	WE ARE ROBIN VOL. 2: JOKERS	BERMEJO, LEE | CORONA, JORGE	$14.99/$17.99 | TP
13.	9781401268114 NOV160336	ROBIN WAR	KING, TOM | VARIOUS	$19.99/$25.99 | TP
14.	9781401250645 NOV140298	DAMIAN: SON OF BATMAN	KUBERT, ANDY; MORRISON, GRANT | KUBERT, ANDY	$16.99/$19.99 | TP
15.	9781401251444 SEP140321	NIGHTWING VOL. 1: BLUDHAVEN	O'NEIL, DENNIS | LAND, GREG; MCDANIEL, SCOTT	$19.99/$23.99 | TP
16.	9781401255336 MAR150281	NIGHTWING VOL. 2: ROUGH JUSTICE	DIXON, CHUCK | MCDANIEL, SCOTT; STORY, KARL	$19.99/$23.99 | TP
17.	9781401258559 SEP150303	NIGHTWING VOL. 3: FALSE STARTS	DIXON, CHUCK | MCDANIEL, SCOTT; STORY, KARL	$19.99/$23.99 | TP
18.	9781401260873 JAN160333	NIGHTWING VOL. 4: LOVE & BULLETS	DIXON, CHUCK | MCDANIEL, SCOTT	$19.99/$24.99 | TP
19.	9781401265021 JUL160412	NIGHTWING VOL. 5: THE HUNT FOR ORACLE	DIXON, CHUCK | MCDANIEL, SCOTT	$19.99/$25.99 | TP
20.	9781401270810 APR170434	NIGHTWING VOL. 6: TO SERVE AND PROTECT	DIXON, CHUCK | LAND, GREG	$24.99/$33.99 | TP
21.	9781401277567 NOV170372	NIGHTWING VOL. 7: SHRIKE	DIXON, CHUCK | LAND, GREG	$24.99/$33.99 | TP
22.	9781401285050	NIGHTWING VOL. 8: LETHAL FORCE	DIXON, CHUCK |	$24.99/$33.99 | TP
23.	9781401237059 JUL120214	NIGHTWING VOL. 1: TRAPS AND TRAPEZES	HIGGINS, KYLE | BARROWS, EDDY	$14.99/$17.99 | TP
24.	9781401240271 APR130225	NIGHTWING VOL. 2: NIGHT OF THE OWLS	HIGGINS, KYLE | BARROWS, EDDY	$14.99/$17.99 | TP
25.	9781401244132 SEP130273	NIGHTWING VOL. 3: DEATH OF THE FAMILY	HIGGINS, KYLE | BARROWS, EDDY	$16.99/$19.99 | TP
26.	9781401246303 APR140258	NIGHTWING VOL. 4: SECOND CITY	HIGGINS, KYLE | BOOTH, BRETT	$14.99/$17.99 | TP
27.	9781401250119 SEP140309	NIGHTWING VOL. 5: SETTING SON	HIGGINS, KYLE | CONRAD, WILL	$16.99/$19.99 | TP
28.	9781401274160 MAY170338	GRAYSON: THE SUPERSPY OMNIBUS	KING, TOM; SEELEY, TIM | JANIN, MIKEL	$99.99/$130.99 | HC
29.	9781401257590 OCT150253	GRAYSON VOL. 1: AGENTS OF SPYRAL	KING, TOM; SEELEY, TIM | JANIN, MIKEL	$14.99/$17.99 | TP
30.	9781401257606 OCT150254	GRAYSON VOL. 2: WE ALL DIE AT DAWN	KING, TOM; SEELEY, TIM | JANIN, MIKEL	$16.99/$19.99 | TP
31.	9781401262761 FEB160227	GRAYSON VOL. 3: NEMESIS	KING, TOM; SEELEY, TIM | JANIN, MIKEL	$16.99/$19.99 | TP
32.	9781401267629 JUL160408	GRAYSON VOL. 4: A GHOST IN THE TOMB	KING, TOM; SEELEY, TIM | JANIN, MIKEL	$16.99/$19.99 | TP
33.	9781401268251 OCT160307	GRAYSON VOL. 5: SPYRAL'S END	KING, TOM; SEELEY, TIM | JANIN, MIKEL; ANTONIO, ROGE	$16.99/$22.99 | TP
34.	9781401268039 OCT160296	NIGHTWING VOL. 1: BETTER THAN BATMAN (REBIRTH)	SEELEY, TIM | FERNANDEZ, JAVIER	$17.99/$22.99 | TP
35.	9781401270858 MAR170406	NIGHTWING VOL. 2: BACK TO BLÜDHAVEN (REBIRTH)	SEELEY, TIM | TAKARA, MARCIO	$16.99/$22.99 | TP
36.	9781401273767 JUN170385	NIGHTWING VOL. 3: NIGHTWING MUST DIE (REBIRTH)	SEELEY, TIM | FERNANDEZ, JAVIER	$16.99/$22.99 | TP
37.	9781401275334 OCT170361	NIGHTWING VOL. 4: BLOCKBUSTER (REBIRTH)	SEELEY, TIM | FERNANDEZ, JAVIER	$16.99/$22.99 | TP
38.	9781401278816 JAN180387	NIGHTWING VOL. 5: RAPTOR'S REVENGE (REBIRTH)	SEELEY, TIM | FERNANDEZ, JAVIER	$14.99/$19.99 | TP
39.	9781401287573 JUN180584	NIGHTWING VOL. 6: THE UNTOUCHABLE	HUMPHRIES, SAM | CHANG, BERNARD	$19.99/$25.99 | TP
40.	9781401273750 JUL170461	NIGHTWING: THE REBIRTH DELUXE EDITION BOOK 1	SEELEY, TIM | FERNANDEZ, JAVIER	$34.99/$45.99 | HC
41.	9781401278922 FEB180287	NIGHTWING: THE REBIRTH DELUXE EDITION BOOK 2	SEELEY, TIM | FERNANDEZ, JAVIER	$34.99/$45.99 | HC
42.	9781401285678	NIGHTWING: THE REBIRTH DELUXE EDITION BOOK 3	SEELEY, TIM | FERNANDEZ, JAVIER	$34.99/$45.99 | HC
43.	9781401285593	NIGHTWING VOL. 1	PERCY, BENJAMIN | MOONEYHAM, CHRIS	$16.99/$22.99 | TP
44.	9781401274993 FEB180308	NIGHTWING: THE NEW ORDER	HIGGINS, KYLE | MCCARTHY, TREVOR	$16.99/$22.99 | TP
45.	9781401237127 AUG120248	RED HOOD AND THE OUTLAWS VOL. 1: REDEMPTION	LOBDELL, SCOTT | ROCAFORT, KENNETH	$14.99 /$17.99 | TP
46.	9781401240905 MAR130273	RED HOOD AND THE OUTLAWS VOL. 2: THE STARFIRE	LOBDELL, SCOTT | ROCAFORT, KENNETH	$14.99 /$17.99 | TP
47.	9781401244125 AUG130301	RED HOOD AND THE OUTLAWS VOL. 3: DEATH OF THE FAMILY	LOBDELL, SCOTT | GREEN, TIMOTHY	$16.99/$19.99 | TP
48.	9781401246365 MAR140256	RED HOOD AND THE OUTLAWS VOL. 4: LEAGUE OF ASSASSINS	TYNION IV, JAMES | GOPEZ, JULIUS; BARRIONUEVO, AL	$16.99/$19.99 | TP
49.	9781401250485 SEP140310	RED HOOD AND THE OUTLAWS VOL. 5: THE BIG PICTURE	TYNION IV, JAMES | GOPEZ, JULIUS	$14.99/$17.99 | TP
50.	9781401253424 MAR150271	RED HOOD AND THE OUTLAWS VOL. 6: LOST AND FOUND	LOBDELL, SCOTT | SANDOVAL, RAFA	$14.99/$17.99 | TP
51.	9781401258566 OCT150260	RED HOOD AND THE OUTLAWS VOL. 7: LAST CALL	LOBDELL, SCOTT | SILVA, R.B.	$14.99/$17.99 | TP
52.	9781401284664 APR180276	RED HOOD AND THE OUTLAWS: THE NEW 52 OMNIBUS VOL. 1	LOBDELL, SCOTT | ROCAFORT, KENNETH	$99.99/$130.99 | HC
53.	9781401261542 DEC150322	RED HOOD/ARSENAL VOL. 1: OPEN FOR BUSINESS	LOBDELL, SCOTT | MEDRI, DENIS	$16.99/$14.99 | TP
54.	9781401264895 JUL160397	RED HOOD/ARSENAL VOL. 2: DEVIL'S DAUGHTER	LOBDELL, SCOTT | FERNANDEZ, JAVIER	$16.99/$22.99 | TP
55.	9781401268756 JAN170381	RED HOOD & THE OUTLAWS VOL. 1: DARK TRINITY (REBIRTH)	LOBDELL, SCOTT | SOY, DEXTER	$16.99/$19.99 | TP
56.	9781401273996 JUL170462	RED HOOD AND THE OUTLAWS VOL. 2: WHO IS ARTEMIS? (REBIRTH)	LOBDELL, SCOTT | SOY, DEXTER	$14.99/$19.99 | TP
57.	9781401278373 JAN180388	RED HOOD AND THE OUTLAWS VOL. 3: BIZARRO REBORN (REBIRTH)	LOBDELL, SCOTT | SOY, DEXTER	$19.99/$25.99 | TP
58.	9781401284886	RED HOOD AND THE OUTLAWS VOL. 4	LOBDELL, SCOTT | SOY, DEXTER	$19.99/$25.99 | TP
		BATGIRL BACKLIST AND SUGGESTED READING ORDER		
1.	9781401276409 JUL170469	BATGIRL: THE BRONZE AGE OMNIBUS VOL. 1	VARIOUS | VARIOUS	$99.99/$130.99 | HC
2.	9781401288419	BATGIRL: THE BRONZE AGE OMNIBUS VOL. 2	VARIOUS | VARIOUS	$99.99/$130.99 | HC
3.	9781401240332 MAR130279	BATGIRL/ROBIN YEAR ONE	DIXON, CHUCK | BEATTY, SCOTT; MARTIN, MARCOS	$24.99 /$28.99 | TP
4.	9781401287931	BATGIRL: YEAR ONE DELUXE EDITION	DIXON, CHUCK | BEATTY, SCOTT	$34.99/$45.99 | TP

DC COMICS READING ORDER

	ISBN	DIAMOND CODE	TITLE	AUTHOR	ARTIST	US$/$CAN	FORMAT
5.	9781401260729	OCT150244	BATGIRL: CASSANDRA CAIN VOL. 1: SILENT KNIGHT	PUCKETT, KELLEY	SCOTT, DAMION	$16.99/$19.99	TP
6.	9781401263522	APR160386	BATGIRL: CASSANDRA CAIN VOL. 2: TO THE DEATH	PUCKETT, KELLEY	SCOTT, DAIMON	$19.99/$23.99	TP
7.	9781401265854	OCT160298	BATGIRL: CASSANDRA CAIN VOL. 3: POINT BLANK	PUCKETT, KELLEY	VARIOUS	$19.99/$25.99	TP
8.	9781401269104	MAY170330	BATGIRL: STEPHANIE BROWN VOL. 1	MILLER, BRYAN Q.	GARBETT, LEE	$29.99/$39.99	TP
9.	9781401277888	DEC170383	BATGIRL: STEPHANIE BROWN VOL. 2	MILLER, BRYAN Q.	NGUYEN, DUSTIN	$24.99/$33.99	TP
10.	9781401238148	NOV120261	BATGIRL VOL. 1: THE DARKEST REFLECTION	SIMONE, GAIL	SYAF, ARDIAN; CIFUENTES, VINCENTE	$14.99/$17.99	TP
11.	9781401238179	JUL130236	BATGIRL VOL. 2: KNIGHTFALL DESCENDS	SIMONE, GAIL	SYAF, ARDIAN; BENES, ED	$16.99/$19.99	TP
12.	9781401246280	FEB140247	BATGIRL VOL. 3: DEATH OF THE FAMILY	SIMONE, GAIL	BENES, ED; SAMPERE, DANIEL	$16.99/$19.99	TP
13.	9781401250409	SEP140305	BATGIRL VOL. 4: WANTED	SIMONE, GAIL	PASARIN, FERNANDO	$16.99/$19.99	TP
14.	9781401255114	FEB150250	BATGIRL VOL. 5: DEADLINE	SIMONE, GAIL	PASARIN, FERNANDO	$17.99/$20.99	TP
15.	9781401257989	DEC148636	BATGIRL VOL. 1: THE BATGIRL OF BURNSIDE	STEWART, CAMERON; FLETCHER, BRENDEN	TARR, BABS	$14.99/$17.99	TP
16.	9781401259662	NOV150268	BATGIRL VOL. 2: FAMILY BUSINESS	STEWART, CAMERON; FLETCHER, BRENDEN	TARR, BABS	$14.99/$16.99	TP
17.	9781401262693	MAY160302	BATGIRL VOL. 3: MINDFIELDS	STEWART, CAMERON; FLETCHER, BRENDEN	TARR, BABS	$16.99/$19.99	TP
18.	9781401268404	DEC160370	BATGIRL VOL. 1: BEYOND BURNSIDE (REBIRTH)	LARSON, HOPE	ALBUQUERQUE, RAFAEL	$16.99/$19.99	TP
19.	9781401274245	JUL170455	BATGIRL VOL. 2: SON OF PENGUIN (REBIRTH)	LARSON, HOPE	WILDGOOSE, CHRISTIAN	$16.99/$22.99	TP
20.	9781401278908	DEC170375	BATGIRL VOL. 3: SUMMER OF LIES (REBIRTH)	LARSON, HOPE	WILDGOOSE, CHRISTIAN	$16.99/$22.99	TP
21.	9781401284657		BATGIRL VOL. 4: STRANGE LOOP	LARSON, HOPE	GODLEWSKI, SCOTT	$19.99/$25.99	TP
22.	9781401289461		BATGIRL VOL. 5: VANISHING POINT	SCOTT, MAIRGHREAD	PELLETIER, PAUL	$16.99/$22.99	TP
23.	9781401268671	JAN170377	BATGIRL AND THE BIRDS OF PREY VOL. 1: WHO IS ORACLE? (REBIRTH)	BENSON, SHAWNA; BENSON, JULIE	ROE, CLAIRE	$16.99/$19.99	
24.	9781401273804	SEP170401	BATGIRL AND THE BIRDS OF PREY VOL. 2: SOURCE CODE (REBIRTH)	BENSON, JULIE; BENSON, SHAWNA	ROE, CLAIRE	$16.99/$22.99	TP
25.	9781401277819	APR180260	BATGIRL AND THE BIRDS OF PREY VOL. 3: FULL CIRCLE	BENSON, JULIE; BENSON, SHAWNA	ANTONIO, ROGE	$19.99/$25.99	TP

SUPERGIRL BACKLIST AND SUGGESTED READING ORDER

	ISBN	DIAMOND CODE	TITLE	AUTHOR	ARTIST	US$/$CAN	FORMAT
1.	9781401262464	JAN160337	SUPERGIRL: THE SILVER AGE OMNIBUS VOL. 1	VARIOUS	VARIOUS	$19.99/$75.00	TP
2.	9781401278618	OCT170378	SUPERGIRL: THE SILVER AGE OMNIBUS VOL. 2	VARIOUS	VARIOUS	$99.99/$130.99	HC
3.	9781401272920	APR170436	SUPERGIRL: THE SILVER AGE VOL. 1	VARIOUS	VARIOUS	$29.99/$33.99	TP
4.	9781401281311	MAY180590	SUPERGIRL: THE SILVER AGE VOL. 2	VARIOUS	VARIOUS	$29.99/$39.99	TP
5.	9781401263461	APR160389	DARING ADVENTURES OF SUPERGIRL VOL. 1	KUPPERBERG, PAUL	INFANTINO, CARMINE	$19.99/$23.99	TP
6.	9781401271152	APR170422	DARING ADVENTURES OF SUPERGIRL VOL. 2	KUPPERBERG, PAUL	INFANTINO, CARMINE	$24.99/$33.99	TP
7.	9781401260927	JUL160420	SUPERGIRL BOOK ONE	DAVID, PETER	FRANK, GARY	$24.99/$33.99	TP
8.	9781401265533	DEC160388	SUPERGIRL BOOK TWO	DAVID, PETER	KIRK, LEONARD	$19.99/$25.99	TP
9.	9781401268794	JUL170484	SUPERGIRL BOOK THREE	DAVID, PETER	KIRK, LEONARD	$29.99/$39.99	TP
10.	9781401273644	APR180279	SUPERGIRL BOOK FOUR	DAVID, PETER	KIRK, LEONARD	$29.99/$39.99	TP
11.	9781401287764		SUPERGIRL BOOK FIVE	DAVID, PETER	KIRK, LEONARD	$29.99/$39.99	TP
12.	9781401270124	JUN160353	SUPERGIRL: BIZARROGIRL NEW EDITION	GATES, STERLING	IGLE, JAMAL	$17.99/$23.99	TP
13.	9781401270155	JUN160352	SUPERGIRL: FRIENDS & FUGITIVES	GATES, STERLING	IGLE, JAMAL	$16.99/$22.99	TP
14.	9781401270148	JUN160351	SUPERGIRL: WHO IS SUPERWOMAN?	GATES, STERLING	IGLE, JAMAL	$16.99/$22.99	TP
15.	9781401260934	OCT150252	SUPERGIRL VOL. 1: THE GIRL OF STEEL	LOEB, JEPH	TURNER, MICHAEL	$16.99/$19.99	TP
16.	9781401264673	MAY160317	SUPERGIRL VOL. 2: BREAKING THE CHAIN	KELLY, JOE	CHURCHILL, IAN	$19.99/$23.99	TP
17.	9781401270797	FEB170316	SUPERGIRL VOL. 3: GHOSTS OF KRYPTON	PUCKETT, KELLEY	JOHNSON, DREW EDWARD	$19.99/$25.99	TP
18.	9781401274825	OCT170377	SUPERGIRL VOL. 4: DAUGHTER OF NEW KRYPTON	GATES, STERLING	IGLE, JAMAL	$19.99/$25.99	TP
19.	9781401285746		SUPERGIRL VOL. 5: THE HUNT FOR REACTRON	GATES, STERLING	IGLE, JAMAL	$19.99/$25.99	TP
20.	9781401236809	JUL120216	SUPERGIRL VOL. 1: LAST DAUGHTER OF KRYPTON	GREEN, MICHAEL; JOHNSON, MIKE	ASRAR, MAHMUD	$14.99/$17.99	TP
21.	9781401240875	APR130223	SUPERGIRL VOL. 2: GIRL IN THE WORLD	GREEN, MICHAEL; JOHNSON, MIKE	ASRAR, MAHMUD	$14.99/$17.99	TP
22.	9781401288358		SUPERGIRL: LAST DAUGHTER (DC ESSENTIAL EDITION)	GREEN, MICHAEL	JOHNSON, MIKE	$24.99/$33.99	TP
23.	9781401243180	NOV130235	SUPERGIRL VOL. 3: SANCTUARY	JOHNSON, MIKE	ASRAR, MAHMUD	$16.99/$19.99	TP
24.	9781401247003	APR140273	SUPERGIRL VOL. 4: OUT OF THE PAST	NELSON, MICHAEL ALAN	ASRAR, MAHMUD	$14.99/$17.99	TP
25.	9781401250515	OCT140364	SUPERGIRL VOL. 5: RED DAUGHTER OF KRYPTON	NELSON, MICHAEL ALAN	NEVES, DIOGENES	$17.99/$20.99	TP
26.	9781401255411	APR150301	SUPERGIRL VOL. 6: CRUCIBLE	BEDARD, TONY	LUPACCHINO, EMANUELA	$16.99/$19.99	TP
27.	9781401268466	FEB170296	SUPERGIRL VOL. 1: REIGN OF THE CYBORG SUPER-MEN (REBIRTH)	ORLANDO, STEVE	CHING, BRIAN	$16.99/$19.99	TP
28.	9781401274337	JUL170464	SUPERGIRL VOL. 2: ESCAPE FROM THE PHANTOM ZONE (REBIRTH)	ORLANDO, STEVE	CHING, BRIAN	$16.99/$22.99	TP
29.	9781401278243	JAN180390	SUPERGIRL VOL. 3: GIRL OF NO TOMORROW (REBIRTH)	ORLANDO, STEVE	ROCHA, ROBSON	$14.99/$19.99	TP
30.	9781401284879		SUPERGIRL VOL. 4: PLAIN SIGHT	ORLANDO, STEVE	CAMPBELL, JAMAL	$16.99/$22.99	TP
31.	9781401289188	JUN188695	SUPERGIRL VOL. 1	ANDREYKO, MARC	MAGUIRE, KEVIN	$16.99/$22.99	TP
32.	9781401268947	FEB180311	SUPERGIRL: BEING SUPER	TAMAKI, MARIKO	JONES, JOELLE	$16.99/$22.99	TP
33.	9781401262655	FEB168236	ADVENTURES OF SUPERGIRL VOL. 1	GATES, STERLING	VARIOUS	$16.99/$22.99	TP
34.	9781401263201	FEB160240	SUPERGIRL: COSMIC ADVENTURES OF THE 8TH GRADE (NEW EDITION)	WALKER, LANDRY	VARIOUS	$12.99/$15.99	TP

JUSTICE SOCIETY BACKLIST AND SUGGESTED READING ORDER

	ISBN	DIAMOND CODE	TITLE	AUTHOR	ARTIST	US$/$CAN	FORMAT
1.	9781401267339	FEB170309	THE LAST DAYS OF THE JUSTICE SOCIETY OF AMERICA	VARIOUS	VARIOUS	$24.99/$33.99	TP
2.	9781401274900	SEP170416	JSA BY GEOFF JOHNS BOOK ONE	JOHNS, GEOFF; GOYER, DAVID S.; ROBINSON, JAMES	SADOWSKI, STEPHEN	$34.99/$45.99	TP
3.	9781401281540	MAY180585	JSA BY GEOFF JOHNS BOOK TWO	JOHNS, GEOFF; GOYER, DAVID	SADOWSKI, STEPHEN	$29.99/$39.99	TP
4.	9781401247614	JAN140343	JSA OMNIBUS VOL. 1	JOHNS, GEOFF; GOYER, DAVID	SADOWSKI, STEPHEN; BAIR, MICHAEL; PACHECO, CARLOS	$125.00/$144.00	HC

	ISBN | DIAMOND CODE	TITLE	AUTHOR | ARTIST	US$/SCAN | FORMAT
5.	9781401251383 JUL140254	JSA OMNIBUS VOL. 2	JOHNS, GEOFF | KRAMER, DON; MORALES, RAGS	$150.00/$172.00 | HC
6.	9781401255305 FEB150261	JSA OMNIBUS VOL. 3	JOHNS, GEOFF | ROSS, ALEX; PEREZ, GEORGE	$125.00/$144.00 | HC
7.	9781401242817 JUL130241	EARTH 2 VOL. 1: THE GATHERING	ROBINSON, JAMES | SCOTT, NICOLA	$14.99/$17.99 | TP
8.	9781401246143 JAN140344	EARTH 2 VOL. 2: THE TOWER OF FATE	ROBINSON, JAMES | SCOTT, NICOLA; CINAR, YILDARAY	$16.99/$19.99 | TP
9.	9781401249380 JUL140241	EARTH 2 VOL. 3: BATTLE CRY	ROBINSON, JAMES | SCOTT, NICOLA	$14.99/$17.99 | TP
10.	9781401254179 JAN150378	EARTH 2 VOL. 4: THE DARK AGE	TAYLOR, TOM | SCOTT, NICOLA	$14.99/$17.99 | TP
11.	9781401257576 AUG150265	EARTH 2 VOL. 5: THE KRYPTONIAN	TAYLOR, TOM | SCOTT, NICOLA	$16.99/$19.99 | HC
12.	9781401257583 JUL150311	EARTH 2 VOL. 6: COLLISION	WILSON, DANIEL | BENNETT, MARGUERITTE	$22.99/$27.99 | TP
13.	9781401256036 FEB150253	EARTH 2: WORLD'S END VOL. 1	WILSON, DANIEL H.; BENNETT, MARGUERITTE; JOHNSON, MIKE | BARROWS, EDDY	$29.99/$35.00 | TP
14.	9781401258443 SEP150294	EARTH 2: WORLD'S END VOL. 2	WILSON, DANIEL H.; BENNETT, MARGUERITE; JOHNSON, MIKE | BENNETT, MARGUERITTE; BARROWS, EDDY	$24.99/$29.99 | TP
15.	9781401262716 JUL160401	CONVERGENCE	KING, JEFF; LOBDELL, SCOTT | PAGULAYAN, CARLO	$19.99/$23.99 | TP
16.	9781401261238 DEC150321	EARTH 2: SOCIETY VOL. 1: PLANETFALL	WILSON, DANIEL H. | JIMENEZ, JORGE	$16.99/$19.99 | TP
17.	9781401264710 MAY160309	EARTH 2: SOCIETY VOL. 2: INDIVISIBLE	ABNETT, DAN | JIMENEZ, JORGE	$14.99/$17.99 | TP
18.	9781401267971 JAN170391	EARTH 2: SOCIETY VOL. 3: A WHOLE NEW WORLD	ABNETT, DAN | VARIOUS	$16.99/$22.99 | TP
19.	9781401271435 MAY170337	EARTH 2: SOCIETY VOL. 4: LIFE AFTER DEATH	ABNETT, DAN | REDONDO, BRUNO	$14.99/$19.99 | TP
20.	9781401278434 JAN180407	JSA: THE GOLDEN AGE (NEW EDITION)	ROBINSON, JAMES | SMITH, PAUL	$19.99/$25.99 | TP

DC COMICS SELECTED BACKLIST

	ISBN | DIAMOND CODE	TITLE	AUTHOR | ARTIST	US$/SCAN | FORMAT
	9781401285791	ADAM STRANGE: THE SILVER AGE VOL. 1	FOX, GARDNER | VARIOUS	$29.99/$39.99 | TP
	9781401272951 FEB170299	ADAM STRANGE: THE SILVER AGE OMNIBUS	FOX, GARDNER | INFANTINO, CARMINE	$99.99/$130.99 | HC
	9781401275341 OCT170362	ANARKY: THE COMPLETE SERIES	GRANT, ALAN | BREYFOGLE, NORM	$19.99/$25.99 | TP
	9781401235079 FEB120247	ANIMAL MAN VOL. 1: THE HUNT	LEMIRE, JEFF | FOREMAN, TRAVEL	$14.99 /$17.99 | TP
	9781401238001 OCT120251	ANIMAL MAN VOL. 2: ANIMAL VS. MAN	LEMIRE, JEFF | PUGH, STEVE; GREEN, TIMOTHY	$16.99 /$19.99 | TP
	9781401242626 JUN130267	ANIMAL MAN VOL. 3: ROTWORLD: THE RED KINGDOM	LEMIRE, JEFF; SNYDER, SCOTT | PUGH, STEVE	$16.99 /$19.99 | TP
	9781401246440 DEC130298	ANIMAL MAN VOL. 4: SPLINTER SPECIES	LEMIRE, JEFF | PUGH, STEVE	$14.99/$17.99 | TP
	9781401249946 AUG140326	ANIMAL MAN VOL. 5: EVOLVE OR DIE!	LEMIRE, JEFF | FOREMAN, TRAVEL	$14.99/$17.99 | TP
	9781401289416	ANIMAL MAN BY JEFF LEMIRE OMNIBUS	LEMIRE, JEFF | FOREMAN, TRAVEL	$99.99/$130.99 | HC
	9781401278861 NOV170371	LEGENDS OF TOMORROW: THE ATOM	VARIOUS | VARIOUS	$19.99/$25.99 | TP
	9781401288426	THE AUTHORITY BY ED BRUBAKER & DUSTIN NGUYEN	BRUBAKER, ED | NGUYEN, DUSTIN	$24.99/$33.99 | TP
	9781401276478 APR170432	ABSOLUTE AUTHORITY VOL. 1 (NEW EDITION)	ELLIS, WARREN | HITCH, BRYAN	$75.00/$99.00 | HC
	9781401281151 JAN180392	ABSOLUTE AUTHORITY VOL. 2 (NEW EDITION)	ELLIS, WARREN | HITCH, BRYAN	$75.00/$99.00 | HC
	9781401284428 JUN180564	BANE: CONQUEST	DIXON, CHUCK | NOLAN, GRAHAM	$29.99/$39.99 | TP
	9781401237844 OCT120253	BATWOMAN VOL. 1: HYDROLOGY	WILLIAMS III, J.H.; BLACKMAN, W. HADEN | WILLIAMS III, J.H.	$14.99 /$17.99 | TP
	9781401237929 JUN130269	BATWOMAN VOL. 2: TO DROWN THE WORLD	WILLIAMS III, J.H.; BLACKMAN, W. HADEN | REEDER, AMY; MCCARTHY, TREVOR	$14.99 /$17.99 | TP
	9781401246105 DEC130300	BATWOMAN VOL. 3: WORLD'S FINEST	WILLIAMS III, J.H.; BLACKMAN, W. HADEN | WILLIAMS III, J.H.	$14.99 /$17.99 | TP
	9781401249991 JUN140271	BATWOMAN VOL. 4: THIS BLOOD IS THICK	WILLIAMS III, J.H.; BLACKMAN, W. HADEN | MCCARTHY, TREVOR	$14.99 /$17.99 | TP
	9781401250829 AUG140335	BATWOMAN VOL. 5: WEBS	ANDREYKO, MARC | HAUN, JEREMY; MCCARTHY, TREVOR	$19.99/$23.99 | TP
	9781401254681 APR150291	BATWOMAN VOL. 6: THE UNKNOWNS	ANDREYKO, MARC | HAUN, JEREMY	$16.99/$17.99 | TP
	9781401274306 AUG170318	BATWOMAN VOL. 1: THE MANY ARMS OF DEATH (REBIRTH)	BENNETT, MARGUERITE; TYNION IV, JAMES IV | EPTING, STEVE	$16.99/$22.99 | TP
	9781401278717 FEB180283	BATWOMAN VOL. 2: WONDERLAND	BENNETT, MARGUERITE | BLANCO, FERNANDO	$14.99/$19.99 | TP
	9781401285777	BATWOMAN VOL. 3: THE FALL OF THE HOUSE OF KANE	BENNETT, MARGUERITE | BLANCO, FERNANDO	$16.99/$22.99 | TP
	9781401258160 JUL150312	BIRDS OF PREY VOL. 1	DIXON, CHUCK | HALEY, MATT	$19.99/$23.99 | TP
	9781401260958 NOV150276	BIRDS OF PREY VOL. 2	DIXON, CHUCK | LAND, GREG	$19.99/$23.99 | TP
	9781401264543 SEP160339	BIRDS OF PREY VOL. 3: THE HUNT FOR ORACLE	SIMONE, GAIL | VARIOUS	$19.99/$25.99 | TP
	9781401261177 DEC150319	BLACK CANARY VOL. 1: KICKING AND SCREAMING	FLETCHER, BRENDEN | WU, ANNIE	$14.99/$17.99 | TP
	9781401265274 AUG160323	BLACK CANARY VOL. 2: NEW KILLER STAR	FLETCHER, BRENDEN | WU, ANNIE	$14.99/$19.99 | TP
	9781401260712 JAN160326	BLACK LIGHTNING VOL. 1	ISABELLA, TONY | O'NEIL, DENNIS	$19.99/$23.99 | TP
	9781401275464 OCT170365	BLACK LIGHTNING VOL. 2	ISABELLA, TONY | CONWAY, GERRY	$19.99/$25.99 | TP
	9781401279646 OCT170366	BLACK LIGHTNING: YEAR ONE (NEW EDITION)	METER, JEN VAN | HAMNER, CULLY	$14.99/$19.99 | TP
	9781401287993	BLACK LIGHTNING: THE COMPLETE 1995 SERIES	ISABELLA, TONY | NEWELL, EDDY	$19.99/$25.99 | TP
	9781401275150	BLACK LIGHTNING: COLD DEAD HANDS	ISABELLA, TONY | HENRY, CLAYTON	$16.99/$22.99 | TP
	9781401268688 FEB170292	BLUE BEETLE VOL. 1: THE MORE THINGS CHANGE (REBIRTH)	GIFFEN, KEITH | KOLINS, SCOTT	$16.99/$19.99 | TP
	9781401275075 SEP170402	BLUE BEETLE VOL. 2: HARD CHOICES (REBIRTH)	GIFFEN, KEITH | KOLINS, SCOTT	$16.99/$22.99 | TP
	9781401280833 APR180266	BLUE BEETLE VOL. 3: ROAD TO NOWHERE	SEBELA, CHRISTOPHER | SILAS, THONY	$16.99/$22.99 | TP
	9781401275303 JAN180360	BUG! THE ADVENTURES OF FORAGER	ALLRED, LEE | ALLRED, MICHAEL	$16.99/$22.99 | TP
	9781401274177 OCT170367	CAPTAIN ATOM: THE FALL AND RISE OF CAPTAIN ATOM	BATES, CARY; WEISMAN, GREG | CONRAD, WILL	$16.99/$22.99 | TP
	9781401207175 MAY098043	CATWOMAN: WHEN IN ROME	LOEB, JEPH | SALE, TIM	$14.99 /$17.99 | TP
	9781401273637 JUN170399	CATWOMAN BY JIM BALENT BOOK ONE	DIXON, CHUCK | BALENT, JIM	$29.99/$39.99 | TP
	9781401288204	CATWOMAN BY JIM BALENT BOOK TWO	DIXON, CHUCK | BALENT, JIM	$29.99/$39.99 | TP
	9781401233846 OCT110246	CATWOMAN VOL. 1	BRUBAKER, ED | COOKE, DARWYN	$29.99/$35.00 | TP
	9781401245924 DEC130309	CATWOMAN VOL. 3: UNDER PRESSURE	BRUBAKER, ED; PALMIOTTI, JIMMY | GULACY, PAUL	$24.99/$28.99 | TP
	9781401260736 FEB160230	CATWOMAN VOL. 5: BACKWARD MASKING	PFEIFER, WILL | LOPEZ, DAVID	$24.99/$29.99 | TP
	9781401265588 OCT160300	CATWOMAN VOL. 6: FINAL JEOPARDY	PFEIFER, WILL | VARIOUS	$24.99/$33.99 | TP

ISBN	DIAMOND CODE	TITLE	AUTHOR	ARTIST	US$/$CAN	FORMAT
9781401234645	FEB120248	CATWOMAN VOL. 1: THE GAME	WINICK, JUDD	MARCH, GUILLEM	$14.99 /$17.99	TP
9781401238391	NOV120260	CATWOMAN VOL. 2: DOLLHOUSE	WINICK, JUDD	MARCH, GUILLEM	$14.99 /$17.99	TP
9781401242725	JUL130237	CATWOMAN VOL. 3: DEATH OF THE FAMILY	NOCENTI, ANN	SANDOVAL, RAFA	$16.99 /$28.99	TP
9781401246273	FEB140253	CATWOMAN VOL. 4: GOTHAM UNDERGROUND	NOCENTI, ANN	SANDOVAL, RAFA; TARROGANA, JORDI	$17.99/$20.99	TP
9781401250638	AUG140332	CATWOMAN VOL. 5: RACE OF THIEVES	NOCENTI, ANN	OLIFFE, PATRICK	$17.99/$20.99	TP
9781401254698	APR150299	CATWOMAN VOL. 6: KEEPER OF THE CASTLE	VALENTINE, GENEVIEVE	BROWN, GARRY	$16.99/$17.99	TP
9781401261184	NOV150275	CATWOMAN VOL. 7: INHERITANCE	VALENTINE, GENEVIEVE	MESSINA, DAVE	$14.99/$17.99	TP
9781401264864	JUL160400	CATWOMAN VOL. 8: RUN LIKE HELL	TIERI, FRANK	MIRANDA, INAKI	$14.99/$17.99	TP
9781401288891	JUN188707	CATWOMAN VOL. 1	JONES, JOELLE	JONES, JOELLE	$16.99/$22.99	TP
9781401260064	JUL150306	CATWOMAN: A CELEBRATION OF 75 YEARS	VARIOUS	VARIOUS	$39.99/$48.99	HC
9781401270827	MAR170396	CAVE CARSON HAS A CYBERNETIC EYE VOL. 1: GOING UNDERGROUND	WAY, GERARD; RIVERA, JON	OEMING, MICHAEL AVON	$16.99/$22.99	TP
9781401277475	NOV170337	CAVE CARSON HAS A CYBERNETIC EYE VOL. 2: EVERY ME, EVERY YOU	RIVERA, JON	OEMING, MICHAEL AVON	$16.99/$22.99	TP
9781401285401		CAVE CARSON HAS AN INTERSTELLAR EYE	RIVERA, JON	OEMING, MICHAEL AVON	$16.99/$22.99	TP
9781401277192	AUG170333	CHALLENGERS OF THE UNKNOWN BY JACK KIRBY	KIRBY, JACK	KIRBY, JACK	$29.99/$39.99	TP
9781401289294	NOV170364	CHALLENGERS OF THE UNKNOWN BY JEPH LOEB AND TIM SALE	LOEB, JEPH	SALE, TIM	$19.99/$25.99	TP
9781401265953	OCT160304	CHECKMATE BY GREG RUCKA VOL. 1	RUCKA, GREG	VARIOUS	$19.99/$25.99	TP
9781401275372	OCT170368	CHECKMATE BY GREG RUCKA BOOK 2	RUCKA, GREG	VARIOUS	$24.99/$33.99	TP
9781401243234	NOV130227	CONSTANTINE VOL. 1: THE SPARK AND THE FLAME	LEMIRE, JEFF; FAWKES, RAY	GUEDES , RENATO	$9.99 /$17.99	TP
9781401247478	MAY140366	CONSTANTINE VOL. 2: BLIGHT	FAWKES, RAY	GUEDES, RENATO	$14.99/$17.99	TP
9781401250850	NOV140296	CONSTANTINE VOL. 3: THE VOICE IN THE FIRE	FAWKES, RAY	ACO	$14.99/$17.99	TP
9781401254704	MAY150240	CONSTANTINE VOL. 4: THE APOCALYPSE ROAD	FAWKES, RAY	SALAZAR, EDGAR	$14.99/$17.99	TP
9781401259723	NOV150263	CONSTANTINE: THE HELLBLAZER VOL. 1: GOING DOWN	DOYLE, MING; TYNION IV, JAMES	ROSSMO, RILEY	$14.99/$17.99	TP
9781401263713	JUN160335	CONSTANTINE: THE HELLBLAZER VOL. 2: THE ART OF THE DEAL	DOYLE, MING; TYNION IV, JAMES	ROSSMO, RILEY	$16.99/$22.99	TP
9781401283476		THE CURSE OF BRIMSTONE (NEW AGE OF HEROES)	JORDAN, JUSTIN	TAN, PHILIP	$16.99/$22.99	TP
9781401268862	DEC160374	THE HELLBLAZER VOL. 1: THE POISON TRUTH (REBIRTH)	OLIVER, SIMON	MORITAT	$16.99/$22.99	TP
9781401273897	JUL170459	THE HELLBLAZER VOL. 2: THE SMOKELESS FIRE (REBIRTH)	OLIVER, SIMON	GUERRA, PIA	$16.99/$22.99	TP
9781401278014	DEC170379	THE HELLBLAZER VOL. 3: THE INSPIRATION GAME (REBIRTH)	SEELEY, TIM	VARIOUS	$16.99/$22.99	TP
9781401286279		THE HELLBLAZER VOL. 4	SEELEY, TIM	VARIOUS	$16.99/$22.99	TP
9781401268152	NOV160329	COSMIC ODYSSEY: THE DELUXE EDITION	STARLIN, JIM	VARIOUS	$29.99/$39.99	HC
9781401261191	DEC150318	CYBORG VOL. 1: UNPLUGGED	WALKER, DAVID	REIS, IVAN; PRADO, JOE	$14.99/$17.99	TP
9781401265311	AUG160334	CYBORG VOL. 2: ENEMY OF THE STATE	WALKER, DAVID F.	WATANABE, FELIPE	$14.99/$19.99	TP
9781401267926	DEC160371	CYBORG VOL. 1: THE IMITATION OF LIFE (REBIRTH)	SEMPER JR., JOHN	CONRAD, WILL; PELLETIER, PAUL	$16.99/$19.99	TP
9781401270872	MAY170323	CYBORG VOL. 2: DANGER IN DETROIT (REBIRTH)	SEMPER JR., JOHN	CONRAD, WILL; PELLETIER, PAUL	$19.99/$25.99	TP
9781401274559	FEB180284	CYBORG VOL. 3: SINGULARITY	SEMPER JR., JOHN	CONRAD, WILL	$16.99/$22.99	TP
9781401285135		CYBORG VOL. 4	GREVIOUX, KEVIN	VARIOUS	$16.99/$22.99	TP
9781401283339	JUN180574	DAMAGE VOL. 1: OUT OF CONTROL (NEW AGE OF HEROES)	VENDITTI, ROBERT	DANIEL, TONY S.	$16.99/$22.99	TP
9781401289034		DAMAGE VOL. 2 (NEW AGE OF HEROES)	VENDITTI, ROBERT	NEVES, DIOGENES	$16.99/$22.99	TP
9781401274610	FEB180300	DASTARDLY & MUTTLEY	ENNIS, GARTH	MAURICET	$16.99/$22.99	TP
9781401242435	JUN130262	DC COMICS ONE MILLION OMNIBUS	MORRISON, GRANT	VARIOUS	$99.99 /$112.00	HC
9781401261320	DEC150323	DC BOMBSHELLS VOL. 1: ENLISTED	BENNETT, MARGUERITE	SAUVAGE, MARGUERITE	$16.99/$19.99	TP
9781401264482	APR160394	DC BOMBSHELLS VOL. 2: ALLIES	BENNETT, MARGUERITE	SAUVAGE, MARGUERITE	$16.99/$19.99	TP
9781401268770	DEC160384	DC BOMBSHELLS VOL. 3: UPRISING	BENNETT, MARGUERITE	SAUVAGE, MARGUERITE	$16.99/$22.99	TP
9781401274078	MAR170418	DC BOMBSHELLS VOL. 4: QUEENS	BENNETT, MARGUERITE	SAUVAGE, MARGUERITE	$19.99/$25.99	TP
9781401276034	JUL170471	DC COMICS: BOMBSHELLS VOL. 5: THE DEATH OF ILLUSION	BENNETT, MARGUERITE	BRAGA, LAURA; ANDOLFO, MIRKA	$16.99/$22.99	TP
9781401276027	DEC170392	DC COMICS: BOMBSHELLS VOL. 6: WAR STORIES	BENNETT, MARGUERITE	BRAGA, LAURA; ANDOLFO, MIRKA	$16.99/$22.99	TP
9781401281687	MAY180574	DC BOMBSHELLS: THE DELUXE EDITION BOOK ONE	BENNETT, MARGUERITE	SAUVAGE, MARGUERITE	$39.99/$53.99	HC
9781401264697	JUN160333	THE ART OF DC BOMBSHELLS	LUCIA, ANT	LUCIA, ANT	$39.99/$53.99	HC
9781401280239	MAR180340	BOMBSHELLS: UNITED VOL. 1: AMERICAN SOIL	BENNETT, MARGUERITE	SAUVAGE, MARGUERITE	$16.99/$22.99	TP
9781401284725		BOMBSHELLS: UNITED VOL. 2: WAR BONDS	BENNETT, MARGUERITE	JARRELL, SANDY	$16.99/$22.99	TP
9781401288266		BOMBSHELLS: UNITED VOL. 3	BENNETT, MARGUERITE	VARIOUS	$16.99/$22.99	TP
9781401238841	AUG120249	DC COMICS: THE NEW 52 ZERO OMNIBUS	VARIOUS	VARIOUS	$150.00 /$112.00	HC
9781401244965	AUG130289	DC COMICS: THE NEW 52 VILLAINS OMNIBUS	VARIOUS	VARIOUS	$150.00 /$176.00	HC
9781401279523	JUL170470	DC'S GREATEST HITS BOX SET	VARIOUS	VARIOUS	$39.96/$50.98	BOXED SET
9781401276041	JUN170407	DC MEETS HANNA-BARBERA	VARIOUS	VARIOUS	$16.99/$22.99	TP
9781401286286		DC MEETS HANNA-BARBERA VOL. 2	VARIOUS	VARIOUS	$16.99/$22.99	TP
9781401277574	NOV170365	DC MEETS LOONEY TUNES	KING, TOM	PALMIOTTI, JIMMY	$19.99/$25.99	TP
9781401288334		DC MEETS LOONEY TUNES VOL. 2	VARIOUS	VARIOUS	$16.99/$22.99	TP
9781401233402	DEC120333	DC UNIVERSE BY ALAN MOORE	MOORE, ALAN	VARIOUS	$24.99 /$28.99	TP
9781401281144	APR180267	DC UNIVERSE BY MIKE MIGNOLA	VARIOUS	MIGNOLA, MIKE	$19.99/$25.99	TP
9781401278274	JAN180396	THE DC UNIVERSE BY BRIAN K. VAUGHAN	VAUGHAN, BRIAN K.	VARIOUS	$19.99/$25.99	TP
9781401274856	SEP170413	DC UNIVERSE BY JOHN BYRNE	BYRNE, JOHN	BYRNE, JOHN	$39.99/$53.99	HC
9781401287870		DC UNIVERSE BY LEN WEIN	WEIN, LEN	JONES, KELLEY	$34.99/$45.99	HC
9781401277734	NOV170366	THE DC UNIVERSE BY NEIL GAIMAN	GAIMAN, NEIL	VARIOUS	$19.99/$25.99	TP

ISBN	DIAMOND CODE	TITLE	AUTHOR	ARTIST	US$/$CAN	FORMAT
9781401287665		DC VALENTINE'S DAY/LOVE STORIES COLLECTION	CONNER, AMANDA; PALMIOTTI, JIMMY; DINI PAUL | LEMIRE, JEFF	$16.99/$22.99 | TP
9781401277338	MAR180321	DC/YOUNG ANIMAL: MILK WARS	WAY, GERARD | DERINGTON, NICK	$19.99/$25.99 | TP
9781401281410	MAY180575	DEADMAN	ADAMS, NEAL | ADAMS, NEAL	$16.99/$22.99 | TP
9781401271671	MAY170336	DEADMAN BY KELLEY JONES: THE COMPLETE COLLECTION	BARON, MIKE | JONES, KELLEY	$24.99/$33.99 | TP
9781401268411	FEB170307	DEADMAN: DARK MANSION OF FORBIDDEN LOVE	VAUGHN, SARAH | MEDINA, LAN	$17.99/$23.99 | TP
9781401290566		DETECTIVE COMICS BEFORE BATMAN VOL. 1	FINGER, BILL | KANE, BOB	$49.99/$65.99 | HC
9781401290573		DETECTIVE COMICS BEFORE BATMAN VOL. 2	FINGER, BILL | KANE, BOB	$49.99/$65.99 | HC
9781401254285	JAN150379	DEATHSTROKE, THE TERMINATOR VOL. 1: ASSASSINS	WOLFMAN, MARV | ERWIN, STEVE; BLYBERG, WILL	$19.99/$23.99 | TP
9781401258429	SEP150293	DEATHSTROKE, THE TERMINATOR VOL. 2: SYMPATHY FOR THE DEVIL	WOLFMAN, MARV; GOLDEN, MICHAEL | NICHOLS, ART	$14.99/$17.99 | TP
9781401260767	JUN170400	DEATHSTROKE, THE TERMINATOR VOL. 3: NUCLEAR WINTER	WOLFMAN, MARV | ERWIN, STEVE	$24.99/$33.99 | TP
9781401270834	FEB180301	DEATHSTROKE, THE TERMINATOR VOL. 4: CRASH OR BURN	WOLFMAN, MARV | VARIOUS	$24.99/$33.99 | TP
9781401285753		DEATHSTROKE, THE TERMINATOR VOL. 5: WORLD TOUR	WOLFMAN, MARV | VARIOUS	$24.99/$33.99 | TP
9781401234812	MAY120282	DEATHSTROKE VOL. 1: LEGACY	HIGGINS, KYLE | BENNET, JOE	$16.99/$19.99 | TP
9781401254711	MAR150267	DEATHSTROKE VOL. 1: GODS OF WAR	DANIEL, TONY S. | DANIEL, TONY S.	$14.99/$17.99 | TP
9781401261207	NOV150272	DEATHSTROKE VOL. 2: GOD KILLER	DANIEL, TONY S. | DANIEL, TONY S.	$14.99/$17.99 | TP
9781401264550	MAY160308	DEATHSTROKE VOL. 3 SUICIDE RUN	DANIEL, TONY S. | KIRKHAM, TYLER	$16.99/$19.99 | TP
9781401267940	SEP160341	DEATHSTROKE VOL. 4: FAMILY BUSINESS	BONNY, JAMES | PANTALENA, PAOLO	$16.99/$22.99 | TP
9781401284756	MAR180339	DEATHSTROKE BY TONY S. DANIEL OMNIBUS	DANIEL, TONY S. | DANIEL, TONY S.	$75.00/$99.00 | HC
9781401268237	DEC160372	DEATHSTROKE VOL. 1: THE PROFESSIONAL (REBIRTH)	PRIEST, CHRISTOPHER | PAGULAYAN, CARLO	$17.99/$23.99 | TP
9781401270988	APR170412	DEATHSTROKE VOL. 2: THE GOSPEL OF SLADE (REBIRTH)	PRIEST, CHRISTOPHER | PAGULAYAN, CARLO	$16.99/$22.99 | TP
9781401274061	JUL170457	DEATHSTROKE VOL. 3: TWILIGHT (REBIRTH)	PRIEST, CHRISTOPHER | BENNET, JOE; PAGULAYAN, CARLO	$16.99/$22.99 | TP
9781401275471	JAN180384	DEATHSTROKE VOL. 4: DEFIANCE (REBIRTH)	PRIEST, CHRISTOPHER | NEVES, DIOGENES	$14.99/$19.99 | TP
9781401278335		DEATHSTROKE VOL. 5: FALL OF SLADE	PRIEST, CHRISTOPHER | NEVES, DIOGENES	$16.99/$22.99 | TP
9781401285890		BATMAN VS. DEATHSTROKE	PRIEST, CHRISTOPHER | NEVES, DIOGENES	$24.99/$33.99 | HC
9781401277185	JUL170472	THE DEMON BY JACK KIRBY	KIRBY, JACK | KIRBY, JACK	$29.99/$39.99 | TP
9781401284824		THE DEMON: HELL IS EARTH	CONSTANT, ANDREW | WALKER, BRAD	$16.99/$22.99 | TP
9781401261214	DEC150320	DOCTOR FATE VOL. 1: THE BLOOD PRICE	LEVITZ, PAUL | LIEW, SONNY	$14.99/$17.99 | TP
9781401264925	JUL160406	DOCTOR FATE VOL. 2: PRISONERS OF THE PAST	LEVITZ, PAUL | LIEW, SONNY	$14.99/$19.99 | TP
9781401281113	APR180268	DOOM PATROL: THE SILVER AGE VOL. 1	VARIOUS | VARIOUS	$29.99/$39.99 | TP
9781401269791	FEB170287	DOOM PATROL VOL. 1: BRICK BY BRICK	WAY, GERARD | DERINGTON, NICK	$16.99/$22.99 | TP
9781401275006		DOOM PATROL VOL. 2: NADA	WAY, GERARD | DERINGTON, NICK	$14.99/$19.99 | TP
9781401285203		ETERNITY GIRL	VISAGGIO, MAGDALENE | LIEW, SONNY	$16.99/$22.99 | TP
9781401275211	MAY180576	EXIT STAGE LEFT: THE SNAGGLEPUSS CHRONICLES	RUSSELL, MARK | FEEHAN, MIKE	$16.99/$22.99 | TP
9781401245177	JAN140352	FINAL CRISIS	MORRISON, GRANT | JONES, J.G.	$19.99/$19.99 | TP
9781401268374	DEC160395	THE FLINTSTONES VOL. 1	RUSSELL, MARK | PUGH, STEVE	$16.99/$22.99 | TP
9781401273989	JUL170475	THE FLINTSTONES VOL. 2: BEDROCK BEDLAM	RUSSELL, MARK | PUGH, STEVE	$16.99/$22.99 | TP
9781401265786	SEP160342	FIRESTORM: THE NUCLEAR MAN	CONWAY, GERRY | PANSICO, EDUARDO	$14.99/$19.99 | TP
9781401274757	JUN170377	FOURTH WORLD BY JACK KIRBY OMNIBUS	KIRBY, JACK | KIRBY, JACK	$150.00/$195.00 | HC
9781401290979	APR180277	FRANK MILLER'S RONIN (DC BLACK LABEL EDITION)	MILLER, FRANK | MILLER, FRANK	$19.99/$25.99 | TP
9781401268077	NOV160344	FUTURE QUEST VOL. 1	PARKER, JEFF | SHANER, EVAN	$16.99/$22.99 | TP
9781401273910	JUN170408	FUTURE QUEST VOL. 2	PARKER, JEFF | VARIOUS	$16.99/$22.99 | TP
9781401278304	FEB180297	FUTURE QUEST PRESENTS VOL. 1	PARKER, JEFF | RUDE, STEVE	$16.99/$22.99 | TP
9781401285425	JUN170408	FUTURE QUEST PRESENTS VOL. 2	PARKER, JEFF | VARIOUS	$16.99/$22.99 | TP
9781401254728	MAR150269	GOTHAM ACADEMY VOL. 1: WELCOME TO GOTHAM ACADEMY	CLOONAN, BECKY; FLETCHER, BRENDEN | KERSCHL, KARL	$14.99/$17.99 | TP
9781401256814	DEC150332	GOTHAM ACADEMY VOL. 2: CALAMITY	CLOONAN, BECKY; FLETCHER, BRENDEN | KERSCHL, KARL	$14.99/$17.99 | TP
9781401264789	AUG160328	GOTHAM ACADEMY VOL. 3: YEARBOOK	FLETCHER, BRENDEN | VARIOUS	$14.99/$19.99 | TP
9781401271190	APR170424	GOTHAM ACADEMY: SECOND SEMESTER VOL. 1: WELCOME BACK	FLETCHER, BRENDEN; CLOONAN, BECKY; KERSCHL, KARL | ARCHER, ADAM	$16.99/$22.99 | TP
9781401274740	AUG170335	GOTHAM ACADEMY: SECOND SEMESTER VOL. 2: THE BALLAD OF OLIVE SILVERLOCK	FLETCHER, BRENDEN; CLOONAN, BECKY; KERSCHL, KARL | ARCHER, ADAM	$14.99/$19.99 | TP
9781401220372	DEC100248	GOTHAM CENTRAL BOOK 1: IN THE LINE OF DUTY	RUCKA, GREG; BRUBAKER, ED | LARK, MICHAEL	$19.99/$23.99 | TP
9781401225438	APR110203	GOTHAM CENTRAL BOOK 2: JOKERS AND MADMEN	RUCKA, GREG; BRUBAKER, ED | LARK, MICHAEL	$19.99/$23.99 | TP
9781401232320	JUL110257	GOTHAM CENTRAL BOOK 3: ON THE FREAK BEAT	RUCKA, GREG; BRUBAKER, ED | LARK, MICHAEL	$19.99/$23.99 | TP
9781401231941	JAN120307	GOTHAM CENTRAL BOOK 4: CORRIGAN	RUCKA, GREG; BRUBAKER, ED | KANO	$19.99/$23.99 | TP
9781401261924	DEC150343	GOTHAM CENTRAL OMNIBUS	BRUBAKER, ED; RUCKA, GREG | LARK, MICHAEL; KANO	$99.00/$112.00 | HC
9781401280192	MAR180344	GOTHAM CITY GARAGE VOL. 1	KELLEY, COLLIN; LANZING, JACKSON | CHING, BRIAN	$16.99/$22.99 | TP
9781401284985		GOTHAM CITY GARAGE VOL. 2	KELLY, COLIN; LANZING, JACKSON | CHING, BRIAN	$16.99/$22.99 | TP
9781401251758	JUL140248	GOTHAM CITY SIRENS BOOK ONE	DINI, PAUL | MARCH, GUILLEM	$24.99/$28.99 | TP
9781401254124	JAN150373	GOTHAM CITY SIRENS BOOK TWO	CALLOWAY, PETER | GUINALDO, ANDRES	$24.99/$28.99 | TP
9781401259730	JAN160314	GRAPHIC INK: THE DC COMICS ART OF JIM LEE	LEE, JIM |	$39.99/$48.99 | HC
9781401289133		DC COMICS: THE ART OF BRUCE TIMM	TIMM, BRUCE | TIMM, BRUCE	$29.99/$39.99 | TP
9781401277970	DEC170393	DC COMICS: THE ART OF DARWYN COOKE	COOKE, DARWYN | COOKE, DARWYN	$29.99/$39.99 | TP
9781401278052	DEC170394	THE HAWK AND THE DOVE: THE SILVER AGE	DITKO, STEVE | VARIOUS	$24.99/$33.99 | TP
9781401272906	MAR170424	HAWKMAN BY GEOFF JOHNS BOOK ONE	JOHNS, GEOFF | MORALES, RAGS	$29.99/$39.99 | TP
9781401278342	JAN180403	HAWKMAN BY GEOFF JOHNS BOOK TWO	JOHNS, GEOFF | MORALES, RAGS	$29.99/$39.99 | TP

ISBN	DIAMOND CODE	TITLE	AUTHOR	ARTIST	US$/SCAN	FORMAT
9781401268244	MAR170423	HAWKMAN & ADAM STRANGE: OUT OF TIME	ANDREYKO, MARC	LOPRESTI, AARON	$16.99/$22.99	TP
9781401240226	APR130245	HE-MAN AND THE MASTERS OF THE UNIVERSE VOL. 1	ROBINSON, JAMES; GIFFEN, KIETH	TAN, PHILIP	$14.99/$17.99	TP
9781401243128	NOV130244	HE-MAN AND THE MASTERS OF THE UNIVERSE VOL. 2: ORIGINS OF ETERNIA	GIFFEN, KEITH; FIALKOV, JOSHUA HALE	IRVING, FRAZER; GIFFEN, KEITH	$14.99/$17.99	TP
9781401258481	JUL150314	HE-MAN: THE ETERNITY WAR VOL. 1	ABNETT, DAN	MAHN, POP	$14.99/$17.99	TP
9781401261283	JAN160329	HE-MAN: THE ETERNITY WAR VOL. 2	ABNETT, DAN	MHAN, POP	$14.99/$17.99	TP
9781401269159	APR170425	HE-MAN/THUNDERCATS	DAVID, ROB	GOLDFINE, LLOYD	$16.99/$22.99	TP
9781401288594		HITMAN BOOK ONE	ENNIS, GARTH	MCCREA, JOHN	$24.99/$33.99	TP
9781401263263	MAR160263	ALL-STAR SECTION EIGHT	ENNIS, GARTH	MCCREA, JOHN	$16.99/$19.99	TP
9781401268138	MAY170349	SIX PACK & DOGWELDER	ENNIS, GARTH	BRAUN, RUSS	$19.99/$25.99	TP
9781401285661	JUN180578	HOUSE OF MYSTERY: THE BRONZE AGE OMNIBUS VOL. 1	VARIOUS	VARIOUS	$99.99/$130.99	HC
9781401276843	JUL170478	HOUSE OF SECRETS: THE BRONZE AGE OMNIBUS VOL. 1	WEIN, LEN	APARO, JIM	$125.00/$163.00	HC
9781401281335	JUN180579	IMPULSE BY MARK WAID & HUMBERTO RAMOS OMNIBUS	WAID, MARK	RAMOS, HUMBERTO	$99.99/$130.99	HC
9781401283308		THE IMMORTAL MEN VOL. 1 (NEW AGE OF HEROES)	TYNION IV, JAMES	LEE, JIM	$16.99/$22.99	TP
9781401280253	APR180271	THE JETSONS	PALMIOTTI, JIMMY	BRITO, PIERRE	$16.99/$22.99	TP
9781401274795	NOV170370	JACK KIRBY 100TH CELEBRATION COLLECTION	VARIOUS	VARIOUS	$19.99/$25.99	TP
9781401242589	AUG130307	THE JOKER: THE CLOWN PRINCE OF CRIME	VARIOUS	VARIOUS	$16.99/$19.99	TP
9781401215811	JUL080124	JOKER	AZZARELLO, BRIAN	BERMEJO, LEE	$19.99/$23.99	HC
9781401245047	APR130219	ABSOLUTE JOKER/LUTHOR	AZZARELLO, BRIAN	BERMEJO, LEE	$99.99/$112.00	HC
9781401274696	SEP170419	KAMANDI BY JACK KIRBY OMNIBUS	KIRBY, JACK	KIRBY, JACK	$125.00/$163.00	HC
9781401289126	JAN180408	THE KAMANDI CHALLENGE	KING, TOM; WILLINGHAM, BILL	ADAMS, NEAL; SIMONSON, WALTER	$24.99/$33.99	TP
9781401263164	MAR160278	LEGENDS 30TH ANNIVERSARY EDITION	OSTRANDER, JOHN	BYRNE, JOHN	$19.99/$23.99	TP
9781401281571	MAY180586	LEGION OF SUPER-HEROES: THE SILVER AGE VOL. 1	VARIOUS	VARIOUS	$24.99/$33.99	TP
9781401271022	MAR170429	LEGION OF SUPER HEROES: THE SILVER AGE OMNIBUS VOL. 1	BINDER, OTTO	PLASTINO, AL	$75.00/$99.00	HC
9781401280550	DEC170397	LEGION OF SUPER-HEROES: THE SILVER AGE OMNIBUS VOL. 2	VARIOUS	VARIOUS	$75.00/$99.00	HC
9781401280857	FEB180309	SUPERBOY AND THE LEGION OF SUPER-HEROES VOL. 2	LEVITZ, PAUL	MANCO, LEONARDO	$49.99/$65.99	HC
9781401268664	JAN170396	LEGIONNAIRES BOOK ONE	WAID, MARK	VARIOUS	$34.99/$45.99	TP
9781401273811	FEB180305	LEGIONNAIRES BOOK TWO	VARIOUS	VARIOUS	$34.99/$45.99	TP
9781401276362	JUN170405	THE LEGION BY DAN ABNETT AND ANDY LANNING VOL. 1	ABNETT, DAN; LANNING, ANDY	COIPEL, OLIVIER	$24.99/$33.99	TP
9781401280406	MAR180350	THE LEGION BY DAN ABNETT AND ANDY LANNING VOL. 2	ABNETT, DAN	COIPEL, OLIVIER	$29.99/$39.99	TP
9781401274771	OCT170373	LOBO BY KEITH GIFFEN & ALAN GRANT VOL. 1	GIFFEN, KEITH	GRANT, ALAN	$24.99/$33.99	TP
9781401285845		LOBO BY KEITH GIFFEN & ALAN GRANT VOL. 2	GIFFEN, KEITH; GRANT, ALAN	BISLEY, SIMON	$24.99/$33.99	TP
9781401263591	MAY160310	LOONEY TUNES: GREATEST HITS VOL. 1: WHAT'S UP DOC?	VARIOUS	VARIOUS	$12.99/$15.99	TP
9781401265946	DEC160394	LOONEY TUNES: GREATEST HITS VOL. 2: YOU'RE DESPICABLE!	VARIOUS	VARIOUS	$12.99/$17.50	TP
9781401271602	MAY170340	LOONEY TUNES: GREATEST HITS VOL. 3: BEEP BEEP	VARIOUS	VARIOUS	$12.99/$17.50	TP
9781401261511	NOV150264	MARTIAN MANHUNTER VOL. 1: THE EPIPHANY	WILLIAMS, ROB	BARROWS, EDDY	$16.99/$19.99	TP
9781401265328	SEP160350	MARTIAN MANHUNTER VOL. 2: THE RED RISING	WILLIAMS, ROB	BARROWS, EDDY	$14.99/$19.99	TP
9781401290498		MASTERS OF THE UNIVERSE OMNIBUS	ROBINSON, JAMES; ABNETT, DAN; GIFFEN, KEITH	TAN, PHILLIP	$99.99/$130.99	HC
9781401285302		MERA: QUEEN OF ATLANTIS	ABNETT, DAN	MEDINA, LAN	$16.99/$22.99	TP
9781401265175	SEP160351	METAL MEN: FULL METAL JACKET	WEIN, LEN	CINAR, YILDIRAY	$14.99/$19.99	TP
9781401265182	SEP160352	METAMORPHO: TWO WORLDS, ONE DESTINY	LOPRESTI, AARON	BANNING, MATT	$14.99/$19.99	TP
9781401267919	APR170430	MIDNIGHTER: THE COMPLETE WILDSTORM SERIES	ENNIS, GARTH	SPROUSE, CHRIS	$34.99/$45.99	TP
9781401259785	NOV150265	MIDNIGHTER VOL. 1: OUT	ORLANDO, STEVE	ACO	$14.99/$17.99	TP
9781401264932	JUL160411	MIDNIGHTER VOL. 2: HARD	ORLANDO, STEVE	ACO	$14.99/$19.99	TP
9781401272012	APR170431	MIDNIGHTER & APOLLO	ORLANDO, STEVE	BLANCO, FERNANDO	$16.99/$22.99	TP
9781401277178	JUN170376	MISTER MIRACLE BY JACK KIRBY (NEW EDITION)	KIRBY, JACK	KIRBY, JACK	$29.99/$39.99	TP
9781401283544	STL096816	MISTER MIRACLE	KING, TOM	GERADS, MITCH	$24.99/$33.99	TP
9781401271114	APR170407	MOTHER PANIC VOL. 1: A WORK IN PROGRESS	WAY, GERARD; HOUSER, JODY	EDWARDS, TOMMY LEE	$16.99/$22.99	TP
9781401277680	NOV170338	MOTHER PANIC VOL. 2: UNDER HER SKIN	HOUSER, JODY	LEON, JOHN PAUL; CRYSTAL, SHAWN	$16.99/$22.99	TP
9781401281007	MAR180351	MOTHER PANIC: GOTHAM A.D.	HOUSER, JODY	CRYSTAL, SHAWN	$16.99/$22.99	TP
9781401257088	JAN150383	MORTAL KOMBAT X VOL. 1 BLOOD TIES	KITTLESEN, SHAWN	SOY, DEXTER	$14.99/$17.99	TP
9781401258535	JUL150317	MORTAL KOMBAT X VOL. 2 BLOOD GODS	KITTLESEN, SHAWN	SOY, DEXTER	$14.99/$17.99	TP
9781401260842	JAN160332	MORTAL KOMBAT X VOL. 3 BLOOD ISLAND	KITTLESEN, SHAWN	SOY, DEXTER	$16.99/$19.99	TP
9781401265250	AUG160336	THE MULTIVERSITY	MORRISON, GRANT	LEE, JIM; QUITELY, FRANK	$29.99/$39.99	TP
9781401280567	MAR180351	MYSTIK U	KWITNEY, ALISA	NORTON, MIKE	$16.99/$22.99	TP
9781401252441	SEP140303	THE NEW 52: FUTURES END VOL. 1	LEMIRE, JEFF; AZZARELLO, BRIAN; JURGENS, DAN; GIFFEN, KEITH	ZIRCHER, PATRICK	$39.99/$47.99	TP
9781401256029	APR150296	THE NEW 52: FUTURES END VOL. 2	LEMIRE, JEFF; AZZARELLO, BRIAN; JURGENS, DAN; GIFFEN, KEITH	ZIRCHER, PATRICK	$29.99/$35.00	TP
9781401258788	JUN150294	THE NEW 52: FUTURES END VOL. 3	LEMIRE, JEFF; AZZARELLO, BRIAN; JURGENS, DAN; GIFFEN, KEITH	ZIRCHER, PATRICK	$29.99/$35.00	TP
9781401272364	MAY170347	THE NEWSBOY LEGION BY JOE SIMON & JACK KIRBY VOL. 2	SIMON, JOE	KIRBY, JACK	$49.99/$65.99	HC
9781401283445		NEW CHALLENGERS	SNYDER, SCOTT; GILLESPIE, AARON	KUBERT, ANDY	$16.99/$22.99	TP
9781401281694	MAY180587	NEW GODS BY JACK KIRBY	KIRBY, JACK	KIRBY, JACK	$29.99/$39.99	TP
9781401270933	MAR170405	NEW SUPER-MAN VOL. 1: MADE IN CHINA (REBIRTH)	YANG, GENE LUEN	BOGDANOVIC, VIKTOR	$16.99/$22.99	TP
9781401273903	JUL170460	NEW SUPER-MAN VOL. 2: COMING TO AMERICA (REBIRTH)	YANG, GENE LUEN	BOGDANOVIC, VIKTOR	$16.99/$22.99	TP
9781401280444	MAR180352	NEW SUPER-MAN VOL. 3: EQUILIBRIUM	YANG, GENE LUEN	TAN, BILLY	$16.99/$22.99	TP

ISBN	DIAMOND CODE	TITLE	AUTHOR	ARTIST	US$/$CAN	FORMAT
9781401288297		NEW SUPER-MAN & THE JLC VOL. 1: JUSTICE LEAGUE CHINA	YANG, GENE LUEN	PEEPLES, BRENT	$16.99/$22.99	TP
9781401274290	JUN170406	NIGHT FORCE BY MARV WOLFMAN AND GENE COLAN: THE COMPLETE SERIES	WOLFMAN, MARV	COLAN, GENE	$39.99/$53.99	HC
9781401261535	MAY160316	OMEGA MEN: THE END IS HERE	KING, TOM	BAGENDA, BARNABY	$24.99/$29.99	TP
9781401274870	APR180275	ORION BY WALT SIMONSON BOOK ONE	SIMONSON, WALT	SIMONSON, WALT	$29.99/$39.99	TP
9781401255350	NOV140312	ORION BY WALTER SIMONSON OMNIBUS	SIMONSON, WALTER	SIMONSON, WALTER	$75.00/$85.00	HC
9781401288518		THE OUTSIDERS BY JUDD WINICK BOOK ONE	WINICK, JUDD	RANEY, TOM	$24.99/$33.99	TP
9781401271664	APR170433	PLANETARY BOOK ONE	ELLIS, WARREN	CASSADAY, JOHN	$29.99/$39.99	TP
9781401277994	DEC170398	PLANETARY BOOK TWO	ELLIS, WARREN	CASSADAY, JOHN	$24.99/$33.99	TP
9781401242381	SEP130279	THE PLANETARY OMNIBUS	ELLIS, WARREN	CASSADAY, JOHN	$75.00 /$85.00	HC
9781401289379		PLASTIC MAN	SIMONE, GAIL	MELO, ADRIANA	$16.99/$22.99	TP
9781401264512	JUN160347	POISON IVY: CYCLE OF LIFE AND DEATH	CHU, AMY	MANN, CLAY	$16.99/$22.99	TP
9781401243074	NOV130247	POWER GIRL: POWER TRIP	PALMIOTTI, JIMMY; JOHNS, GEOFF	CONNER, AMANDA	$29.99/$35.00	TP
9781401263171	MAR160274	PREZ: THE FIRST TEEN PRESIDENT	BRUBAKER, ED	SIMON, JOE	$19.99/$23.99	TP
9781401259792	NOV150266	PREZ VOL. 1: CORNDOG IN CHIEF	RUSSELL, MARK	CALDWELL, BEN	$14.99/$17.99	TP
9781401280871	APR180274	RAGMAN	FAWKES, RAY	MIRANDA, INAKI	$16.99/$22.99	TP
9781401268985	FEB170314	RAVEN	WOLFMAN, MARV	BORGES, ALISSON	$14.99/$19.99	TP
9781401284732		RAVEN: DAUGHTER OF DARKNESS VOL. 1	WOLFMAN, MARV	MHAN, POP	$16.99/$22.99	TP
9781401248956	JUN140284	RONIN DELUXE EDITION	MILLER, FRANK	MILER, FRANK	$29.99/$35.00	TP
9781401274986	MAR180353	THE RUFF AND REDDY SHOW	CHAYKIN, HOWARD	REY, MAC	$16.99/$22.99	TP
9781401249465	NOV140323	SCOOBY-DOO TEAM-UP VOL. 1	FISCH, SHOLLY	BRIZUELA, DARIO	$12.99/$15.99	TP
9781401258597	NJUN150277	SCOOBY-DOO TEAM-UP VOL. 2	FISCH, SHOLLY	BRIZUELA, DARIO	$12.99/$15.99	TP
9781401268015	JAN170397	SCOOBY-DOO TEAM-UP VOL. 3	VARIOUS	VARIOUS	$12.99/$17.50	TP
9781401274948	SEP170424	SCOOBY-DOO TEAM-UP VOL. 4	FISCH, SHOLLY	VARIOUS	$12.99/$17.50	TP
9781401284190	FEB180310	SCOOBY-DOO TEAM-UP VOL. 5	FISCH, SHOLLY	VARIOUS	$12.99/$17.50	TP
9781401285760		SCOOBY-DOO TEAM-UP VOL. 6	FISCH, SHOLLY	VARIOUS	$12.99/$17.50	TP
9781401267902	NOV160345	SCOOBY APOCALYPSE VOL. 1	GIFFEN, KEITH; LEE, JIM	PORTER, HOWARD	$16.99/$22.99	TP
9781401273736	JUN170409	SCOOBY APOCALYPSE VOL. 2	GIFFEN, KEITH; DEMATTEIS, J.M.	EAGLESHAM, DALE	$16.99/$22.99	TP
9781401277482	NOV170376	SCOOBY APOCALYPSE VOL. 3	GIFFEN, KEITH; DEMATTEIS, J.M.	EAGLESHAM, DALE	$16.99/$22.99	TP
9781401284459	JUN180587	SCOOBY APOCALYPSE VOL. 4	GIFFEN, KEITH; DEMATTEIS, J.M.	VARIOUS	$16.99/$22.99	TP
9781401289577		SCOOBY APOCALYPSE VOL. 5	GIFFEN, KEITH; DEMATTEIS, J.M.	VARIOUS	$16.99/$22.99	TP
9781401281519	FEB180312	SEVEN SOLDIERS BY GRANT MORRISON OMNIBUS	MORRISON, GRANT	WILLIAMS III, J.H.; SOOK, RYAN; STEWART, CAMERON	$75.00/$99.00	HC
9781401254858	NOV150288	SECRET SIX VOL. 1: FRIENDS IN LOW PLACES	SIMONE, GAIL	LASHLEY, KEN; EAGLESHAM, DALE	$14.99/$17.99	TP
9781401264536	SEP160354	SECRET SIX VOL. 2: THE GAUNTLET	SIMONE, GAIL	EAGLESHAM, DALE	$14.99/$19.99	TP
9781401270995	APR170410	SHADE THE CHANGING GIRL VOL. 1: EARTH GIRL MADE EASY	CASTELLUCCI, CECIL	ZARCONE, MARLEY	$16.99/$22.99	TP
9781401275457	OCT170347	SHADE, THE CHANGING GIRL VOL. 2: LITTLE RUNAWAY	CASTELLUCCI, CECIL	ZARCONE, MARLEY	$16.99/$22.99	TP
9781401285708		SHADE, THE CHANGING WOMAN	CASTELLUCCI, CECIL	ZARCONE, MARLEY	$16.99/$22.99	TP
9781401288150		SHAZAM!: THE GOLDEN AGE OMNIBUS VOL. 1	PARKER, BILL	VARIOUS	$99.99/$130.99	HC
9781401287696		SHAZAM AND THE MONSTER SOCIETY OF EVIL DELUXE EDITION	SMITH, JEFF	SMITH, JEFF	$49.99/$65.99	HC
9781401274849	SEP170425	SHAZAM: A NEW BEGINNING 30TH ANNIVERSARY DELUXE EDITION	THOMAS, ROY	VARIOUS	$34.99/$45.99	HC
9781401288228		SHAZAM!: POWER OF HOPE DELUXE EDITION	DINI, PAUL	ROSS, ALEX	$17.99/$23.99	HC
9781401288396		SHAZAM BY DENNIS O'NEIL VOL. 1	O'NEIL, DENNIS	VARIOUS	$49.99/$65.99	HC
9781401246990	FEB140251	SHAZAM! VOL. 1	JOHNS, GEOFF	FRANK, GARY	$16.99/$19.99	TP
9781401287894		SHAZAM! (NEW EDITION)	JOHNS, GEOFF	FRANK, GARY	$12.99/$17.50	TP
9781401255381	NOV140315	SHAZAM!: A CELEBRATION OF 75 YEARS	PARKER, BILL	BECK, C.C.	$39.99/$47.99	HC
9781401283377		SIDEWAYS VOL. 1: STEPPIN' OUT (NEW AGE OF HEROES)	DIDIO, DAN; JORDAN, JUSTIN	ROCAFORT, KENNETH	$16.99/$22.99	TP
9781401283353	JUN180589	THE SILENCER VOL. 1: CODE OF HONOR (NEW AGE OF HEROES)	ABNETT, DAN	ROMITA JR., JOHN; BOGDANOVIC, VIKTOR	$16.99/$22.99	TP
9781401289232		THE SILENCER VOL. 2 (NEW AGE OF HEROES)	ABNETT, DAN	BOGDANOVIC, VIKTOR	$16.99/$22.99	TP
9781401267643	AUG160342	SPACE GHOST (NEW EDITION)	KELLY, JOE	OLIVETTI, ARIEL	$16.99/$22.99	TP
9781401261603	DEC150325	STARFIRE VOL. 1: WELCOME HOME	PALMIOTTI, JIMMY; CONNER, AMANDA	LUPACCHINO, EMANUELA	$22.99/$14.99	TP
9781401270384	OCT160312	STARFIRE VOL. 2	PALMIOTTI, JIMMY; CONNER, AMANDA	CONNER, AMANDA; LUPACCHINO, EMANUELA	$14.99/$14.99	TP
9781401247072	FEB140257	THE AUTHORITY VOL. 1	ELLIS, WARREN	HITCH, BRYAN	$19.99/$23.99	TP
9781401250805	SEP140316	THE AUTHORITY VOL. 2	MILLAR, MARK	QUITELY, FRANK	$24.99/$28.99	TP
9781401276478	APR170432	ABSOLUTE AUTHORITY VOL. 1 (NEW EDITION)	ELLIS, WARREN	HITCH, BRYAN	$75.00/$99.00	HC
9781401264826	AUG160343	SUGAR & SPIKE	GIFFEN, KEITH	EVELY, BILQUIS	$14.99/$19.99	TP
9781401271404	OCT170376	SUPER POWERS BY JACK KIRBY	KIRBY, JACK	KIRBY, JACK	$39.99/$53.99	TP
9781401268428	MAY170350	SUPER POWERS VOL. 1	BALTAZAR, ART; FRANCO	BALTAZAR, ART; FRANCO	$12.99/$17.50	TP
9781401274016	JUL170465	SUPER SONS VOL. 1: WHEN I GROW UP (REBIRTH)	TOMASI, PETER J.	JIMENEZ, JORGE	$12.99/$17.50	TP
9781401278465	DEC170381	SUPER SONS VOL. 2: PLANET OF THE CAPES (REBIRTH)	TOMASI, PETER J.	JIMENEZ, JORGE	$14.99/$19.99	TP
9781401282394	MAR180354	SUPER SONS OF TOMORROW	TOMASI, PETER J.	GLEASON, PATRICK; JIMENEZ, JORGE; MAHNKE, DOUG	$14.99/$19.99	TP
9781401284466	JUN180588	SUPER SONS VOL. 3: PARENT TRAP	TOMASI, PETER J.	BARBERI, CARLO; PELLETIER, PAUL	$14.99/$19.99	TP
9781401285579		SUPER SONS OMNIBUS	TOMASI, PETER J.	JIMENEZ, JORGE	$49.99/$65.99	HC
9781401290580		ADVENTURES OF THE SUPER SONS VOL. 1	TOMASI, PETER J.	BARBERI, CARLO	$16.99/$22.99	TP
9781401275136	OCT170375	SUPERBOY BOOK ONE: TROUBLE IN PARADISE	KESEL, KARL	GRUMMETT, TOM	$24.99/$33.99	TP
9781401285869		SUPERBOY BOOK TWO: WATERY GRAVE	KESEL, KARL	GRUMMETT, TOM	$24.99/$33.99	TP

DC COMICS SELECTED BACKLIST

ISBN	DIAMOND CODE	TITLE	AUTHOR	ARTIST	US$/$CAN	FORMAT
9781401267803	FEB170297	SUPERWOMAN VOL. 1: WHO IS SUPERWOMAN? (REBIRTH)	JIMENEZ, PHIL | JIMENEZ, PHIL	$16.99/$19.99 | TP
9781401274733	AUG170326	SUPERWOMAN VOL. 2: REDISCOVERY (REBIRTH)	JIMENEZ, PHIL | SEGOVIA, STEPHEN	$14.99/$19.99 | TP
9781401278526	FEB180291	SUPERWOMAN VOL. 3: THE MIDNIGHT HOUR (REBIRTH)	PERKINS, K. | SEGOVIA, STEPHEN	$16.99/$22.99 | TP
9781401284404		SWAMP THING: THE BRONZE AGE VOL. 1	WEIN, LEN | WRIGHTSON, BERNIE	$29.99/$39.99 | TP
9781401273781	MAY170351	SWAMP THING: THE BRONZE AGE OMNIBUS VOL. 1	WEIN, LEN | WRIGHTSON, BERNIE	$99.99/$130.99 | HC
9781401234621	MAY120280	SWAMP THING VOL. 1: RAISE THEM BONES	SNYDER, SCOTT | PAQUETTE, YANICK	$14.99/$17.99 | TP
9781401238438	JAN130301	SWAMP THING VOL. 2: FAMILY TREE	SNYDER, SCOTT | PAQUETTE, YANICK	$14.99/$17.99 | TP
9781401290986		SWAMP THING: PROTECTOR OF THE GREEN (DC ESSENTIAL EDITION)	SNYDER, SCOTT | PAQUETTE, YANICK	$24.99/$33.99 | TP
9781401242640	AUG130299	SWAMP THING VOL. 3: ROTWORLD: THE GREEN KINGDOM	SNYDER, SCOTT; LEMIRE, JEFF | PAQUETTE, YANICK	$16.99/$19.99 | TP
9781401258702	MAY150248	SWAMP THING BY SCOTT SNYDER DELUXE EDITION	SNYDER, SCOTT | PAQUETTE, YANICK	$49.99/$58.00 | HC
9781401246396	MAR140257	SWAMP THING VOL. 4: SEEDER	SOULE, CHARLES | KANO	$14.99/$17.99 | TP
9781401250522	SEP140313	SWAMP THING VOL. 5: THE KILLING FIELD	SOULE, CHARLES | SAIZ, JESUS	$14.99/$17.99 | TP
9781401254902	MAR150275	SWAMP THING VOL. 6: THE SUREEN	SOULE, CHARLES | SAIZ, JESUS	$16.99/$19.99 | TP
9781401257705	OCT150262	SWAMP THING VOL. 7: SEASON'S END	SOULE, CHARLES | SAIZ, JESUS; PINA, JAVI	$16.99/$19.99 | TP
9781401270018	JUL160416	SWAMP THING: THE DEAD DON'T SLEEP	WEIN, LEN | JONES, KELLEY	$16.99/$19.99 | TP
9781401263744	MAY160320	TELOS	KING, JEFF | PAGULAYAN, CARLO	$14.99/$19.99 | TP
9781401283360		THE TERRIFICS VOL. 1: MEET THE TERRIFICS (NEW AGE OF HEROES)	LEMIRE, JEFF | SHANER, EVAN "DOC"; REIS, IVAN	$16.99/$22.99 | TP
9781401274382	AUG170344	TWO FACE: A CELEBRATION OF 75 YEARS	VARIOUS | VARIOUS	$39.99/$53.99 | HC
9781401283513		THE UNEXPECTED VOL. 1 (NEW AGE OF HEROES)	ORLANDO, STEVE | SOOK, RYAN	$16.99/$22.99 | TP
9781401284961		A VERY DC HOLIDAY SEQUEL	DINI, PAUL; RUCKA, GREG; KING, TOM | LEMIRE, JEFF	$16.99/$22.99 | TP
9781401276058	AUG170328	A VERY DC REBIRTH HOLIDAY	SNYDER, SCOTT; KING, TOM; DINI, PAUL | FINCH, DAVID	$16.99/$22.99 | TP
9781401268725	DEC160387	VIGILANTE BY MARV WOLFMAN VOL. 1	WOLFMAN, MARV | POLLARD, KEITH	$19.99/$25.99 | TP
9781401268732	OCT170382	VIGILANTE: SOUTHLAND	PHILLIPS, GARY | CASAGRANDE, ELENA	$16.99/$22.99 | TP
9781401268275	DEC160396	WACKY RACELAND	PONTAC, KEN | MANCO, LEONARDO	$16.99/$22.99 | TP
9781401245122	MAR140269	BEFORE WATCHMEN: MINUTEMEN/SILK SPECTRE	COOKE, DARWYN; CONNER, AMANDA | COOKE, DARWYN; CONNER, AMANDA	$19.99/$23.99 | TP
9781401245139	MAR140270	BEFORE WATCHMEN: COMEDIAN/RORSCHACH	AZZARELLO, BRIAN | BERMEJO, LEE; JONES, J.G.	$19.99/$23.99 | TP
9781401245146	MAR140271	BEFORE WATCHMEN: NITE OWL/DR. MANHATTAN	STRACZYNSKI, J. MICHAEL | HUGHES, ADAM; KUBERT, ANDY; KUBERT, JOE	$19.99/$23.99 | TP
9781401245153	MAR140272	BEFORE WATCHMEN: OZYMANDIAS/CRIMSON CORSAIR	WEIN, LEN; HIGGINS, JOHN | LEE, JAE; HIGGINS, JOHN	$19.99/$23.99 | TP
9781401285517	JUN180573	BEFORE WATCHMEN OMNIBUS	AZZARELLO, BRIAN; COOKE, DARWYN; STRACZYNSKI, J. MICHAEL; WEIN, LEN | CONNER, AMANDA; HUGHES, ADAM; JONES, J.G.; BERMEJO, LEE	$125.00/$163.00 | HC
9781401245252	FEB140265	WATCHMEN	MOORE, ALAN | GIBBONS, DAVE	$19.99/$23.99 | TP
9781401248192	FEB140266	WATCHMEN: INTERNATIONAL EDITION	MOORE, ALAN | GIBBONS, DAVE	$19.99/$23.99 | HC
9781401238964	FEB130225	WATCHMEN: THE DELUXE EDITION	MOORE, ALAN | GIBBONS, DAVE	$39.99/$47.99 | HC
9781401270346	JUN160362	WATCHMEN COLLECTOR'S EDITION SLIPCASE SET	MOORE, ALAN | GIBBONS, DAVE	$125.00/$163.00 | BOXED SET
9781401265298	JUL160393	WATCHMEN NOIR	MOORE, ALAN | GIBBONS, DAVE	$39.99/$48.99 | HC
9781401265564	APR170439	WATCHMEN: THE ANNOTATED EDITION	KLINGER, LESLIE S.; MOORE, ALAN | GIBBONS, DAVE	$49.99/$65.99 | HC
9781401284718	AUG180662	WATCHMEN (DC MODERN CLASSICS EDITION)	MOORE, ALAN | GIBBONS, DAVE	$49.99/$65.99 | HC
9781401274955	JUL170485	ABSOLUTE WILDC.A.T.S. BY JIM LEE	LEE, JIM | LEE, JIM	$125.00/$163.00 | HC
9781401276522	MAY170352	WILDSTORM: A CELEBRATION OF 25 YEARS	VARIOUS | VARIOUS	$29.99/$39.99 | HC
9781401274184	JUL170486	THE WILD STORM VOL. 1	ELLIS, WARREN | DAVIS-HUNT, JON	$16.99/$22.99 | TP
9781401278656	FEB180316	THE WILD STORM VOL. 2	ELLIS, WARREN | DAVIS-HUNT, JON	$16.99/$22.99 | TP
9781401285272		THE WILD STORM VOL. 3	ELLIS, WARREN | DAVIS-HUNT, JON	$16.99/$22.99 | TP
9781401281052	APR180284	THE WILD STORM: MICHAEL CRAY VOL. 1	HILL, BRYAN | HARRIS, N. STEPHEN	$16.99/$22.99 | TP
9781401285586		THE WILD STORM: MICHAEL CRAY VOL. 2	HILL, BRYAN | HARRIS, N. STEPHEN	$16.99/$22.99 | TP
9781401271657	MAY170335	WONDER GIRL: ADVENTURES OF A TEEN TITAN	VARIOUS | VARIOUS	$14.99/$19.99 | TP
9781401271169	JAN170404	YOUNG JUSTICE BOOK ONE	DAVID, PETER | NAUCK, TODD	$24.99/$33.99 | TP
9781401277666	NOV170377	YOUNG JUSTICE BOOK TWO	DAVID, PETER | NAUCK, TODD	$29.99/$39.99 | TP
9781401285104		YOUNG JUSTICE BOOK THREE	DAVID, PETER | NAUCK, TODD	$29.99/$39.99 | TP
9781401268824	DEC160393	ZATANNA BY PAUL DINI	DINI, PAUL | QUINONES, JOE; ROUX, STÉPHANE	$34.99/$45.99 | TP

DC BOOKS FOR YOUNG READERS

ISBN	DIAMOND CODE	TITLE	AUTHOR	ARTIST	US$/$CAN	FORMAT
9781401283391	JUN188690	MERA: TIDEBREAKER	PAIGE, DANIELLE | BYRNE, STEPHEN	$16.99/$22.99 | TP
9781401285913	JUN188706	UNDER THE MOON: A CATWOMAN TALE	MYRACLE, LAUREN | GOODHART, ISAAC	$16.99/$22.99 | TP
9781401286392	JUN188694	SUPER SONS: THE POLARSHIELD PROJECT	PEARSON, RIDLEY | GONZALEZ, ILE	$9.99/$13.50 | TP
9781401262471	APR160322	DC SUPER HERO GIRLS: FINALS CRISIS	FONTANA, SHEA | LABAT, YANCEY	$9.99/$13.50 | TP
9781401267612	AUG160270	DC SUPER HERO GIRLS: HITS AND MYTHS	FONTANA, SHEA | LABAT, YANCEY	$9.99/$13.50 | TP
9781401272357	MAR170353	DC SUPER HERO GIRLS: SUMMER OLYMPUS	FONTANA, SHEA | LABAT, YANCEY	$9.99/$13.50 | TP
9781401273835	JUN170333	DC SUPER HERO GIRLS: PAST TIMES AT SUPER HERO HIGH	FONTANA, SHEA | GARBOWSKA, AGNES; LABAT, YANCEY	$9.99/$13.50 | TP
9781401278786	NOV170216	DC SUPER HERO GIRLS: DATE WITH DISASTER!	FONTANA, SHEA | LABAT, YANCEY	$9.99/$13.50 | TP
9781401274832	FEB180156	DC SUPER HERO GIRLS: OUT OF THE BOTTLE	FONTANA, SHEA | DICHIARA, MARCELO; GARBOWSKA, AGNES	$9.99/$13.50 | TP
9781401283537	JUN180439	DC SUPER HERO GIRLS: SEARCH FOR ATLANTIS	FONTANA, SHEA | LABAT, YANCEY	$9.99/$13.50 | TP
9781401282561	JUN188673	DC SUPER HERO GIRLS: SPACED OUT	FONTANA, SHEA | GARBOWSKA, AGNES	$9.99/$13.50 | TP
9781401279530	SEP170412	DC SUPER HERO GIRLS BOX SET	FONTANA, SHEA | LABAT, YANCEY	$34.99/$45.99 | BOXED SET

DC COMICS SELECTED BACKLIST

ISBN	DIAMOND CODE	TITLE	AUTHOR	ARTIST	US$/$CAN	FORMAT

JINXWORLD

9781401290535		FIRE	BENDIS, BRIAN MICHAEL	BENDIS, BRIAN MICHAEL	$19.99/$19.99	TP
9781401290542		FORTUNE AND GLORY: A TRUE HOLLYWOOD COMIC BOOK STORY	BENDIS, BRIAN MICHAEL	BENDIS, BRIAN MICHAEL	$14.99/$19.99	TP
9781401287498	JUN188680	GOLDFISH	BENDIS, BRIAN MICHAEL	BENDIS, BRIAN MICHAEL	$24.99/$33.99	TP
9781401287504	JUN188685	JINX	BENDIS, BRIAN MICHAEL	BENDIS, BRIAN MICHAEL	$24.99/$33.99	TP
9781401290610	JUN188691	PEARL VOL. 1	BENDIS, BRIAN MICHAEL	GAYDOS, MICHAEL	$16.99/$22.99	TP
9781401287450	JUL180773	POWERS BOOK ONE	BENDIS, BRIAN MICHAEL	OEMING, MICHAEL AVON	$29.99/$39.99	TP
9781401287481	JUN188692	POWERS BOOK TWO	BENDIS, BRIAN MICHAEL	OEMING, MICHAEL AVON	$29.99/$39.99	TP
9781401290504		POWERS BOOK THREE	BENDIS, BRIAN MICHAEL	OEMING, MICHAEL AVON	$29.99/$39.99	TP
9781401290511		POWERS BOOK FOUR	BENDIS, BRIAN MICHAEL	OEMING, MICHAEL AVON	$29.99/$39.99	TP
9781401287443	JUL180782	SCARLET BOOK ONE	BENDIS, BRIAN MICHAEL	MALEEV, ALEX	$14.99/$19.99	TP
9781401287474	JUN188693	SCARLET BOOK TWO	BENDIS, BRIAN MICHAEL	MALEEV, ALEX	$14.99/$19.99	TP
9781401289720		ABSOLUTE SCARLET	BENDIS, BRIAN MICHAEL	MALEEV, ALEX	$75.00/$99.00	HC
9781401290627		SCARLET VOL. 1	BENDIS, BRIAN MICHAEL	MALEEV, ALEX	$16.99/$22.99	TP
9781401290634	JUN188699	TAKIO: THE COMPLETE COLLECTION	BENDIS, BRIAN MICHAEL	OEMING, MICHAEL AVON	$16.99/$22.99	TP
9781401287467	JUN180585	THE UNITED STATES OF MURDER INC. VOL. 1	BENDIS, BRIAN MICHAEL	OEMING, MICHAEL AVON	$16.99/$22.99	TP
9781401290528		TORSO	BENDIS, BRIAN MICHAEL; ANDREYKO, MARC	BENDIS, BRIAN MICHAEL	$24.99/$33.99	TP

VERTIGO SELECTED BACKLIST

9781401250560	JUL140274	100 BULLETS BOOK ONE	AZZARELLO, BRIAN	RISSO, EDUARDO	$24.99/$28.99	TP
9781401254315	JAN150409	100 BULLETS BOOK TWO	AZZARELLO, BRIAN	RISSO, EDUARDO	$24.99/$28.99	TP
9781401257958	JUN150323	100 BULLETS BOOK THREE	AZZARELLO, BRIAN	RISSO, EDUARDO	$24.99/$29.99	TP
9781401257941	OCT150272	100 BULLETS BOOK FOUR	AZZARELLO, BRIAN	RISSO, EDUARDO	$24.99/$29.99	TP
9781401261337	DEC150363	100 BULLETS BOOK FIVE	AZZARELLO, BRIAN	RISSO, EDUARDO	$24.99/$29.99	TP
9781401229740	JUL110284	AMERICAN VAMPIRE VOL. 1	SNYDER, SCOTT; KING, STEPHEN	ALBUQUERQUE, RAFAEL	$19.99/$23.99	TP
9781401230708	FEB120289	AMERICAN VAMPIRE VOL. 2	SNYDER, SCOTT	ALBUQUERQUE, RAFAEL	$17.99/$20.99	TP
9781401233341	JUN120280	AMERICAN VAMPIRE VOL. 3	SNYDER, SCOTT	ALBUQUERQUE, RAFAEL	$16.99/$19.99	TP
9781401237196	JUN130293	AMERICAN VAMPIRE VOL. 4	SNYDER, SCOTT	ALBUQUERQUE, RAFAEL; BERNETT, JORDI	$16.99/$19.99	TP
9781401237714	DEC130346	AMERICAN VAMPIRE VOL. 5	SNYDER, SCOTT	ALBUQUERQUE, RAFAEL; NGUYEN, DUSTIN	$16.99/$19.99	TP
9781401249298	AUG140356	AMERICAN VAMPIRE VOL. 6	SNYDER, SCOTT	ALBUQUERQUE, RAFAEL	$14.99/$17.99	TP
9781401254322	AUG150288	AMERICAN VAMPIRE VOL. 7	SNYDER, SCOTT	ALBUQUERQUE, RAFAEL	$14.99/$17.99	TP
9781401262587	APR160416	AMERICAN VAMPIRE VOL. 8	SNYDER, SCOTT	ALBUQUERQUE, RAFAEL	$14.99/$17.99	TP
9781401284831	APR180291	AMERICAN VAMPIRE OMNIBUS VOL. 1	SNYDER, SCOTT; KING, STEPHEN	ALBUQUERQUE, RAFAEL	$99.99/$130.99	HC
9781401278359	JAN180417	AMERICAN WAY: THOSE ABOVE AND BELOW	RIDLEY, JOHN	JEANTY, GEORGES	$16.99/$22.99	TP
9781401285470		ANIMAL MAN BY GRANT MORRISON BOOK ONE 30TH ANNIVERSARY DELUXE EDITION	MORRISON, GRANT	TRUOG, CHAS	$29.99/$39.99	HC
9781401256876	FEB160254	ART OPS VOL. 1: HOW TO START A RIOT	SIMON, SHAUN	ALLRED, MICHAEL	$14.99/$17.99	TP
9781401267414	SEP150320	ART OPS VOL. 2: POPISM	ALLRED, MIKE	SIMON, SHAUN	$14.99/$19.99	TP
9781401268282	DEC160403	ASTRO CITY: HONOR GUARD	BUSIEK, KURT	ANDERSON, BRENT; ROSS, ALEX	$19.99/$25.99	TP
9781401274924	SEP170438	ASTRO CITY VOL. 14: REFLECTIONS	BUSIEK, KURT	ANDERSON, BRENT	$16.99/$22.99	TP
9781401274931	SEP170439	ASTRO CITY VOL. 15: ORDINARY HEROES	BUSIEK, KURT	ANDERSON, BRENT	$24.99/$33.99	HC
9781401281496	MAY180567	ASTRO CITY VOL. 16: BROKEN MELODY	BUSIEK, KURT	ANDERSON, BRENT	$24.99/$33.99	HC
9781401289447		ASTRO CITY VOL. 17	BUSIEK, KURT	ANDERSON, BRENT	$24.99/$33.99	HC
9781401240356	APR130261	BLACK ORCHID	GAIMAN, NEIL	MCKEAN, DAVE	$16.99/$19.99	TP
9781401268763	FEB170335	BOOKS OF MAGIC BOOK ONE	RIEBER, JOHN NEY	GROSS, PETER	$24.99/$33.99	TP
9781401262754	MAR160289	CLEAN ROOM VOL. 1: THE IMMACULATE CONCEPTION	SIMONE, GAIL	DAVIS-HUNT, JON	$14.99/$17.99	TP
9781401267407	SEP160367	CLEAN ROOM VOL. 2: EXILE	SIMONE, GAIL	DAVIS-HUNT, JON	$14.99/$19.99	TP
9781401271091	APR170448	CLEAN ROOM VOL. 3: WAITING FOR THE STARS TO FALL	SIMONE, GAIL	DAVIS-HUNT, JON	$16.99/$22.99	TP
9781401264598	JUN160373	THE DARK & THE BLOODY VOL. 1	ALDRIDGE, SHAWN	GODLEWSKI, SCOTT	$14.99/$19.99	TP
9781401271367	NAR170445	DARK NIGHT: A TRUE BATMAN STORY	DINI, PAUL	RISSO, EDUARDO	$16.99/$22.99	TP
9781401229696	NOV100268	DAYTRIPPER	MOON, FABÍO; BÁ, GABRIEL	MOON, FABÍO; BÁ, GABRIEL	$19.99/$23.99	TP
9781401245115	DEC130340	DAYTRIPPER DELUXE EDITION	MOON, FABÍO; BÁ, GABRIEL	MOON, FABÍO; BÁ, GABRIEL	$34.99/$41.99	HC
9781401287634		ABSOLUTE DAYTRIPPER	BA, GABRIEL	MOON, FABIO	$99.99/$130.99	HC
9781401247164	DEC130341	DEATH	GAIMAN, NEIL	VARIOUS	$19.99/$23.99	TP
9781401278540		DEATHBED	WILLIAMSON, JOSHUA	ROSSMO, RILEY	$16.99/$22.99	TP
9781401261351	FEB160255	DMZ BOOK ONE	WOOD, BRIAN	BURCHIELLI, RICCARDO	$24.99/$29.99	TP
9781401263577	APR160420	DMZ BOOK TWO	WOOD, BRIAN	BURCHIELLI, RICCARDO	$24.99/$29.99	TP
9781401268435	DEC160406	DMZ BOOK THREE	WOOD, BRIAN	BURCHIELLI, RICCARDO	$24.99/$33.99	TP
9781401274634	NOV170388	DMZ BOOK FOUR	WOOD, BRIAN	BURCCHIELLI, RICCARDO	$24.99/$33.99	TP
9781401285838	NOV170388	DMZ BOOK FIVE	WOOD, BRIAN	BURCCHIELLI, RICCARDO	$24.99/$33.99	TP
9781401263126	NOV150304	DOOM PATROL BOOK ONE	MORRISON, GRANT	CASE, RICHARD	$24.99/$29.99	TP
9781401263799	APR160421	DOOM PATROL BOOK TWO	MORRISON, GRANT	CASE, RICHARD	$29.99/$34.99	TP
9781401265977	DEC160407	DOOM PATROL BOOK THREE	MORRISON, GRANT	CASE, RICHARD	$29.99/$39.99	TP

ISBN	DIAMOND CODE	TITLE	AUTHOR	ARTIST	US$/$CAN	FORMAT
9781401245627	MAR140282	THE DOOM PATROL OMNIBUS	MORRISON, GRANT	VARIOUS	$150.00/$172.00	HC
9781401247027	JAN140382	FLEX MENTALLO: MAN OF MUSCLE MYSTERY	MORRISON, GRANT	QUITELY, FRANK	$14.99/$17.99	TP
9781401244989	OCT130291	EX MACHINA BOOK ONE	VAUGHAN, BRIAN K.	HARRIS, TONY	$19.99/$23.99	TP
9781401246914	FEB140292	EX MACHINA BOOK TWO	VAUGHAN, BRIAN K.	HARRIS, TONY; SPROUSE, CHRIS	$19.99/$23.99	TP
9781401250034	JUN140307	EX MACHINA BOOK THREE	VAUGHAN, BRIAN K.	HARRIS, TONY; LEON, JOHN PAUL	$19.99/$23.99	TP
9781401250027	OCT140387	EX MACHINA BOOK FOUR	VAUGHAN, BRIAN K.	HARRIS, TONY	$19.99/$23.99	TP
9781401254223	FEB150282	EX MACHINA BOOK FIVE	VAUGHAN, BRIAN K.	HARRIS, TONY	$19.99/$23.99	TP
9781401280680	DEC170409	EX MACHINA: THE COMPLETE SERIES OMNIBUS	VAUGHAN, BRIAN K.	HARRIS, TONY	$150.00/$195.00	HC
9781401237554	FEB120285	FABLES VOL. 1: LEGENDS IN EXILE	WILLINGHAM, BILL	MEDINA, LAN	$12.99/$15.99	TP
9781401200770	DEC138056	FABLES VOL. 2: ANIMAL FARM	WILLINGHAM, BILL	BUCKINGHAM, MARK	$14.99/$17.99	TP
9781401202569	SEP128354	FABLES VOL. 3: STORYBOOK LOVE	WILLINGHAM, BILL	BUCKINGHAM, MARK	$17.99/$20.99	TP
9781401202224	OCT058021	FABLES VOL. 4: MARCH OF THE WOODEN SOLDIERS	WILLINGHAM, BILL	BUCKINGHAM, MARK	$17.99/$20.99	TP
9781401204860	SEP128332	FABLES VOL. 5: THE MEAN SEASONS	WILLINGHAM, BILL	BUCKINGHAM, MARK	$17.99/$20.99	TP
9781401205003	JAN148352	FABLES VOL. 6: HOMELANDS	WILLINGHAM, BILL	BUCKINGHAM, MARK	$17.99/$20.99	TP
9781401210007	MAR060384	FABLES VOL. 7: ARABIAN NIGHTS (AND DAYS)	WILLINGHAM, BILL	BUCKINGHAM, MARK	$14.99/$17.99	TP
9781401210014	SEP060313	FABLES VOL. 8: WOLVES	WILLINGHAM, BILL	BUCKINGHAM, MARK	$17.99/$20.99	TP
9781401213169	MAR070271	FABLES VOL. 9: SONS OF EMPIRE	WILLINGHAM, BILL	BUCKINGHAM, MARK	$17.99/$20.99	TP
9781401216863	FEB080297	FABLES VOL. 10: THE GOOD PRINCE	WILLINGHAM, BILL	BUCKINGHAM, MARK	$17.99/$20.99	TP
9781401219130	AUG080229	FABLES VOL. 11: WAR AND PIECES	WILLINGHAM, BILL	BUCKINGHAM, MARK	$17.99/$20.99	TP
9781401223168	MAY090236	FABLES VOL. 12: THE DARK AGES	WILLINGHAM, BILL	BUCKINGHAM, MARK	$17.99/$20.99	TP
9781401225728	NOV090228	FABLES VOL. 13: THE GREAT FABLES CROSSOVER	WILLINGHAM, BILL	BUCKINGHAM, MARK	$17.99/$20.99	TP
9781401228804	SEP100304	FABLES VOL. 14: WITCHES	WILLINGHAM, BILL	BUCKINGHAM, MARK	$17.99/$20.99	TP
9781401230005	JAN110422	FABLES VOL. 15: ROSE RED	WILLINGHAM, BILL	BUCKINGHAM, MARK	$17.99/$20.99	TP
9781401233068	SEP110221	FABLES VOL .16: SUPER TEAM	WILLINGHAM, BILL	BUCKINGHAM, MARK	$14.99/$17.99	TP
9781401235161	APR120282	FABLES VOL. 17: INHERIT THE WIND	WILLINGHAM, BILL	BUCKINGHAM, MARK	$14.99/$17.99	TP
9781401237691	OCT120296	FABLES VOL. 18: CUBS IN TOYLAND	WILLINGHAM, BILL	BUCKINGHAM, MARK	$16.99/$19.99	TP
9781401242480	SEP130305	FABLES VOL. 19: SNOW WHITE	WILLINGHAM, BILL	BUCKINGHAM, MARK	$16.99/$19.99	TP
9781401245160	MAY140403	FABLES VOL. 20: CAMELOT	WILLINGHAM, BILL	BUCKINGHAM, MARK	$19.99/$23.99	TP
9781401251321	JAN150397	FABLES VOL. 21: HAPPILY EVER AFTER	WILLINGHAM, BILL	BUCKINGHAM, MARK	$17.99/$21.99	TP
9781401252335	APR150316	FABLES VOL. 22: FAREWELL	WILLINGHAM, BILL	BUCKINGHAM, MARK	$17.99/$21.99	TP
9781401203696	DEC070297	FABLES: 1001 NIGHTS OF SNOWFALL	WILLINGHAM, BILL	VARIOUS	$14.99/$17.99	TP
9781401224271	MAY090235	FABLES THE DELUXE EDITION BOOK ONE	WILLINGHAM, BILL	BUCKINGHAM, MARK	$29.99/$35.00	HC
9781401228798	JUL100251	FABLES THE DELUXE EDITION BOOK TWO	WILLINGHAM, BILL	BUCKINGHAM, MARK	$29.99/$35.00	HC
9781401230975	APR110244	FABLES THE DELUXE EDITION BOOK THREE	WILLINGHAM, BILL	BUCKINGHAM, MARK	$29.99/$35.00	HC
9781401233907	OCT110292	FABLES THE DELUXE EDITION BOOK FOUR	WILLINGHAM, BILL	BUCKINGHAM, MARK	$29.99/$35.00	HC
9781401234966	JAN120330	FABLES THE DELUXE EDITION BOOK FIVE	WILLINGHAM, BILL	BUCKINGHAM, MARK	$29.99/$35.00	HC
9781401237240	OCT120295	FABLES THE DELUXE EDITION BOOK SIX	WILLINGHAM, BILL	BUCKINGHAM, MARK	$29.99/$35.00	HC
9781401240400	APR130253	FABLES THE DELUXE EDITION BOOK SEVEN	WILLINGHAM, BILL	BUCKINGHAM, MARK	$29.99/$35.00	HC
9781401242794	OCT130286	FABLES THE DELUXE EDITION BOOK EIGHT	WILLINGHAM, BILL	BUCKINGHAM, MARK	$29.99/$35.00	HC
9781401250041	JUN140304	FABLES THE DELUXE EDITION BOOK NINE	WILLINGHAM, BILL	BUCKINGHAM, MARK	$29.99/$35.00	HC
9781401255213	JAN150396	FABLES THE DELUXE EDITION BOOK TEN	WILLINGHAM, BILL	BUCKINGHAM, MARK; HAMILTON, CRAIG	$29.99/$35.00	HC
9781401258269	JUN150322	FABLES THE DELUXE EDITION BOOK ELEVEN	WILLINGHAM, BILL	BUCKINGHAM, MARK	$29.99/$35.00	HC
9781401261382	JAN160352	FABLES THE DELUXE EDITION BOOK TWELVE	WILLINGHAM, BILL	BUCKINGHAM, MARK	$29.99/$35.00	HC
9781401264499	MAY160342	FABLES THE DELUXE EDITION BOOK 13	WILLINGHAM, BILL	BUCKINGHAM, MARK	$29.99/$39.99	HC
9781401268565	JAN170418	FABLES THE DELUXE EDITION BOOK 14	WILLINGHAM, BILL	BUCKINGHAM, MARK	$29.99/$39.99	HC
9781401274641	AUG170356	FABLES: THE DELUXE EDITION BOOK 15	WILLINGHAM, BILL	BUCKINGHAM, MARK	$39.99/$53.99	HC
9781401268367	FEB170333	EVERAFTER VOL. 1: THE PANDORA PROTOCOL	STURGES, MATTHEW; JUSTUS, DAVE	MOORE, TRAVIS	$16.99/$22.99	TP
9781401275020	SEP170444	EVERAFTER VOL. 2: THE UNSENTIMENTAL EDUCATION	STURGES, LILAH	JUSTUS, DAVE; MOORE, TRAVIS	$16.99/$22.99	TP
9781401256845	JUL150340	FABLES: THE WOLF AMONG US VOL. 1	STURGES, MATTHEW	JUSTUS, DAVE; MCMANUS, SHAWN	$19.99/$23.99	TP
9781401261375	MAR160290	FABLES: THE WOLF AMONG US VOL. 2	STURGES, MATTHEW	NGUYEN, ERIC	$19.99/$23.99	TP
9781401252816	AUG140365	FABLES COVERS: THE ART OF JAMES JEAN (NEW EDITION)	JEAN, JAMES; WILLINGHAM, BILL	JEAN, JAMES	$49.99/$58.00	HC
9781401235505	AUG120283	FAIREST VOL. 1: WIDE AWAKE	WILLINGHAM, BILL	JIMENEZ, PHIL	$14.99/$17.99	TP
9781401240219	APR130255	FAIREST VOL. 2: HIDDEN KINGDOM	WILLINGHAM, BILL; BEUKES, LAUREN	MIRANDA, INAKI	$14.99/$17.99	TP
9781401245931	FEB140288	FAIREST VOL. 3: THE RETURN OF THE MAHARAJA	WILLIAMS, SEAN E.	SADOWSKI, STEPHEN; JIMENEZ, PHIL	$14.99/$17.99	TP
9781401250058	JUL140278	FAIREST VOL. 4: CINDERELLA - OF MEN AND MICE	ANDREYKO, MARC; WILLINGHAM, BILL	MCMANUS, SHAWN	$14.99/$17.99	TP
9781401254261	MAY150265	FAIREST VOL. 5: THE CLAMOR FOR GLAMOR	BUCKINGHAM, MARK	BRAUN, RUSS	$14.99/$17.99	TP
9781401270445	JAN170419	THE FILTH NEW EDITION	MORRISON, GRANT	WESTON, CHRIS	$19.99/$25.99	TP
9781401261399	MAR160291	FLINCH BOOK TWO	QUITELY, FRANK; ENNIS, GARTH; AZZARELLO, BRIAN	LEE, JIM	$14.99/$17.99	TP
9781401271343	APR170452	FROSTBITE	WILLIAMSON, JOSHUA	ALEXANDER, JASON SHAWN	$16.99/$22.99	TP
9781401267872	AUG160360	FREE COUNTRY: A TALE OF THE CHILDREN'S CRUSADE	GAIMAN, NEIL	VARIOUS	$17.99/$23.99	TP
9781401228286	FEB130242	GET JIRO!	BOURDAIN, ANTHONY; ROSE, JOEL	FOSS, LANGDON	$14.99/$17.99	TP
9781401265007	JUL160433	GET JIRO: BLOOD & SUSHI	BOURDAIN, ANTHONY; ROSE, JOEL	GARZA, ALE	$14.99/$19.99	TP
9781401264772	JUL160435	THE GIRL WHO KICKED THE HORNET'S NEST	MINA, DENISE	MUTTI, ANDREA	$19.99/$25.99	TP

ISBN	DIAMOND CODE	TITLE	AUTHOR	ARTIST	US$/$CAN	FORMAT
9781401278205	JAN180401	GLOBAL FREQUENCY: THE DELUXE EDITION	ELLIS, WARREN	VARIOUS	$34.99/$45.99	HC
9781401267957	NOV160356	THE INVISIBLES BOOK ONE	MORRISON, GRANT	YEOWELL, STEVE; THOMPSON, JILL	$24.99/$33.99	TP
9781401274818	AUG170355	THE INVISIBLES BOOK TWO	MORRISON, GRANT	YEOWELL, STEVE	$24.99/$33.99	TP
9781401281021	APR180293	THE INVISIBLES BOOK THREE	MORRISON, GRANT	VARIOUS	$24.99/$33.99	TP
9781401285197		THE INVISIBLES BOOK FOUR	MORRISON, GRANT	VARIOUS	$24.99/$33.99	TP
9781401234591	APR120288	THE INVISIBLES OMNIBUS	MORRISON, GRANT	VARIOUS	$150.00/$172.00	TP
9781401272883	APR170453	IT'S A BIRD...(NEW EDITION)	SEAGLE, STEVEN T.	KRISTIANSEN, TEDDY	$17.99/$23.99	TP
9781401229658	DEC100299	IZOMBIE VOL. 1: DEAD TO THE WORLD	ROBERSON, CHRIS	ALLRED, MIKE	$14.99/$17.99	TP
9781401232962	JUN110353	IZOMBIE VOL. 2: UVAMPIRE	ROBERSON, CHRIS	ALLRED, MIKE	$14.99/$17.99	TP
9781401233709	NOV110232	IZOMBIE VOL. 3: SIX FEET UNDER AND RISING	ROBERSON, CHRIS	ALLRED, MIKE	$14.99/$17.99	TP
9781401236977	SEP120261	IZOMBIE VOL. 4: REPOSSESSED	ROBERSON, CHRIS	ALLRED, MIKE	$19.99/$23.99	TP
9781401262037	SEP150327	IZOMBIE OMNIBUS	ROBERSON, CHRIS	ALLRED, MICHAEL	$75.00/$85.00	HC
9781401262709	MAR160294	JACKED	KRIPKE, ERIC	HIGGINS, JOHN	$16.99/$19.99	TP
9781401264635	SEP160369	JACK OF FABLES THE DELUXE EDITION BOOK 1	WILLINGHAM, BILL; STURGES, MATTHEW	AKINS, TONY	$29.99/$39.99	HC
9781401277710	NOV170389	JACK OF FABLES: THE DELUXE EDITION BOOK TWO	WILLINGHAM, BILL	STURGES, MATTHEW	$39.99/$53.99	HC
9781401230067	DEC100302	JOHN CONSTANTINE, HELLBLAZER VOL. 1: ORIGINAL SINS	DELANO, JAMIE	RIDGWAY, JOHN	$19.99 /$23.99	TP
9781401233020	SEP110218	JOHN CONSTANTINE, HELLBLAZER VOL. 2: THE DEVIL YOU KNOW	DELANO, JAIME	LLOYD, DAVID	$19.99/$23.99	TP
9781401235192	MAR120279	JOHN CONSTANTINE, HELLBLAZER VOL. 3: THE FEAR MACHINE	DELANO, JAMIE	BUCKINGHAM, MARK	$24.99/$28.99	TP
9781401236908	AUG120288	JOHN CONSTANTINE, HELLBLAZER VOL. 4: THE FAMILY MAN	VARIOUS	LLOYD, DAVID	$19.99/$23.99	TP
9781401238025	JAN130335	JOHN CONSTANTINE: HELLBLAZER VOL. 5: DANGEROUS HABITS	DELANO, JAIME	ENNIS, GARTH	$19.99/$23.99	TP
9781401240431	MAY130258	JOHN CONSTANTINE, HELLBLAZER VOL. 6: BLOODLINES	ENNIS, GARTH	SIMPSON, WILLIAM	$19.99/$23.99	TP
9781401243036	OCT130283	JOHN CONSTANTINE, HELLBLAZER VOL. 7: TAINTED LOVE	ENNIS, GARTH	DILLON, STEVE	$19.99/$23.99	TP
9781401247492	MAR140283	JOHN CONSTANTINE, HELLBLAZER VOL. 8: RAKE AT THE GATES OF HELL	ENNIS, GARTH	DILLON, STEVE	$19.99/$23.99	TP
9781401250720	JUL140283	JOHN CONSTANTINE, HELLBLAZER VOL. 9: CRITICAL MASS	JENKINS, PAUL	CAMPBELL, EDDIE; PHILLIPS, SEAN	$19.99/$23.99	TP
9781401251376	NOV140338	JOHN CONSTANTINE, HELLBLAZER VOL. 10: IN THE LINE OF FIRE	JENKINS, PAUL	PHILLIPS, SEAN	$19.99/$23.99	TP
9781401255299	MAY150266	JOHN CONSTANTINE, HELLBLAZER VOL. 11: LAST MAN STANDING	JENKINS, PAUL	PHILLIPS, SEAN	$24.99/$29.99	TP
9781401258108	OCT150281	JOHN CONSTANTINE, HELLBLAZER VOL. 12: HOW TO PLAY WITH FIRE	JENKINS, PAUL	PLEECE, WARREN	$19.99/$23.99	TP
9781401261412	FEB160259	JOHN CONSTANTINE, HELLBLAZER VOL. 13: HAUNTED	ENNIS, GARTH	JENKINS, PAUL	$19.99/$23.99	TP
9781401263737	MAY160346	JOHN CONSTANTINE, HELLBLAZER VOL. 14: GOOD INTENTIONS	VARIOUS	VARIOUS	$24.99/$29.99	TP
9781401265793	OCT160323	JOHN CONSTANTINE, HELLBLAZER VOL. 15: HIGHWATER	VARIOUS	VARIOUS	$19.99/$25.99	TP
9781401269098	FEB170336	JOHN CONSTANTINE, HELLBLAZER VOL. 16: THE WILD CARD	VARIOUS	VARIOUS	$24.99/$33.99	TP
9781401273668	JUN170419	JOHN CONSTANTINE, HELLBLAZER VOL. 17: OUT OF SEASON	CAREY, MIKE	MANCO, LEONARDO	$29.99/$39.99	TP
9781401275389	OCT170391	JOHN CONSTANTINE, HELLBLAZER VOL. 18: THE GIFT	CAREY, MIKE	MANCO, LEONARDO	$29.99/$39.99	TP
9781401280802	APR180292	JOHN CONSTANTINE, HELLBLAZER VOL. 19: RED RIGHT HAND	MINA, DENISE	VARIOUS	$24.99/$33.99	TP
9781401285692		JOHN CONSTANTINE, HELLBLAZER VOL. 20: SYSTEMS OF CONTROL	CAREY, MIKE	VARIOUS	$24.99/$33.99	TP
9781401284794		JOHN CONSTANTINE, HELLBLAZER: 30TH ANNIVERSARY CELEBRATION	VARIOUS	VARIOUS	$39.99/$53.99	HC
9781401268145	NOV160357	KID ETERNITY BOOK ONE	NOCENTI, ANN	PHILLIPS, SEAN	$19.99/$25.99	TP
9781401261429	OCT150282	KILL YOUR BOYFRIEND/VINAMARAMA DELUXE	MORRISON, GRANT	BOND, PHILIP	$19.99/$23.99	HC
9781401257736	AUG150292	THE KITCHEN	MASTERS, OLLY	DOYLE, MING	$16.99/$19.99	TP
9781401264734	JUL160434	LAST GANG IN TOWN VOL. 1	OLIVER, SIMON	DAYGLO, RUFUS	$14.99/$17.99	TP
9781563898587	MAY118167	THE LEAGUE OF EXTRAORDINARY GENTLEMEN VOL. 1	MOORE, ALAN	O'NEILL, KEVIN	$16.99/$19.99	TP
9781401201180	MAY118168	THE LEAGUE OF EXTRAORDINARY GENTLEMEN VOL. 2	MOORE, ALAN	O'NEILL, KEVIN	$16.99/$19.99	TP
9781401284169	FEB180306	THE LEAGUE OF EXTRAORDINARY GENTLEMEN: THE BLACK DOSSIER	MOORE, ALAN	O'NEILL, KEVIN	$19.99/$25.99	TP
9781401289003		THE LEAGUE OF EXTRAORDINARY GENTLEMEN OMNIBUS	MOORE, ALAN	O'NEILL, KEVIN	$75.00/$99.00	HC
9781401271459	MAY170362	THE LOST BOYS VOL. 1	SEELEY, TIM	GODLEWSKI, SCOTT	$16.99/$22.99	TP
9781401240264	FEB130247	LUCIFER BOOK ONE	CAREY, MIKE	GROSS, PETER; HAMPTON, SCOTT	$29.99 /$35.00	TP
9781401242602	JUL130266	LUCIFER BOOK TWO	CAREY, MIKE	GROSS, PETER	$29.99 /$35.00	TP
9781401246044	DEC130345	LUCIFER BOOK THREE	CAREY, MIKE	GROSS, PETER	$29.99/$35.00	TP
9781401246051	MAY140408	LUCIFER BOOK FOUR	CAREY, MIKE	GROSS, PETER	$29.99/$35.00	TP
9781401249458	SEP140346	LUCIFER BOOK FIVE	CAREY, MIKE	GROSS, PETER; KELLY, RYAN	$29.99/$35.00	TP
9781401261931	MAY160345	LUCIFER VOL. 1: COLD HEAVEN	BLACK, HOLLY	GARBETT, LEE	$14.99/$17.99	TP
9781401265410	DEC160412	LUCIFER VOL. 2	BLACK, HOLLY	GARBETT, LEE	$14.99/$19.99	TP
9781401271398	JUL170491	LUCIFER VOL. 3: BLOOD IN THE STREETS	KADREY, RICHARD; BLACK, HOLLY	GARBETT, LEE	$16.99/$22.99	TP
9781401259051	MAY150271	MAD MAX: FURY ROAD	MILLER, GEORGE	VARIOUS	$14.99/$17.99	TP
9781401283469		MOTHERLANDS	SPURRIER, SI	STOTT, RACHAEL	$16.99/$22.99	TP
9781401265625	MAR160295	MR. PUNCH 20TH ANNIVERSARY EDITION	GAIMAN, NEIL	MCKEAN, DAVE	$17.99/$23.99	TP
9781401265014	JUL160436	NEIL GAIMAN'S MIDNIGHT DAYS	GAIMAN, NEIL	MCKEAN, DAVE; WAGNER, MATT	$19.99/$25.99	TP
9781401287849		NEIL GAIMAN'S STARDUST (NEW EDITION)	GAIMAN, NEIL	VESS, CHARLES	$19.99/$25.99	TP
9781401263515	MAY160343	NEW ROMANCER VOL. 1	MILLIGAN, PETER	PARSONS, BRETT	$14.99/$17.99	TP
9781401263317	MAR160295	NORTHLANDERS BOOK 1: THE ANGLO-SAXON SAGA	WOOD, BRIAN	GIANFELICE, DAVIDE	$29.99/$35.00	TP
9781401265083	AUG160358	NORTHLANDERS VOL. 2: THE ICELANDIC SAGA	WOOD, BRIAN	KELLY, RYAN	$29.99/$39.99	TP
9781401273798	AUG170357	NORTHLANDERS BOOK 3: THE EUROPEAN SAGA	WOOD, BRIAN	VARIOUS	$34.99/$45.99	TP
9781401240455	MAR130303	PREACHER BOOK ONE	ENNIS, GARTH	DILLON, STEVE	$19.99 /$23.99	TP

VERTIGO SELECTED BACKLIST

ISBN	DIAMOND CODE	TITLE	AUTHOR	ARTIST	US$/$CAN	FORMAT
9781401242558	JUN130299	PREACHER BOOK TWO	ENNIS, GARTH	DILLON, STEVE	$19.99 /$23.99	TP
9781401245016	OCT130293	PREACHER BOOK THREE	ENNIS, GARTH	DILLON, STEVE	$19.99 /$23.99	TP
9781401230944	MAR140292	PREACHER BOOK FOUR	ENNIS, GARTH	DILLON, STEVE	$19.99 /$23.99	TP
9781401250744	MAY140409	PREACHER BOOK FIVE	ENNIS, GARTH	DILLON, STEVE	$19.99 /$23.99	TP
9781401252793	JUL140282	PREACHER BOOK SIX	ENNIS, GARTH	DILLON, STEVE	$19.99 /$23.99	TP
9781401264413	JAN160353	ABSOLUTE PREACHER VOL. 1	ENNIS, GARTH	DILLON, STEVE	$150.00/$172.00	HC
9781401268091	NOV160355	ABSOLUTE PREACHER VOL. 2	ENNIS, GARTH	DILLON, STEVE	$150.00/$195.00	HC
9781401278489	SEP170442	ABSOLUTE PREACHER VOL. 3	ENNIS, GARTH	DILLON, STEVE	$150.00/$195.00	HC
9781401203153	FEB118119	PRIDE OF BAGHDAD	VAUGHAN, BRIAN K.	HENRICHON, NIKO	$14.99 /$17.99	TP
9781401248949	AUG140360	PRIDE OF BAGHDAD DELUXE EDITION	VAUGHAN, BRIAN K.	HENRICHON, NIKO	$24.99 /$28.99	HC
9781563896675	APR108106	PROMETHEA BOOK 1	MOORE, ALAN	WILLIAMS III, J.H.	$17.99 /$20.99	TP
9781401200947	AUG128046	PROMETHEA BOOK 2	MOORE, ALAN	WILLIAMS III, J.H.	$17.99 /$20.99	TP
9781563896675	AUG128047	PROMETHEA BOOK 3	MOORE, ALAN	WILLIAMS III, J.H.	$17.99 /$20.99	TP
9781401200312	OCT098137	PROMETHEA BOOK 4	MOORE, ALAN	WILLIAMS III, J.H.	$17.99 /$20.99	TP
9781401206208	DEC138192	PROMETHEA BOOK 5	MOORE, ALAN	WILLIAMS III, J.H.	$17.99 /$20.99	TP
9781401288662		PROMETHEA: THE DELUXE EDITION BOOK ONE	MOORE, ALAN	WILIAMS III, J.H.	$49.99/$65.99	HC
9781401237684	JAN130330	PUNK ROCK JESUS	MURPHY, SEAN	MURPHY, SEAN	$16.99 /$19.99	TP
9781401263614	APR160426	RED THORN VOL. 1: GLASGOW KISS	BAILLIE, DAVID	HETRICK, MEGHAN	$14.99 /$17.99	TP
9781401267254	NOV160358	RED THORN VOL. 2: MAD GODS AND SCOTSMEN	BAILLIE, DAVID	HETRICK, MEGHAN	$14.99/$19.99	TP
9781401220839	JAN120343	SAGA OF THE SWAMP THING BOOK ONE	MOORE, ALAN	BISETTE, STEPHEN	$19.99 /$23.99	TP
9781401225445	JUN120283	SAGA OF THE SWAMP THING BOOK TWO	MOORE, ALAN	BISETTE, STEPHEN	$19.99 /$23.99	TP
9781401227678	OCT120301	SAGA OF THE SWAMP THING BOOK THREE	MOORE, ALAN	BISETTE, STEPHEN	$19.99 /$23.99	TP
9781401240462	APR130262	SAGA OF THE SWAMP THING BOOK FOUR	MOORE, ALAN	BISSETTE, STEPHEN, WOCH, STAN	$19.99 /$23.99	TP
9781401230968	SEP130310	SAGA OF THE SWAMP THING BOOK FIVE	MOORE, ALAN	VEITCH, RICK	$14.99 /$17.99	TP
9781401246921	FEB140293	SAGA OF THE SWAMP THING BOOK SIX	MOORE, ALAN	VEITCH, RICK; ALCALA, ALFREDO	$19.99 /$23.99	TP
9781401263379	MAR160299	SWAMP THING: TRIAL BY FIRE	MILLAR, MARK	HESTER, PHIL	$19.99 /$23.99	TP
9781401265199	AUG160359	THE SANDMAN: OVERTURE	GAIMAN, NEIL	WILLIAMS III, J.H.	$19.99 /$25.99	TP
9781401280475	NOV170387	ABSOLUTE SANDMAN OVERTURE	GAIMAN, NEIL	WILLIAMS III, J.H.	$125.00/$163.00	HC
9781401284770	JUN180595	THE SANDMAN VOL. 1: PRELUDES & NOCTURNES 30TH ANNIVERSARY EDITION	GAIMAN, NEIL	KIETH, SAM	$19.99/$25.99	TP
9781401285067	AUG180642	THE SANDMAN VOL. 2: THE DOLL'S HOUSE 30TH ANNIVERSARY EDITION	GAIMAN, NEIL	DRINGENBERG, MIKE	$19.99/$25.99	TP
9781401285487		THE SANDMAN VOL. 3: DREAM COUNTRY 30TH ANNIVERSARY EDITION	GAIMAN, NEIL	JONES, KELLEY	$19.99/$25.99	TP
9781401285814	JUN188701	THE SANDMAN VOL. 4: SEASON OF MISTS 30TH ANNIVERSARY EDITION	GAIMAN, NEIL	JONES, KELLEY	$19.99/$25.99	TP
9781401288075	JUN188702	THE SANDMAN VOL. 5: A GAME OF YOU 30TH ANNIVERSARY EDITION	GAIMAN, NEIL	MCMANUS, SHAWN; GIORDANO, DICK	$19.99/$25.99	TP
9781401288464	JUN188703	THE SANDMAN VOL. 6: FABLES & REFLECTIONS 30TH ANNIVERSARY EDITION	GAIMAN, NEIL	RUSSELL, P. CRAIG	$19.99/$25.99	TP
9781401289089	JUN188704	THE SANDMAN VOL. 7: BRIEF LIVES 30TH ANNIVERSARY EDITION	GAIMAN, NEIL	THOMPSON, JILL	$19.99/$25.99	TP
9781401289591	JUN188705	THE SANDMAN VOL. 8: WORLD'S END 30TH ANNIVERSARY EDITION	GAIMAN, NEIL	TALBOT, BRYAN	$19.99/$25.99	TP
9781401235451	FEB120298	THE SANDMAN VOL. 9: THE KINDLY ONES	GAIMAN, NEIL	HEMPEL, MARC	$19.99 /$23.99	TP
9781401237547	AUG120292	THE SANDMAN VOL. 10: THE WAKE	GAIMAN, NEIL	ZULLI, MICHAEL	$19.99 /$23.99	TP
9781401224288	JUN100280	THE SANDMAN: THE DREAM HUNTERS	GAIMAN, NEIL	RUSSELL, P. CRAIG	$19.99 /$23.99	TP
9781401242336	JUL130264	THE SANDMAN: ENDLESS NIGHTS	GAIMAN, NEIL	VARIOUS	$19.99 /$23.99	TP
9781401233327	AUG110277	THE ANNOTATED SANDMAN VOL. 1	GAIMAN, NEIL	VARIOUS	$49.99/$58.00	HC
9781401235666	JUN120271	THE ANNOTATED SANDMAN VOL. 2	GAIMAN, NEIL	VARIOUS	$49.99/$58.00	HC
9781401241025	APR140291	THE ANNOTATED SANDMAN VOL. 3	KLINGER, LESLIE S.; GAIMAN, NEIL	VARIOUS	$49.99/$58.00	HC
9781401243227	JUL150334	THE ANNOTATED SANDMAN VOL. 4	GAIMAN, NEIL	KLINGER, LESLIE	$49.99/$58.00	HC
9781401287733	MAR180353	THE SANDMAN OMNIBUS VOL. 3	GAIMAN, NEIL	BACHALO, CHRIS; QUIETLY, FRANK; RUSSELL, P. CRAIG	$150.00/$195.00	HC
9781401263270	MAR160298	SANDMAN MYSTERY THEATRE BOOK 1	WAGNER, MATT	DAVIS, GUY	$29.99/$35.00	TP
9781401265694	SEP160370	SANDMAN MYSTERY THEATRE BOOK 2	WAGNER, MATT	VARIOUS	$24.99/$33.99	TP
9781401275365	OCT170392	SAVAGE THINGS	JORDAN, JUSTIN	MOUSTAFA, IBRAHIM	$19.99/$25.99	TP
9781401271268	APR170454	SCALPED BOOK ONE	AARON, JASON	GUERA, R.M.	$24.99/$33.99	TP
9781401277864	DEC170410	SCALPED BOOK TWO	AARON, JASON	GUERA, R.M.	$24.99/$33.99	TP
9781401281564	MAY180589	SCALPED BOOK THREE	AARON, JASON	GUERA, R.M.	$24.99/$33.99	TP
9781401285395		SCALPED BOOK FOUR	AARON, JASON	GUERA, R.M.	$24.99/$33.99	TP
9781401288488		SCALPED BOOK FIVE	AARON, JASON	GUERA, R.M.	$24.99/$33.99	TP
9781401274191	JUL170492	SEBASTIAN O/MYSTERY PLAY BY GRANT MORRISON	MORRISON, GRANT	YEOWELL, STEVE; MUTH, JON J	$29.99/$39.99	HC
9781401264666	APR160424	SHERIFF OF BABYLON VOL. 1: BANG. BANG. BANG.	KING, TOM	GERADS, MITCH	$14.99/$17.99	TP
9781401267261	NOV160359	SHERIFF OF BABYLON VOL. 2: POW. POW. POW.	KING, TOM	GERADS, MITCH	$14.99/$19.99	TP
9781401277918	DEC170411	THE SHERIFF OF BABYLON: THE DELUXE EDITION	KING, TOM	GERADS, MITCH	$39.99/$53.99	HC
9781401290719		SIX DAYS	VENDITTI, ROBERT; MAURER, KEVIN		$24.99/$33.99	HC
9781401262778	MAY160350	SLASH & BURN	SPENCER, SI	DUNBAR, MAX	$14.99/$17.99	TP
9781401278441	JAN180416	SLEEPER BOOK ONE	BRUBAKER, ED	PHILLIPS, SEAN	$29.99/$39.99	TP
9781401287689		SLEEPER BOOK TWO	BRUBAKER, ED	PHILLIPS, SEAN	$29.99/$39.99	TP
9781401264956	AUG160357	THE COMPLETE SUICIDERS: THE BIG SHAKE	BERMEJO, LEE	BERMEJO, LEE	$29.99/$39.99	TP
9781401265540	JUN160377	SURVIVORS' CLUB: THE COMPLETE SERIES	BEUKES, LAUREN	KELLY, RYAN	$19.99/$25.99	TP

VERTIGO SELECTED BACKLIST

ISBN	DIAMOND CODE	TITLE	AUTHOR	ARTIST	US$/$CAN	FORMAT
9781401276805	JUN170420	SWEET TOOTH BOOK ONE	LEMIRE, JEFFFLEMIRE, JEFF	$24.99/$33.99	TP
9781401280468	MAR180363	SWEET TOOTH BOOK TWO	LEMIRE, JEFF	LEMIRE, JEFF	$24.99/$33.99	TP
9781401285654		SWEET TOOTH BOOK THREE	LEMIRE, JEFF	LEMIRE, JEFF	$24.99/$33.99	TP
9781401220846	DEC080220	TRANSMETROPOLITAN VOL. 1: BACK ON THE STREET	ELLIS, WARREN	ROBERTSON, DARICK	$14.99/$17.99	TP
9781401222611	FEB090264	TRANSMETROPOLITAN VOL. 2: LUST FOR LIFE	ELLIS, WARREN	ROBERTSON, DARICK	$14.99/$17.99	TP
9781401223120	DEC098262	TRANSMETROPOLITAN VOL. 3: YEAR OF THE BASTARD	ELLIS, WARREN	ROBERTSON, DARICK	$14.99/$17.99	TP
9781401224905	JUL090291	TRANSMETROPOLITAN VOL. 4: THE NEW SCUM	ELLIS, WARREN	ROBERTSON, DARICK	$14.99/$17.99	TP
9781401228194	SEP090228	TRANSMETROPOLITAN VOL. 5. LONELY CITY	ELLIS, WARREN	ROBERTSON, DARICK	$14.99/$17.99	TP
9781401228187	DEC090284	TRANSMETROPOLITAN VOL. 6: GOUGE AWAY	ELLIS, WARREN	ROBERTSON, DARICK	$14.99/$17.99	TP
9781401228156	FEB100264	TRANSMETROPOLITAN VOL. 7: SPIDER'S THRASH	ELLIS, WARREN	ROBERTSON, DARICK	$14.99/$17.99	TP
9781401229368	JUN100282	TRANSMETROPOLITAN VOL. 8: DIRGE	ELLIS, WARREN	ROBERTSON, DARICK	$14.99/$17.99	TP
9781401230494	JAN110435	TRANSMETROPOLITAN VOL. 9: THE CURE	ELLIS, WARREN	ROBERTSON, DARICK	$14.99/$17.99	TP
9781401231248	MAY110296	TRANSMETROPOLITAN VOL. 10: ONE MORE TIME	ELLIS, WARREN	ROBERTSON, DARICK	$19.99/$23.99	TP
9781401287955		TRANSMETROPOLITAN BOOK ONE	ELLIS, WARREN	ROBERTSON, DARICK	$19.99/$25.99	TP
9781401254308	OCT140403	ABSOLUTE TRANSMETROPOLITAN VOL. 1	ELLIS, WARREN	ROBERTSON, DARICK; RAMOS, RODNEY	$125.00/$144.00	HC
9781401254308	OCT150280	ABSOLUTE TRANSMETROPOLITAN VOL. 2	ELLIS, WARREN	ROBERTSON, DARICK	$125.00/$144.00	HC
9781401285456	MAR180362	ABSOLUTE TRANSMETROPOLITAN VOL. 3	ELLIS, WARREN	ROBERTSON, DARICK	$125.00/$163.00	HC
9781401249007	MAY140407	TRILLIUM	LEMIRE, JEFF	LEMIRE, JEFF	$16.99/$19.99	TP
9781401274528	AUG170358	TRILLIUM: THE DELUXE EDITION	LEMIRE, JEFF	LEMIRE, JEFF	$34.99/$45.99	HC
9781401262457	FEB160268	THE TWILIGHT CHILDREN	HERNANDEZ, JAMIE	COOKE, DARWYN	$14.99/$17.99	TP
9781401262747	FEB160269	UNFOLLOW VOL. 1: 140 CHARACTERS	WILLIAMS, ROB	DOWLING, MICHAEL	$14.99/$17.99	TP
9781401267230	OCT160327	UNFOLLOW VOL. 2: GOD IS WATCHING	WILLIAMS, ROB	DOWLING, MIKE	$14.99/$19.99	TP
9781401270964	MAY170363	UNFOLLOW VOL. 3: TURN IT OFF	WILLIAMS, ROB	DOWLING, MIKE	$16.99/$22.99	TP
9781401225650	APR128238	THE UNWRITTEN VOL. 1: TOMMY TAYLOR AND THE BOGUS IDENTITY	CAREY, MIKE	GROSS, PETER	$14.99/$17.99	TP
9781401228736	MAY100283	THE UNWRITTEN VOL. 2: INSIDE MAN	CAREY, MIKE	GROSS, PETER	$12.99/$15.99	TP
9781401230463	DEC100305	THE UNWRITTEN VOL. 3: DEAD MAN'S KNOCK	CAREY, MIKE	GROSS, PETER	$14.99/$17.99	TP
9781401232924	JUL110296	THE UNWRITTEN VOL. 4: LEVIATHAN	CAREY, MIKE	GROSS, PETER	$14.99/$17.99	TP
9781401233594	OCT110301	THE UNWRITTEN VOL. 5: ON TO GENESIS	CAREY, MIKE	GROSS, PETER	$14.99/$17.99	TP
9781401235604	JUL120262	THE UNWRITTEN VOL. 6: TOMMY TAYLOR AND THE WAR OF WORDS	CAREY, MIKE	GROSS, PETER	$16.99/$19.99	TP
9781401238063	DEC120368	THE UNWRITTEN VOL. 7: THE WOUND	CAREY, MIKE	GROSS, PETER	$14.99/$17.99	TP
9781401243012	OCT130295	THE UNWRITTEN VOL. 8: ORPHEUS IN THE UNDERWORLDS	CAREY, MIKE	GROSS, PETER	$16.99/$19.99	TP
9781401246945	APR140302	THE UNWRITTEN VOL. 9: THE UNWRITTEN FABLES	CAREY, MIKE	GROSS, PETER; BUCKINGHAM, MARK	$14.99/$17.99	TP
9781401250553	JUL140285	THE UNWRITTEN VOL. 10: WAR STORIES	CAREY, MIKE	GROSS, PETER	$14.99/$17.99	TP
9781401253486	FEB150288	THE UNWRITTEN VOL. 11: APOCALYPSE	CAREY, MIKE	GROSS, PETER	$16.99/$19.99	TP
9781401265434	AUG160361	THE UNWRITTEN THE DELUXE EDITION BOOK 1	CAREY, MIKE	GROSS, PETER	$29.99/$39.99	HC
9781401208417	SEP088030	V FOR VENDETTA	MOORE, ALAN	LLOYD, DAVID	$19.99/$23.99	TP
9781401282011		V FOR VENDETTA 30TH ANNIVERSARY DELUXE EDITION	MOORE, ALAN	LLOYD, DAVID	$49.99/$65.99	HC
9781401282011	AUG180495	VERTIGO: A CELEBRATION OF 25 YEARS	GAIMAN, NEIL; ELLIS, WARREN	ENNIS, GARTH; JOCK	$49.99/$65.99	HC
9781401254919	MAR150313	THE WAKE	SNYDER, SCOTT	MURPHY, SEAN	$17.99/$20.99	TP
9781401243029	NOV130270	WE3	MORRISON, GRANT	QUIETLY, FRANK	$14.99/$17.99	TP
9781401251512	JUN140312	Y: THE LAST MAN BOOK ONE	VAUGHAN, BRIAN K.	GUERRA, PIA	$19.99/$23.99	TP
9781401254391	DEC140421	Y: THE LAST MAN BOOK TWO	VAUGHAN, BRIAN K.	GUERRA, PIA	$19.99/$23.99	TP
9781401258801	JUN150324	Y: THE LAST MAN BOOK THREE	VAUGHAN, BRIAN K.	GUERRA, PIA	$19.99/$23.99	TP
9781401261689	NOV150300	Y: THE LAST MAN BOOK FOUR	VAUGHAN, BRIAN K.	GUERRA, PIA	$19.99/$23.99	TP
9781401263720	MAY160352	Y: THE LAST MAN BOOK FIVE	VAUGHAN, BRIAN K.	GUERRA, PIA	$19.99/$23.99	TP
9781401254292	DEC140420	ABSOLUTE Y: THE LAST MAN VOL. 1	VAUGHAN, BRIAN K.	GUERRA, PIA	$125.00/$144.00	HC
9781401264918	APR160415	ABSOLUTE Y: THE LAST MAN VOL. 2	VAUGHAN, BRIAN K.	GUERRA, PIA	$125.00/$163.00	HC
9781401271008	MAR170450	ABSOLUTE Y: THE LAST MAN VOL. 3	VAUGHAN, BRIAN K.	GUERRA, PIA	$125.00/$163.00	HC

Published by DC Comics. Copyright © 2019 DC Comics. All books, titles, characters, character names, logos and related indicia are trademarks and copyright of their respective owners. DC VERTIGO is a trademark of DC Comics. MAD ™ and © E.C. Publications, Inc. The stories, characters and incidents mentioned in this publication are entirely fictional. DC Comics does not read or accept unsolicited submissions of ideas, stories or artwork.

Cover art by Ben Oliver and Hi-FI
Intro story by Robert Venditti and Scott Kolins

2900 West Alameda Ave., Burbank, CA 91505
Printed by Times Printing, Random Lake, WI. Ship date 8/31/18.

ISBN: 9781401292911
Diamond Code: JUN188753

ORDER INFORMATION

BOOK TRADE

DC Entertainment titles are distributed to the book trade by Penguin Random House Publishers Services and are eligible for cooperative advertising and free freight. Please contact the Penguin Random House sales representative in your region.

UNITED STATES

Random House Customer Service
400 Hahn Road
Westminster, MD 21157
To order by phone or for customer service:
1-800-733-3000
Available daily 8:30AM to 5:00PM EST
(Eastern and Central Accounts)
10:30AM to 7:00PM EST
(Fax: 1-800-659-2436
csorders@penguinrandomhouse.com

Visit the website at www.penguinrandomhouse.com. You can place an order, check on an order, file claims, check title availability; request invoice copies and much more.

ELECTRONIC ORDERING (EDI):
1-800-726-0600
Minimum orders:
Initials: $100 retail value
Reorders: $200 retail value

SCHOOLS AND LIBRARIES
The Library and Academic Marketing Department
is available to provide title information, review copies, desk and examination copies, and any other educational materials.

http://www.penguinrandomhouse.biz/libraries/
or email: library@randomhouse.com

For High Schools, visit visit www.randomhouse.com/highschool or email: highschool@randomhouse.com

For Colleges and Universities, visit www.randomhouse.com/academic or email: RHAcademic@randomhouse.com

SPECIAL MARKETS
Penguin Random House Special Markets
Penguin Random House
375 Hudson Street
New York, NY 10014
Website: www.penguinrandomhouse.biz/specialmarkets
Email: specialmarkets@penguinrandomhouse.com
Fax: 212-572-4961

CANADA

Penguin Random House of Canada Limited
Mississauga Distribution Centre (Random House)
6971 Columbus Road, Mississauga, ON L5T 1K1
To order by phone or for customer service:
+1-416-364-4449
8:30AM to 5:00PM EST (Monday through Friday)
Canadian Telebook I.D. S2013975
Fax ordering: 1-888-562-9924
customerservicescanada@penguinrandomhouse.com
Shipping Minimum (Reorders and New Title): $100
Retail notice to all Canadian customers:
Suggested Canadian list prices do not include the Federal Goods and Services Tax (GST)

Returns: Random House of Canada, Ltd.
Mississauga Distribution Centre (Random House)
6971 Columbus Road, Mississauga, ON L5T 1K1

INTERNATIONAL

Penguin Random House, Inc. International Department
1745 Broadway
New York, NY 10019
1-212-829-6712
Fax: 1-212-572-6045; 1-212-829-6700
http://www.penguinrandomhouse.biz/international/
Email: international@penguinrandomhouse.com
Minimum order: $100 retail value

COMIC BOOK SPECIALTY MARKET

Diamond Comic Distributors
reorders@diamondcomics.com
(800) 45-COMIC

RESOURCES

For more information about DC books, sell sheets, downloadable classroom activities and academic reading guides, please visit our resources pages for educators and librarians: www.dccomics.com/resources

Follow us on

VISIT US AT DCCOMICS.COM & VERTIGOCOMICS.COM